Becoming Immortal

Becoming Immortal

Combining Cloning
and Stem-Cell Therapy

Stanley Shostak

State University of New York Press

Cover Photo: Culture trays containing human embryonic stem cells being stored in heat-controlled storage in the research laboratory of James Thomson. Photo by Jeff Miller, Courtesy of University of Wisconsin-Madison.

Published by
State University of New York Press, Albany

© 2002 State University of New York

For information, address State University of New York Press,
90 State Street, Suite 700, Albany, NY 12207

Production by Michael Haggett
Marketing by Jennifer Giovani

Library of Congress Cataloging-in-Publication Data

Shostak, Stanley.
    Becoming immortal : combing cloning and stem-cell therapy / Stanley Shostak.
      p. cm.
    Includes index.
    ISBN 0-7914-5401-0 (alk. paper) — ISBN 0-7914-5402-9 (pbk. : alk. paper)
      1. Human cloning. 2. Stem cells—Research. I. Title.

QH442.2 .S564 2002
612.6—dc21   2001054944

10 9 8 7 6 5 4 3 2 1

Dedication

To Carl Partanen and to the memory of Mac V. Edds, Jr. and Dick Russell.

Contents

Preface

Expecting to relax during a routine flight home, I casually glanced through the contents of the airline's magazine and practically suffered a heart attack. The first feature article was entitled, "How to Live Forever"![1] Believing for a moment that *Becoming Immortal* had been scooped, I tore through the magazine only to find that the article concerned achieving enduring fame not eternal life. Relieved but not soothed, I imagined that others, glancing at the title of my book, might think that I was writing out of narcissism or wishful thinking. I was not.

Becoming Immortal was conceived as the last of three books intended to critique current concepts of change in the biological sciences. The first two books, *Death of Life*[2] and *Evolution of Sameness and Difference,*[3] examined the legacy of molecular biology and provided a perspective on the human genome project. *Becoming Immortal* was supposed to anticipate further directions in research on biological change, but my plan was overtaken by events. The book ultimately took its direction from a lamb named "Dolly" and prospects of cloning and stem cell research.[4]

My object in writing *Becoming Immortal* was to give the possibility of immortalizing human beings a realistic face so that it would be looked at seriously. These objectives were broad enough for me, and as I pursued them, I discovered that my narrow interests were shared by numerous friends who made themselves available to help and guide me. I discovered the work of authors who are, to put it simply, soul mates in this work. They have undoubtedly shaped my thinking around such issues as the universality of evolution and development, as well as the possibilities for change outside of or beyond accepted notions of biology.

Which brings me to acknowledgments. I begin with Marcia Landy, Distinguished Service Professor of English/Film Studies whose own work on the Gramscian organic intellectual and on popular culture brought me to questions of mortality, and who, as the first reader and critic of record for all my work over the last thirty years, keeps me focused on immortality. Laurens Schwartz, my friend and mentor, gave *Becoming Immortal* a critical reading that sent it back to the drawing board—and me to the library—on numerous occasions. Yoram Schiffmann, of Cambridge's Department of Applied Mathematics and Theoretical Physics got me through many a "sticky wicket." Lynn Margulis inspired much of what I have accomplished by her own efforts and by introducing me to new friends and helpmates, including Professor Donald Williamson, whose notions of larval transfer inspired my ideas on nomadic development and illicit fusion, and Richard Doyle, who helped me appreciate the seriousness of my work through his own sense of humor.

    Becoming Immortal would never have been written without the help of Drynda Lee Johnston, head librarian at Langley Library, University of Pittsburgh, Ann-Marie Tärnström, head librarian at the Biology Library, Stockholm University, and the staff at Cambridge University's Scientific Periodicals Library (SPL) and Genetics Library. I must also thank Professor James Pipas, chair of the Department of Biological Sciences, Professor John Cooper, Dean of the Faculty of Arts and Sciences at the University of Pittsburgh, who provided me with sabbatical leave in the fall of 2000, and the President and Fellows of Hughes Hall at the University of Cambridge who made available their ample facilities for me to finish this book.

Prologue

If you want to produce an immortal human being, you must produce an immortal mind.

—Tom Ryan, Dublin Ireland

Looking into my mind's rearview mirror, I see that research for *Becoming Immortal* actually began when, as a child, like many other children, I was prone to ask "Why?" questions. The most burning of these questions was, "Why do we have to grow up [and die]?" This question burns with an even hotter flame today but now in a more academic form: Why did life evolve a dynamics in which living things are constantly exchanged? Why didn't a stasis evolve in which living things remained more or less constant?

What I failed to appreciate as a child and throughout most of my adult life was that in order to achieve immortality, human life, as we know it, would have to change biologically in ways that were virtually excluded by evolution and development. The idea of biological change without natural selection and contrary to the central dogma was precisely the idea that had eluded me until I began to realize that what we know about evolution and development touches on only a part of the biological changes that shape life. This realization came to me as a consequence of my efforts to study biological change historically, before or beyond the confines of today's life forms.

I am interested in all the manifold qualities of life that appear in life's multifarious forms, both present, recent, and long past. I am interested in explaining where developmental differences come from and how they are maintained physiologically. Does life embody forms that are products of horizontal mixtures as opposed to the vertical mixtures brought about by sexual reproduction? Are there mixtures in proportions rather than the mere presence or absence of life's forms?

The answers to these questions began to take form in *Death of Life* and *Evolution of Sameness and Difference* with the help of the concept of *devolution*. Devolution is biological change brought about by the *fusion* (mixing) and *fission* (fragmentation) of biological forms. Fleshing out devolution in *Becoming Immortal* will, I hope, provide a new prospective on cloning and stem-cell research, a perspective that may shape attitudes toward life in the future.

Academic scientists are frequently at a loss when writing about the future, about science's products and applications in the future. The future seems out of bounds for science, since it is the territory of uncertainty. Attempts by scientists to take a hand in shaping the future have sometimes led to tragic results, most notoriously, to the genocide practiced in Nazi Germany. On the other hand, ignoring or being unconcerned with the future is blatantly irresponsible. Therefore, like the star ship Enterprise of *Star Trek* fame, I intend *Becoming Immortal* "to go where no one has gone before" and ask what direction human biological change might take if human beings took charge of their own destiny, setting aside evolution and development in the pursuit of immortality.

Chapter 1

Quo Vadis?

"Life is, after all, very much the same everywhere," said Miss Marple in her placid voice. "Getting born, you know, and growing up—and coming into contact with other people—getting jostled—and then marriage and more babies—"

—Agatha Christie, *Murder at the Vicarage*

At issue here is nothing less than taking seriously the question whether a science can depend on something like a circumcision.

—Jacques Derrida, *Archive Fever*

Seen from the point of view of death, the product of the corpse is life.

—Walter Benjamin, *Origin of German Tragic Drama*

Why, in short, do we seek, in the mobility of the whole, tracks that are supposed to be followed by bodies supposed to be in motion? A *moving continuity* is given to us, in which everything changes and yet remains: why then do we dissociate the two terms, permanence and change, and then represent permanence by *bodies* and change by *homogeneous movements* in space?

—Henri Bergson, *Matter and Memory*

What are human beings, biologically, and where are they heading? Fossils indicate that human life has changed, or evolved, ever since vaguely human forms appeared several million years ago. Sequences of nitrogenous bases in the human genome also suggest that we have changed even more recently, since *Homo sapiens* became the only species in the genus *Homo* some tens of thousands years ago. Nothing it would seem, short of extinction, will stop further change, but, by and large, scientists are not thinking about our present status as a species and are hardly contemplating how we might change in the future.

Biologists do not get serious for several reasons about characterizing human life as such and projecting its future. The most compelling reason is that there would be hell to pay from both left and right of the political spectrum. Charges of "Fascist!" would roar from the left, and accusations of "playing God" would fly from the right. Even political moderates might feel that anything remotely resembling a scientific statement on our present condition, to say nothing of a prognosis for our species' future, goes beyond the legitimate province of science. Biologists, therefore, limit their public pronouncements to the realm of nature, alluding to human nature and its evolution by natural selection as a remote consequence of being alive. Biologists wish us *bon chance,* to be sure, but they would sooner abandon us to chance than make serious assessments about our present position and potential.

I am not saying that we should, or can, correct all of our design flaws. For example, the crossing of our nasal and oral passages, which causes more deaths by asphyxiation than is generally realized, seems to have originated in early chordates and is probably too deeply rooted in vertebrate development to be readily altered. We can, nevertheless, improve upon ourselves in several respects, and I do not mean changing unattractive features. For example, birth could be made a lot easier, and a few vestigial structures, such as the appendix (which ruptures with devastating consequences) and breast tissue in males (occasionally the source of a rampant form of breast cancer) might be dispensed with without causing harm.[1] Above all, and what interests me here, is the great prize of achieving immortality. Eliminating old age and death is now within reach.

Imagine what life would be like if we did not get gray, lose hair, suffer tight and fragile skin, cataracts, diabetes mellitus, hypogonadism, osteoporosis, vascular diseases such as atherosclerosis (both myocardial and cerebrovascular), and age-related cancers? Wouldn't it be nice if we lived well and vigorously forever—in permanent, healthy, youthful life! I certainly do not mean growing old forever or even having access to some quick fixes by recall and restart buttons in the event of a crash. I mean a youthful immortality, built in, determined, reliable, and automatic!

I am not talking about believe-it-or-not poultices, miracle cures, and life-enhancing procedures currently in the pipeline for extending life. I leave that hopeful terrain to the perambulation of others.[2] Nor is *Becoming Immortal* an examination of the consequences of immortality for society and culture, of the bioethics of morality or immorality. I am confident that sociologists and social workers, bioethicists, and moralists will pick up on immortality without my impromptu prodding. My objective here is merely to promote a course of research at the end of which achieving immortality becomes a feasible alternative to aging and death. Mortal *Homo sapiens* forma *mortalis* can give rise to immortal *Homo sapiens* forma *immortalis! Becoming Immortal* shows how.

Most of what I have learned and have to say on making us immortal will come as no surprise to biologists. I have ascertained why, biologically speaking, we are not immortal; why we did not evolve immortality; and why at present we cannot develop immortality. But the history of life on Earth suggests how large, important changes in organisms have come about outside of Darwinian evolution and canonical developmental theories, and how, therefore, a change as portentous as becoming immortal might be achieved in extant forms. My recommendations for a course of research leading to the technology required for immortalization is not a science fiction fabrication. It is a serious attempt to foment debate on "Quo vadis?"

WHY BECOME IMMORTAL?

My guess is that the inspiration to become immortal is an extension of the awe experienced merely contemplating human life.

> What is the tie which conjoins these several aspects of mind [the human and the infrahuman] so inseparably? What is it else than "urge-to-live"? Human cognition may like the winged horse take at times its flights toward the stars and forget earth. None the less it is harnessed to life's car, whose charioteer is "urge-to-live" sublimed to "zest-to-live." It and its fellow-steeds, endeavour, will, emotion, passion or whatever else we call them pull under the same lash.[3]

Human life is so impressive that aging seems hardly worthy of it, and death seems a criminal affront.

Aesthetics and vanity aside, there is a more practical, and compelling, reason for becoming immortal: to effect prolonged space travel when Earth becomes uninhabitable and we have to abandon our solar system. Human beings will ultimately have to escape from Earth for any of a number of reasons, including those that have caused the mass extinctions of living forms in the past, namely "death from the sky" or "death from the mantle."[4] In our case, a still more likely scenario would seem to be death from ourselves.[5] I might also mention that the Sun will prove the ultimate and irresistible foe to life on Earth. If all goes according to schedule, the Sun will expand and swallow up Earth in a few billion years, but before that, it will "wipe out the entire biosphere,"[6] and, long before that, the Sun's increased luminosity will end human life.

No matter where the disaster comes from, if we are to preserve human life, we will have to send representatives of humanity to solar systems capable of sustaining human life. That such a solar system exists somewhere in our galaxy is reasonably certain. Where it is, is yet to be discovered. The trip through space to reach this solar system will undoubtedly take hundreds if not thousands of years, even at a maximally feasible velocity. The human beings flying the spaceship will have to be sterile, because reproduction would be disastrous on a space ship with limited resources, and immortal, because accumulated wisdom would permit flight in the face of contingency and monitoring a cargo of mortal human beings in suspended animation. The logistical problems will be enormous, but immortality is nonnegotiable.

Here then is the choice for humanity: Become immortal or accept the inevitable end of humanity. My preference is to make the effort to create immortal human beings in time to move a sizable part of humanity to safe ground.

HAS LIFE CHANGED?

In an age when cellular is as likely to refer to a mobile phone as a living thing, and clones[7] can be genes or ewes or even bunches of carrots and patches of strawberries on a field, one must be especially vigilant about the meaning of biology's terms. Even death, instead of being one of the two certainties of life (the other being taxes [thank you, Benjamin Franklin]), is now equivocal—*brain dead* is not dead vis-à-vis organs for transplant. Moreover, from the cover of *The New York Times Magazine*[8] to the recesses of academic journals one encounters uncertainty over life's determination by genes versus its regulation by the environment.[9] Has life changed? No, although parameters may have shifted.

Life is the state of existence prior to death. Life is always a precarious condition, maintained in a delicate balance between opportunity and contingency, but, even under the best of all possible circumstances, life is succeeded by death.

Death's inevitability is easily explained. Citing the deplorable statistics for preserving human life in long-term care facilities, the physician and popular-medicine writer, Sherwin Nuland, explains

> [t]hough their doctors dutifully record such distinct entities as stroke, or cardiac failure, or pneumonia, these aged folk have in fact died because something in them has worn out.[10]

Richard Lewontin, the evolutionary geneticist and philosopher of biology, relies on a mechanical metaphor to make the same point:

> [T]he cause of death is that living organisms are electro-mechanical devices, made up of articulated physical parts which, for purely thermodynamic reasons, eventually wear out and fail to function. Different parts wear out at different times in different individuals, and some parts are more prone to failure than others, or are located in the functional articulation at a place that is more critical.[11]

"Old age" and "worn out" are not categories accepted by the Department of Health and Human Services, the Bureau of Vital Statistics, or the World Health Organization, while cardiovascular accidents, cerebral thrombosis (stroke), various forms of cancer, and that old standby, pneumonia, are recognized as terminal events, but death is only secondarily a consequence of acute disease. It is primarily the sequela of a lifetime.

Leonard Hayflick, the doyen of cell-aging research, makes a similar point:

> More than 75% of all human deaths in developed countries now occur in those over the age of 75. If the causes of these deaths are resolved we will not become immortal but we will have revealed how death occurs in the absence of disease. What will be found is that the underlying cause of these deaths is the inexorable loss of physiological capacity in the cells of vital organs—the hallmark of ageing.[12]

And aging results from built-in obsolescence, from the disposability of soma, from the limits of the organism's repair capacity, or from the accumulation of genetic dust-beneath-the-cupboard, but not from aging genes.[13] Aging is not inherited in the ordinary way blue eye color is inherited. Rather, aging is inherited in a covert way—the way enfeebled metarterioles blossom on the bulb of your nose.[14]

LONGEVITY RESEARCH

Possibilities for foiling obsolescence are studied by longevity researchers, and their efforts to push the envelope of life-expectancy outward to its limit have been rewarded. Good health care, especially during one's youth, sufficient nutrition, adequate rest, and time to recuperate from exertion, injury, and abuse have already added years to the average human life-expectancy. One can also buy one or another commodity or service—or not buy other commodities or services—to good effect. How many more years can be added to the average human lifetime is uncertain, and estimates are all over the map, from no more than 15 years to more than 500 years.[15] But death still looms beyond that limit. Prolonged longevity is not immortality; it is only postponing the inevitable.

Once upon a time, humanity's answer to certain death was Heaven or some such extraterrestrial world, a working hypothesis for the preservation of the spirit.[16] Hypotheses for preserving the body were not equally robust, and solutions to the problem of the body's perishability have eluded all but the most imaginative. Science fiction writers have certainly worked immortality to death without creating anything especially new since Count Dracula. Scientists have not done much better. Even if the Human Genome Project, recently reaching its fruition,[17] allows us to inscribe our sequences of nucleotides (the monomers of deoxyribonucleic acid, better known as DNA) into a database, the encrypted message would not translate into a formula for material immortality—we would not achieve nirvana *in silico*.

The best hope for immortality would seem to be offered by cryonics, a program for freezing the newly dead, or at least the deceased's head, and resurrecting the individual at a future time when death is no longer a threat and when heads may be rejoined to bodies—although access to a headless body would seem to present another problem. Yes, you must die, but not without hope of corporeal revival.

Of course, the premise of cryonics is seriously encumbered not only by problems of revitalization but by uncertainty over restoring a persona. Personality and idiosyncrasies are unlikely to be preserved in ice even at the temperature of liquid nitrogen, and the defrosted body may resist reprogramming with the experience of a previous lifetime.

Alternatively, a great deal of popular literature offers programs for putting off the inevitable as long as possible, if not indefinitely. The fiction and nonfiction writer, Ben Bova, for example, prescribes a route to a semblance of immortality. He accepts the genetic determination of a lifetime but points out "that cancerous cells have found the trick of immortality."[18] Bova rests his case on the bevy of scientific work suggesting that various procedures and products, including improved general nutrition,[19] near-starvation (or caloric restriction [CR]),[20] antioxidants (superoxide dismutase/catalase mimetics),[21] early medical intervention against childhood diseases, rest and relaxation, and castration will allow more of us to achieve the longest possible life-expectancy.

Other programs for prolonging life center on reproduction as either conflicting or convergent with longevity. For example, early birthing and protracted lactation may prolong life by reducing the risk of breast and colon cancer but not without introducing other hazards that tend to reduce life-span.

On the other hand, given the hazards of birthing, increased longevity might be achieved merely by suspending birthing and having fewer offspring. Indeed, the relationship between delayed fecundity and longevity may be so profound that the average duration of a lifetime in future generations will be increased merely by selecting women exhibiting delayed childbearing, as suggested by Michael Rose, one of the parents of Darwinian medicine.[22] Longer lifetimes might be achieved by concentrating genes already in the human gene pool for delayed childbearing.

THE GENETICS OF LONGEVITY

One very ambitious program for promoting longevity consists of finding genes that cause or prevent aging and, utilizing the yet-to-be-discovered technology of gene therapy to prevent or promote the expression of these genes, thereby warding off their dire effects or enhancing their salubrious ones. The problem with this technique begins with traditional geneticists' habit of identifying normal genes by their opposite members—their mutations. In order to find genes influencing longevity, traditional geneticists look for mutations. In the case of longevity, the relevant mutations would be those that either accelerate aging or extend an individual's lifetime beyond the average life-span for members of the species. The first problem is that

> [e]ven in species where senescence does make some contribution to mortality in the wild . . . any hypothetical "accelerated ageing gene" would be disadvantageous to the individual. It is therefore difficult to see how genes for accelerated ageing could be maintained in stable equilibrium, as individuals in whom the genes were inactivated . . . would enjoy a selection advantage.[23]

On the other hand, several mutations extending an average life-span (among other things) have been discovered in model organisms living in the laboratory.[24] For example, in the fruit fly, *Drosophila melanogaster*,[25] the *chico*[26] and *methuselah* mutants extend life-span; in the round worm, *Caenorhabditis elegans*, *age-1*, *daf-2*, and other mutants in the insulin-like signaling pathway do likewise, possibly by enhancing the ability to respond to oxidative stress;[27] in yeast, *Saccharomyces cerevisiae*, *LAG1* and *LAC1* determine mean and maximum number of cell divisions (equated to life-span), *RAS1* is life-shortening, *RAS2* is life-extending; *SIR2* and *SIR4*, containing a specific *AGE* locus, may influence yeast's longevity through transcriptional silencing of genes mediating stress or caloric restriction.[28] Remarkably, *C. elegans*, containing a chromosome IV duplication, including a *sir-2* locus resembling yeast's *SIR2*,[29] and transgenic worms bearing this locus may live as much as 50% longer than normal adults. The products of the *sir* family of genes may all be involved in the insulin-like signaling pathway coupling longevity to nutrient availability.

In mice (and men?), life-span is influenced by a small number of mutant genes.[30] For example, mutations in the gene encoding the p66[shc] protein extend the life-span of mice about 30%, and mutants that inhibit the development of the pituitary gland, such as the gene-defective Prophet in Ames dwarf mice, extend life-span approximately 50%. The activities of life-span regulating genes and mutants may be positively correlated with high immune responsiveness, or negatively correlated with metabolic rate (body temperature) and oxidative damage (the mitochondrial free radical theory).

The relevance to human beings of genes discovered in laboratory organisms is certainly a hypothesis worth testing, but only a hypothesis until tested. No doubt genes will influence all the things that keep cells alive or kill them, but larger, longer-lived animals, such as human beings, will have different problems preserving their lives than shorter-lived animals. Longevity will probably depend on genes controlling different enzymes and metabolic pathways, such as antioxidant enzymes and DNA repair pathways.

Quantitative differences between large and small animals illustrate the problem of genetic relevance. Large animals have vastly more cells than smaller animals and maintain some of their latae cell populations by producing enormous numbers of cells per day by cellular proliferation. Unfortunately, cancer cells crop up among the normal cells constantly in production, and some cancers arise in older, larger, longer-lived animals that are virtually unknown in smaller, shorter-lived animals. Unlike short-lived animals whose lifetime may be determined by the preservation of small numbers of cells, large, long-lived animals have to apply

> a brake against the accumulation of the multiple mutations needed for a cell to become malignant. A 70-kg man who lives for 80 years has to be 14,000 times as resistant to developing cancer as a 0.2-kg rat that lives 2 years.[31]

Genes promoting longevity in the rat, therefore, may represent only a fraction of the genes promoting longevity in human beings.

Longevity-gene mutants do not kill an organism by firing a shot, and the normal gene does not prevent an organism's death by outfitting it in body armor. Rather, these genes set processes in motion which, operating through long cascades of actions and reactions, ultimately affect longevity. The hope of gene therapists is to deliver the right human gene to the right cells while replacing or silencing the wrong genes and ultimately preventing or reversing downstream cellular aging and promoting organismic longevity.[32] The possibility of transferring life-span expanding genes from other organisms to human beings is all the more problematic, since it is not clear whether genes influencing life-span in other animals will operate comparably in human beings.

Candidates for gene therapy are found among sufferers of several inherited aging disorders: genetic instability syndromes, mutants causing aberrations in DNA metabolism, such as *WRN* (null mutations in a helicase[33]) responsible for Werner syndrome (WS or progeria of adults),[34] Rothmund-Thomson syndrome, Cockayne syndrome, possibly Hutchinson-Gilford syndrome (progeria of childhood), and others.[35] The mutations causing these disorders result in the early onset of complex senescent phenotypes (progeria and progeroid syndromes). However,

> [i]t is an oversimplification to refer to these [senescent] disease as "premature ageing syndromes". To do so suggests that they will invariably reveal the mechanisms underlying "usual" or "normal" ageing. But their phenotypic features may sometimes be quite unusual, and some features may result from gross abnormalities in development.[36]

Moreover, genes involved with dementias and other symptoms of senescence which do not show up in progeria are usually associated with physiological activities, such as complex responses to stress mediated by reactive oxygen species (ROS), and hence with tangled interactions unsuitable for gene therapy. In any case, one enters unknown territory with gene therapy and even potent possibilities offer no guarantees.

"HELLO, DOLLY!" AND SALUTATIONS TO STEM CELLS

And then came Dolly, cloning, and stem-cell research, providing, in combination, a cure for mortality! This miracle cure does not merely cater to our long-time anxieties over longevity; it closes the gap between body and soul, offering for the first time, genuine corporeal immortality!

Together, cloning and stem cells can work miracles. Separately, they are just pieces of the puzzle, neither alone capable of making immortal organisms. Cloning only promises to replicate organisms (their parts or stem cells), and stem cells are merely self-renewing, pluripotential cells (having the ability to differentiate into other kinds of cells[37]).

CLONING

The first mammal cloned with a nucleus from a differentiated adult cell was born at the Roslin Institute in 1996[38] and whimsically named Dolly.[39] Speaking genetically, she was a replica of the organism whose cell donated a nucleus.[40] Dolly's nuclear parent was demonstrated morphologically and by high-tech DNA fingerprinting with polymorphic microsatellite DNA fragments. Dolly, the clone, inherited her genetic traits from a pregnant, 6-year old Finn-Dorset ewe killed in 1994 and not the Scottish Blackface which supplied the egg cytoplasm.[41] In all other ways, the pale faced Dolly is as normal as any Finn-Dorset ewe produced by ordinary sexual reproduction, as demonstrated in the Autumn of 1998 by her giving birth to Bonnie and, a year later, to even more lambs.[42]

The Roslin Institute "is a government laboratory, one of a network of institutes throughout Britain that now answer to the Biotechnology and Biological Sciences Research Council (BBSRC) which in turn is one of seven such councils that together form the core and umbrella of Britain's government-supported science and technology."[43] The cultured,[44] mammary gland cell providing the clone's original nucleus was supplied by the biotech startup,

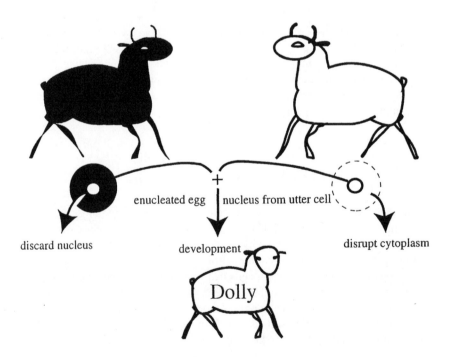

Pharmaceutical Proteins Ltd. (PPL) Inc., and PPL scientists were the "principal investigators" involved in the project.[45]

Dolly was no accident (although success with cloning is rare enough). Her birth was the climax of a series of experiments designed to promote pharming, the harvesting of biologically active materials from livestock. She joined an elite stable of cloned sheep made with nuclei donated by cultured embryonic cells (Megan and Morag, Cedric, Cyril, Cecil and Tuppence), fetal fibroblasts (Taffy and Tweed), and a genetically modified (transformed) culture cell (Polly)[46] carrying the human gene encoding clotting factor IX later secreted in her milk.[47]

Other announcements of cloning with nuclei from differentiated (adult) cells and fetal fibroblasts[48] followed on Dolly's coattails: a calf (Marguerite) in France and eight more in Japan (although only four survived the early antenatal period),[49] mice (Cumulina, named after the cumulus oophorus nuclear donor) in Hawaii,[50] a pig[51] (Xena presumably named for the prospects of using pigs as a source of xenotransplants to human beings) followed by more pigs,[52] and goats[53] if not a monkey.[54] Copycat cloning burgeoned, although frequently reported at press conferences and not in the strictly scientific style required by professional journals. The patented procedure for making Dolly (and hence the patenting of Dolly herself) also provoked turf battles around licensing and royalties, since cloned mammals might prove economically advantageous.[55] The biotech firms sponsoring the cloning of large mammals expect cloning to become as common in the twenty-first century as genetically modified plants were in the closing decade of the twentieth, at least in the United States and the Pacific Rim.[56]

In the public imagination, Dolly became a breakthrough in the struggle against perishability, and many pondered the possibility of extending life through facsimiles. Some simply hoped that cloning technology would make it possible to recreate loved ones from preserved tissue (in the mode of *Creator,* starring Peter O'Toole) from recently deceased children or favorite pets, but, inevitably, self-love conquered, and the idea of perpetuating oneself became a preoccupation of wistful dreamers. Richard Dawkins, the evolutionist and popular science writer, stated his own preference to recreate himself through cloning and challenged the rest of us:

> Mightn't even you, in your heart of hearts, quite like to be cloned? . . . I think I would. . . . My feeling is founded on pure curiosity. . . . I find it a personally riveting thought that I could watch a small copy of myself, fifty years younger and wearing a baseball hat instead of a British Empire pith helmet, nurtured through the early decades of the twenty-first century. Mightn't it feel almost like turning back your personal clock fifty years? And mightn't it be

wonderful to advise your junior copy on where you went wrong, and how to do it better?[57]

Cloning did not, however, embody the essence of immortality, that is, personal continuity. The microneedle sometimes used in cloning to inject the nucleus of an adult's cell into the cytoplasm of an egg is hardly a fountain of youth, and cloning hardly reanimates the nuclear donor (e.g., the long dead ewe whose udder cell donated the nucleus used in the cloning of Dolly).[58] Cloning is not about rejuvenating individuals. Cloning only replicates them, and then, only as far as their nuclear-genetically encoded traits.

A clone is supposed to be a facsimile of the nuclear-donor, but a human being, clone or not, is inevitably its own person, not the nuclear donor carried over to a new body. In all likelihood, one's clone would develop its own personality, living in its own time and place, even if one tutors one's clone personally. A personality is something acquired over a lifetime, influenced heavily by nurture, experience, and learning, and such a lifetime is unlikely to be transferred to the new body by a mere nucleus (even with a good dose of donor cytoplasm).[59]

Inevitably, individuals are no more likely to see their clones as themselves as they are likely to see their offspring, as currently conceived, as themselves. The break between nuclear donor and clone is just as large as the break between parents and ordinary offspring, especially since the clone would develop in utero much the same way as any normally fertilized egg or an egg following in vitro fertilization and embryo transfer to a prenatal foster mother or surrogate. Furthermore, no matter how much one's clone looks and behaves like oneself as an infant, one's own ego is likely to balk and leave one unable to identify one's clone with oneself as an adult. In the final analysis or moment, one is unlikely to "go quietly into that gentle sleep" believing that one's clone is oneself.

Dolly also inspired a flurry of ethical controversies, duly raised and aired from the highest echelon of government to the lowest rungs of the tabloid press. These issues were set off by a Geron bombshell when Michael West, chief executive officer of Advanced Cell Technology, announced that a mammalian blastocyst (a preembryo[60]) had developed from a cow's egg (sans its own nucleus) and a human nuclear transplant.[61] The private sector had only been motivated to create bovine/human chimeras for research as a way of economizing, since cow eggs cost $1.00 while human eggs cost no less than $1,000, but the specter of "playing God" would thereafter haunt cloning.

One day, or so it seemed to the casual observer, cloning one's pets and even oneself was as American as apple pie, the next day, cloning was strictly verboten, if not a crime against humanity![62] As a consequence, like a meteor careening toward Earth, by 1998 cloning human beings seemed doomed to follow a trajectory to oblivion. After all, cloning had already been done in fiction and movies (e.g., *Boys from Brazil*), only to be repudiated as a means for preserving "desirable" individuals. Yet, before hurdling to a fiery death, cloning received a boost and became relevant to immortality again. The thrust came from another breakthrough technology in this struggle against perishability.

STEM CELLS

Long before stem cells became prime subjects in immortality research, stem cells were studied for their role in normal tissue maintenance.[63] The idea was that individuals were constantly refurbished by stem cells, thereby maintaining life. The constant turnover of cells in the outer layer of skin (epidermis), the inner layer of the digestive track (absorptive cells), and blood and lymphatic systems were known since World War II. At that time, the advent of radioactive elements and labeled materials (especially tritiated thymidine) had made it practical to track cellular turnover.

Diminished production of particular materials associated with some diseases (e.g., insulin and diabetes) suggested that the sufferer's primary defect

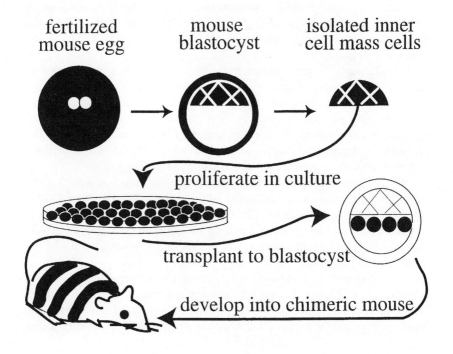

fertilized mouse egg   mouse blastocyst   isolated inner cell mass cells

proliferate in culture

transplant to blastocyst

develop into chimeric mouse

might be abnormally low concentrations of replacement-stem cells. The potential of stem cells in therapy seemed enormous, and attempts to use stem cells therapeutically were well underway in the closing decades of the twentieth century: Fetal nerve precursors were transplanted to the brains of Parkinson's disease patients, and bone marrow was transplanted to patients suffering from leukemias, lymphomas, and other cancers.[64]

Most of the fundamental research on stem cells was done on embryonic or embryonal stem (ES) cells obtained from mouse preembryos or blastocysts and raised in tissue culture. These cells could differentiate into virtually any adult mouse cell upon reintroduction into developing mouse blastocysts. But, in the November 6, 1998 issue of the weekly science magazine, *Science,* the team led by James Thomson at the University of Wisconsin with funding from Geron Corporation of Menlo Park, California, announced that it had isolated and cultured human ES cells from 20 of 36 human blastocysts left over from *in vitro* fertilization.[65] Thus, a virtually endless supply of human stem cells became available for research.

The November 10, 1998 issue of the journal, *Proceedings of the National Academy of Sciences,* followed with the announcement by John Gearhart and others at The Johns Hopkins University School of Medicine,[66] likewise with funding from Geron Corporation, that primordial germ cells (PGCs), or germ stem (GS) cells had been isolated and cultured from the gonadal ridges and mesenteries of 5- to 9-week post-fertilization human embryos obtained by therapeutic abortion. These cells not only proliferated in tissue culture, but differentiated into a variety of cell types, including representatives of all three embryonic germ layers.[67]

The Thomson/Gearhart research did more than answer the question of whether human embryos and fetuses contain stem cells. Their research demonstrated that human stem cells could be amplified in tissue culture, theoretically removing the greatest block to stem-cell replacement therapy, namely, the difficulty of obtaining sufficient quantities of high-quality stem cells. The problem of quantity had plagued attempts to re-nervate the substantia nigra of Parkinson's disease patients with dopamine producing cells.

Like the cloning of Dolly, the isolation of stem cells had been accomplished in the private sector, and Geron stock nearly doubled its value following news of the breakthroughs. The United States Congress and parliaments in many countries had driven research on human stem cells into the private sector by placing human embryos and fetuses on the proscribed list of national granting agencies.

The politics of stem-cell research is as murky as the politics of cloning. Human stem-cell research with ES cells derived from preembryos and GS cells from aborted fetuses quickly runs afoul of abortion politics. After much hand wringing, on December 19, 2000, in an open vote, the British House of

Commons approved 366 to 174 new rules allowing scientists to derive and use stem cells from human embryos and perform experiments with nuclear transfer.[68] In the United States, the National Bioethics Advisory Commission recommended easing the strictures on research utilizing human embryos and fetuses.[69] President Clinton partially lifted the ban on cloning and President Bush has decided to allow research utilizing ES cells, although United States scientists will not receive support from the National Institutes of Health allowing them to cull human stem cells from the detritus of *in vitro* fertility clinics. Of course, entrepreneurial scientists will perform human stem-cell research, and the possibility of immortality research through stem cells will soon become global business.[70]

Stem-cell researchers will add ways for increasing longevity with the help of cybernetic devices and electronic prostheses, performing one or another miracle and enhancing well-being for great numbers of individuals who can afford the cost of these technologies. However, stem-cell therapy as such, like other longevity-enhancing devices, only delays the inevitable, and, like cloning, is not in and of itself the long-sought cure for mortality. The panacea for aging, however, is close at hand: It lies in combining the technologies of cloning and stem-cell therapy.

COMBINING CLONING AND STEM CELLS FOR IMMORTALITY

The possibility of biological immortality rests on two premises: (1) *Anyone able to perpetually regenerate, reinvigorate, and replace aged or diseased parts of their body could live in the same body from birth to eternity with their persona intact.* (2) *A clone of one's own cells could serve as a source of embryonic stem cells able to support cellular renewal.*

Neither of the above premises is controversial. The idea of perpetual replacement is as old as the industrial revolution and the manufacture of interchangeable parts. That ES cells could serve as a source of such parts is a new but not too novel permutation on older concepts of stem-cell therapy.

According to the science writer, Gina Kolata, the idea of clones serving as a source of stem cells was first articulated by the Harvard hematologist Stuart Orkin.

> Ultimately, Orkin said, [if] scientists . . . could learn how the egg reprograms a cell's DNA, bringing it back to its primordial state, they might someday be able to force a cell to reprogram its *own* DNA and then differentiate into any sort of cell that the scientists want. That, of course is the most futuristic scenario of all, Orkin warned, but it shows what might someday be possible. That process

of learning to reprogram a cell's DNA would have to begin, however, with cloning.[71]

Indeed, the desire to reprogram the genome had motivated Ian Wilmut's and Keith Campbell's efforts that led to Dolly. In their words, they found ways of "*restoring* totipotency to cell lines that once would have seemed to be differentiated beyond recall . . . creating new embryos from cells that are already differentiated, by reprogramming their genomes."[72]

The novel idea introduced here is that *grafting a clone to an embryo would create a permanent generator of embryonic stem cells and immortalize the host organism* (see Chapter 5 for details). A certain amount of difficulty or hesitance may greet this idea, since little in the history of biology prepares biologists to think synthetically about changing human life. Indeed, biologists can hardly be expected to think about creating new organs and tissues, since the evolution of tissues and organs in organisms is not even explained in standard works of evolutionary theory. Furthermore, standard works of developmental biology sometimes pay attention to correcting errors of metabolism caused by mutations but never pay so much as lip service to the possibility of developing new organs capable of solving old problems.

Little-known studies of parasitism (see discussion of devolution in Chapter 4) suggest how tissues and organs might have originated by fission and fragmentation. These studies suggest that implanting a preembryo in an embryo would be a direct route to providing the developing host with a new organ. Were that organ capable of generating ES cells indefinitely, the host would be capable of living indefinitely.

A clone would seem an ideal source of stem cells for a variety of reasons, not the least of which is the untrammeled tolerance, or self-recognition, of the body for the clone and the clone for the body. Likewise, a blastocyst, or preembryo, would seem the ideal stage for implantation into a developing host, since the portion of the blastocysts known as the inner cell mass (ICM) is the traditional source of ES cells—proliferating cells not yet on their way to differentiate in particular pathways.

The idea of human immortality may still seem like a fairy tale, but if an organ can be created via implantation into an embryo, little else in all this theorizing will be biologically contentious. Cloning and stem-cell research are already the premier topics of immortality research because they can work as sources of immunologically acceptable stem cells. What is added here is merely the idea of implanting the clone and turning it into a permanent source of ES cells, thereby turning the host into a permanent living being.

The solution to the ancient problem of mortality seems in retrospect so simple that one may wonder why biologists have not thought of it before. The answer resides in biology's historic predilection to ponder old problems instead of new possibilities.

WHY WE ARE NOT IMMORTAL OR WHAT IS LIFE ANYWAY?

Mortality is part and parcel of biologists' conception of life which goes back to Aristotle in the fourth century B.C. This conception matured materially following the days of idyllic nature, and, in the seventeenth century, some natural philosophers separated themselves from religious philosophers in order to investigate life's mechanisms.[73] Later, eighteenth century nature philosophers declared their allegiance to natural law and attempted to attract acolytes to their rigorous version of life on Earth. Early nineteenth century biologists attempted to offer solutions to life's transcendent problems as well as answers to questions such as what life is doing here, where life comes from, and how it got to where it is now, if not where it is heading in the long term. At the same time, biologists entered the ranks of professional scientists, earning wages and other perquisites for their trouble. Now, at the advent of the twenty-first century, biologists have become the engineers of entrepreneurial enterprises with a little help from their friends, from venture capital, and from those holding the purse strings of national granting agencies and nonprofits.

A synthetic branch of biology never quite germinated from its root and stem. Instead, biologists became mired in a theory of life consisting of three down and dirty parts: 1) flux, 2) discontinuity, and 3) waste. Flux moves the sameness of life from cell to cell and organism to organism, and everything else living things share with each other; discontinuity creates individuals and allows them to gamble and compete or trade off differences with each other; waste is life's great resource, supporting everything within life's capability. Taken together, the three parts of this theory of biological life circumscribe and prescribe mortality. This version of life also encapsulates the obstacles to both thinking about and achieving immortality.

FLUX

Briefly, from the point of view of contemporary biology, life is impermanent. Living things, such as adult organisms, are unstable, and groups of living things, such as species, are transient. Indeed, life's most abiding feature may be its constant flux, for example, the turnover of animals brought about by birth and death. In order to turn the tables on mortality and change us from mortals into immortals, turnover has to be turned into equilibrium. This will not be as hard as it might seem on first blush, since life's flux, in practice, is continuous.

August (Friedrich Leopold) Weismann (1834–1914), a professor at the University of Freiburg at Breisgau, first appreciated life's flux and continuity in essentially modern terms in the closing decades of the nineteenth century.[74] Weismann's place in history was guaranteed, however, when his language was translated into the vernacular of twentieth century genetics by the Oxford Professor of Zoology, Richard (Clinton) Dawkins (b. 1941).[75] Essentially, living things, or organisms, consist of two elements, one of which, called the germplasm by Weismann, is continuous from generation to generation; the other element, called the somatoplasm by Weismann, is discontinuous, only emerging as an offshoot of germplasm as a mark of succeeding generations. Translated into modern terms, germplasm is a complete set of genes (a genome), and somatoplasm comprises the body of an organism.

Operationally, germplasm passes from parent to offspring and generation to generation in a germ line comprised of germ cells or gametes, commonly eggs and spermatozoa. In contrast, all the cell types making up all the tissues, organs, and organ systems comprise the somatoplasm. It takes its origin from the fertilized egg or zygote and fans out into somatic cell lines in the course

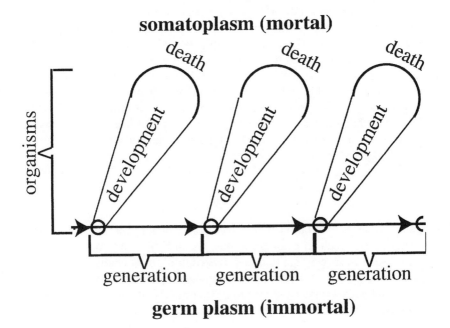

of development. As differentiated cells, eggs or spermatozoa represent unique cell lines. As germ cells belonging to the germ line, they can escape the confines of the organism to reach new generations.

Everyone alive today has acquired germplasm from biological parents who have acquired germplasm from biological parents, and all these biological parents would seem to have acquired germplasm from biological parents back to some time in the Precambrian when sexual reproduction was consolidated in animal reproduction. Moreover, everyone born in the future will have acquired their germplasm from biological parents,[76] and this continuity will last as long as one leaves progeny and one's progeny leave progeny.[77] Clones might seem to be an exception, but their biological parents will inevitably be located one or more generations removed. The quality of continuity in germplasm as opposed to the discontinuity in somatoplasm—popping up in every generation—means that germplasm is immortal, while somatoplasm is not!

Arguably, twentieth century biology consists of deciphering the operations of Weismann's germ- and somatoplasm. The idea of an immortal germplasm has merged with the idea of permanent, particulate conveyors of heredity, known originally as Mendelian factors and rechristened *genes*. Germplasm was virtually ready-made for transformation into self-replicating DNA, but somatoplasm continues to confront biologists with some of life's most bewildering mysteries.

The Secret of Life

Life's deepest secret, and the one that has preoccupied naturalists and biologists for centuries, is the quality that distinguishes life in all living things from death. If one were to rank biological problems by the status of individuals trying to solve them, this secret of life would be the highest. No end of eminent biologists have discussed their work in terms of this secret and have tried finding its solution.

As late as the 1930s, the physicist-turned-biologist, Max Perutz, thought that "the Secret of Life—in capital letters—consisted of the function of enzymes."[78] Linus Pauling imagined protein as concealing the solution to the "secret of life."[79] Today, the consensus of opinion is that Perutz and Pauling were wrong.

The physicist, Erwin Schrödinger, is generally credited with articulating in 1944 the modern secret of life in his book *What is Life?*[80] although he does not literally use the phrase—it would have been out of character for a physicist. Other words, "conundrum"[81] and "enigmatic"[82] appear, but "secret" escapes him. "Secret" is, nevertheless, implied by the questions and clues around which he organizes his book, a secret, moreover, waiting to be solved by the methods of physics:

How can the events *in space and time,* which take place within the spatial boundary of a living organism be accounted for by physics and chemistry? (Pg. 3; emphasis original.)

[I]ncredibly small groups of atoms . . . have control of the observable large scale features which the organism acquires in the course of its development . . . [and] determine important characteristics of its functioning. (Pg. 21.)

How can we . . . reconcile the facts that the gene structure seem [*sic*] to involve only a comparatively small number of atoms . . . , and that nevertheless it displays a most regular and lawful activity—with a durability or permanence that borders upon the miraculous? (Pg. 49.)

Are these structures [genes] . . . capable of withstanding for long periods the disturbing influence of heat motion to which the hereditary substance is continually exposed? (Pg. 61.)

Thus it would appear that the "new" principle, the order-from-order principle, to which we have pointed with great solemnity as being the real clue to the understanding of life, is not at all new to physics (Pg. 87.).

Schrödinger predicts that revelation will come from "the material carrier of life" (pg. 5)—the self-reproducing unit of hereditary information or gene found on the chromosome which he considered "an aperiodic crystal" (Pg. 5) or "solid" (Pg. 65),

or probably only an axial skeleton fibre of what we actually see under the microscope as the chromosome, that contain in some kind of code-script the entire patterns of the individual's future development and of its functioning in the mature state (Pg. 22).

Furthermore,

chromosome structures . . . are law-code and executive power—or, to use another simile, they are architect's plan and builder's craft— in one. (Pg. 23.)

Biologists—not to short-change physicists and chemists—have sought to solve life's secret through genes ever since.

What is Life? had an enormous impact, especially among war-weary physicists, and was responsible for Francis Crick "leaving physics and developing an interest in biology."[83] *What is Life?* "very elegantly propounded the belief that genes were the key components of living cells and that, to understand what life is, we must know how genes act."[84]

Another development in biology also had enormous impact. Evidence accumulated that DNA, not protein, was the gene. From London to Pasadena, researchers had linked genes to DNA, but the breakthrough came when James Dewey Watson (b. 1928) heard Maurice Wilkins (b. 1916) describe an X-ray diffraction picture of DNA made by Rosalind Elsie Franklin (1920–1958). Watson believed that the continuity of life was structural, and that "when the structure of DNA was known, we might be in a better position to understand how genes work."[85] He conveyed his recollections of Franklin's picture to his collaborator, Francis Harry Compton Crick (b. 1916), and, with a little help from Max Perutz, they set out to turn this "potential key to the secret of life."[86]

Watson's and Crick's fundamental belief in "order-from-order" or structure from structure led them to conceive of the double-helical structure of DNA—two strands of nucleic acids coiling around a common axis like two spiral rails joined by steps made of complementary nitrogenous bases. And when, in 1953, tinkering with structural models finally produced a model consistent with Franklin's X-ray diffraction picture, "Francis winged into the Eagle [a well-known Cambridge bar] to tell everyone within hearing distance that we had found the secret of life." Quieter by nature, Watson seems to have reserved his announcement of their discovering the "secret of life" for a letter to his informal mentor and idol, Max Delbrück.[87]

Actually, a great deal was already known about DNA at the time, but what had escaped notice, and what Watson and Crick brought to everyone's attention, was that the nitrogenous bases in one strand of DNA were complementary to the nitrogenous bases in the other strand.[88] One strand could therefore determine the nitrogenous bases in the other strand. Watson and Crick concluded their seminal report in the British scientific weekly, *Nature*, "It has not escaped our notice that the specific pairing we have postulated immediately suggests a possible copying mechanism for the genetic material."[89]

The idea of DNA as the gene—the DNA/gene—is wondrously simple: Each strand of DNA is supposed to direct the synthesis of a complementary strand. A new strand of DNA is synthesized by assembling nucleotides bearing complementary nitrogenous bases in place and zippering them up into another strand with complementary nucleotides.[90] Today, the molecular reproduction of the DNA/gene, or the synthesis of one strand of DNA as a complement to a preexisting DNA strand, is known as replication—DNA-dependent DNA synthesis—and is possibly the best known reaction in molecular biology, if not biochemistry. Replication is not simple, however, dependent as it is on a multitude of enzymes, primers, engines, and editors.[91]

Life's Other Secrets

From the beginning, expectations for DNA were unreasonably high—DNA was expected to play all the roles of genes while remaining essentially a simple molecule. Biologists may be masters of reductionism, but heredity could not be reduced quite this far and genes could not be as simple as the pairing of complementary bases in DNA. The enthusiasm shared by biologists the world over for the DNA/gene was justified, nevertheless, by the high achievements of the bio-technical sciences and the biotech industry.

As things turned out, the two-dimensional sequence of nitrogenous bases in DNA did not live up to the requirements for genes in four-dimensional life. The double helix was not the "formula," "recipe" or "blue print" for making and maintaining somatoplasm or germplasm. A great deal more had to be added to cells, especially to eukaryotic cells[92] of animals, plants, fungi, and protoctistans.[93] Among the additions were the self-reproducing organelles (mitochondria and chloroplasts), the self-generating surface (cortex), and a dynamic cytoskeleton. Only then could a eukaryotic cell begin to perform all the functions of heredity attributed originally (naively) to DNA/genes.

Gradually, biologists appreciated the limitations of DNA/genes and began to uncover other secrets of life, especially those controlling DNA/genes. In the 1960s, Jacques Monod[94] held out for a new "secret of life"—the control of gene activity.[95] Monod studied mutant strains of the colonic bacillus, *Escherichia coli* (*E. coli*) and demonstrated that its genes' activity consisted of producing single strands of ribonucleic acid (RNA). These RNA strands, subsequently identified as messenger RNA (mRNA), directed the synthesis of particular proteins. Some genes were continuously engaged in mRNA synthesis, while others were turned on or off or tuned up or down. Gene activity was controlled by the action of gene-controlling proteins known as regulators and repressors, or, more recently, transcription factors. Monod's "second secret" was bound up with the control of substances controlling gene activity.

By the 1970s, life's secrets had proliferated again, and, with the introduction of chaos theory by mathematical biophysicists, the number of life's secrets expanded exponentially.[96] Then, in the late 1980s, the last, great secret,[97] the sequence of nucleotides in the human genome, became the objective, or what Walter Gilbert called "the grail," of high-tech laboratories around the world.[98] The Human Genome Project rapidly became the most expensive biological project ever funded. It was supported internationally by governmental agencies, as well as pharmaceutical firms. In the words of the science critic, Richard Doyle:

> The action and manipulation of nucleic acids became the hallmark
> of a molecular biology that no longer simply analyses organisms
> but—in symbiosis with stock markets and venture capitalists—trans-
> forms them, generating life forms without precedent.[99]

What then has been learned from the molecular biologist's ruminations on life's secrets? What is now known about the DNA/gene that was not already implied by Weismann's germplasm? Probably the most important thing is that the modern search for life's secrets has put biologists in a position to control life beyond anyone's wildest dreams, and it is precisely that control which brings immortality within the realm of palpable possibility.

Life's Aporia

As dazzling as biology's accomplishments are in making sense of genes, biologists are still bewildered by the immortality of germplasm and the mortality of somatoplasm. Indeed, the problem of immortality would disappear if the situation were reversed and, instead of germplasm, somatoplasm were immortal. Why are germ- and somatoplasm different in this crucial respect?

Weismann had proposed the existence of different germ- and somatoplasms in order to explain the results of experiments intended to test the Lamarckian principle of the "inheritance of acquired characteristics." According to Weismann's reading of Lamarck, changes acquired by an organism in the course of its lifetime should be passed to offspring through heredity. Thus, Weismann had tails amputated from new-born mice over many generations. No effect on succeeding generations was noted, indicating to Weismann that Lamarck was not only wrong but indubitably wrong.

Many objections are easily raised to Weismann's method, and his results are no longer interpreted as an incontrovertible refutation of Lamarck's principle.[100] Today, neither the experiment nor its negative results are discussed much, but Weismann's theory of separate germ- and somatoplasm remains a powerful canon of biology's lore. In its modern incarnation, known as the "central dogma," Weismann's theory is a pillar of biological rectitude.

Simply put, the central dogma states that the flow of information from DNA to RNA to protein is a one-way street. Characteristics influenced by DNA/genes and hence the body (somatoplasm)—or more precisely, enzymes and the products of enzymatic activities and their structural interactions—have no influence on hereditary material (germplasm), or DNA/genes.

Biologists do not mean that genes operate in a vacuum or that their activities are not influenced by events and processes in the cytoplasm. The central dogma merely asserts that messages encoded in genes are "engraved in concrete"—or germplasm, as the case may be. The messages are encoded in DNA's sequence of nitrogenous bases, or primary structure, and sequences are neither specified by cytoplasm nor modified by cytoplasm.[101] On the other hand, everything about the cytoplasm, the cell, and the organism is supposed to be determined by the messages encoded in DNA. According to the central dogma, the solutions to all of life's problems begins with DNA/genes and ends with cytoplasm, cells, organs, and organism.

The history of modern biotechnology is the tale of the central dogma—mainly how to violate it. With the help of massive infusions of cash, biologists have worked out the techniques for targeting genes for change, for combining DNA from different sources—recombinant DNA technology—for amplifying genes through gene cloning and the polymerase chain reaction (PCR), getting genes into cells with the help of vectors and electroporation, and screening for genetically modified cells. As a result, human hormones are presently manufactured by bacteria and cultured cells, genetically modified food is presently available in supermarkets around the world, and human proteins are harvested from the secretions of livestock—so-called pharming.

Cloning and stem-cell research are only the latest efforts to violate the central dogma. They can only accelerate the production of genetically modified organisms.

The Riddle of Life

At the same time some biologists were solving the secret of life, others were riveted by the riddle of life: the enigma of death in the midst of life. A rich literature grew from the nineteenth century examination of life as an open thermodynamic system in contrast to death as the lowest free-energy point. At one time, it seemed that life was only the reaction of macromolecules to each other and to the solvents and solutes in their environment. The riddle permeated the early literature of twentieth century molecular biology. For example, Wendell M. Stanley, who crystallized the tobacco mosaic viral protein in 1935, struggled with "finding the key to the riddle of life,"[102] and Max Delbrück spoke of the "riddle of life" in a 1937 "preliminary write-up" in which he considered viral replication as "a particular trick of organic chemistry."[103] By 1970, Delbrück announced, prematurely as it turned out, "This riddle of life has been solved."[104]

Later in the twentieth century, speculations on life at the interstices of order and chaos dominated the scientific imagination, and, it seemed, life was an emergent property, a fractal crystallized between dimensions, while death lay outside the sleeve of probabilities surrounding the living state and too far from one or another attractor state.[105] But genes had yet to take their place in this ordered disorder.

Once again, August Weismann had anticipated the modern solution by expounding the power of germplasm—alias genes—to determine the duration of life.[106] The most provocative evidence that something inherited through germplasm determined the duration of life came from the literature on protozoan reproduction: Purely asexually reproducing populations of some protozoans (*Paramecium*) degenerated, while sexually reproducing, or conjugating, organisms, restored the population's vitality.[107] Still, it was difficult to imagine why the duration of a lifetime should be determined at all.

In the first years of the twentieth century, Weismann's ideas on the determination of life's duration were broadly rejected, especially since they seemed utterly in conflict with the dominant view of neoDarwinian evolution, namely, that everything that evolved through genes was adaptive. What could genes be adaptive to while determining the length of a lifetime? What could possibly be advantageous about genes that caused the death of the organism at any time?

Several possibilities are now tendered in the marketplace of evolutionary ideas. For example, genes that delayed death in the young and fecund might backfire in old age and cause death.[108] Alternatively, genes for death might once have managed to hitchhike their way into generations by attaching themselves to other genes that actually provided substantial advantages for reproduction and without which organisms would survive and reproduce for shorter periods.

Programmed Cell Death and Apoptosis: A major problem with Weismann's ideas on the inheritance of lifetime was posed by the results of the first experiment with tissue culture. Ross Grainville Harrison (1870–1959) invented hanging-drop tissue culture in 1907 in order to see if pre-nerve cells could grow neural processes as they differentiated into nerves. His experiment answered the question positively, but the nerves died in tissue culture despite their being young and having everything they needed to survive.[109]

Weismann had predicted that cells would die at their appointed hour, but nerves are among the longest lived cells in organisms and should not have died in Harrison's experiment when they did. The apparent contradiction with Weismann's ideas has never been resolved, but history was kind to Weismann again, and the issue was decided in Weismann's favor: Cells in tissue culture that die after differentiating are said to have committed suicide by genetically determined, "programmed cell death." The idea is that, following differentiation, genes force the cells to release a cascade of events which end in the cells' demise. Cytologically, the dying cell's nucleus has the appearance of falling apart, hence, cells are said to undergo "apoptosis"—from the Greek word for the falling away of petals from a flower or leaves from a tree.

The direct command to commence apoptosis seems to be given by mitochondria, a cell organelle and most important source of consumable energy.[110] It seems that when cells cannot maintain the level of energy required to keep ion-transport channels functioning, mitochondria inform the cell of its impending doom, and it shuts down systematically. Apoptosis provides a classic example of organellar-cellular interactions.

Apoptosis seems to offer organisms several adaptive advantages. In multicellular organisms and yeast, the systematic shutdown of one effete cell might reduce the spread of damage to other, related cells. In animals, DNA replicated with serious errors triggers fail-safe devices, and, if the cell determines that the errors cannot be corrected, the signal for apoptosis is broadcast. Similarly, cells which have accumulated too many bad genes might decide to give up the ghost when the bad genes' products would turn the cell into an invasive and destructive cancer. Apoptosis, or death at the cellular level, may thereby actually prolong the organism's life rather than forecast its doom.

Programmed cell death may kill cells, but it is not necessarily destructive. Apoptosis is widespread in organisms where excess tissue is whittled down (the fibrocartilaginous callus joining parts of a fractured bone, for example), in fetuses where parts are sculptured into new configurations (e.g., freeing the embryonic limb from the body wall), and embryonically where cavitation via programmed cell death carves out major embryonic and extraembryonic cavities. In insects, amphibians, and other organisms which undergo metamorphosis between larva and juvenile stages, apoptosis may remove larval tissue.

Programmed cell death also serves as a preemptive strike in adults against the encroachments of cancer. The major tumor-suppressor genes are linked to apoptotic cascades. But programmed cell death and apoptosis do not seem to be the cause of normal aging or dying.

Cell Longevity *in vitro* and the Hayflick Number: Harrison's hanging drop technique was the forerunner of modern tissue culture, or *in vitro* cell techniques, the mainstay of many molecular biology laboratory and biotech firm.[111] But contrary to the pre-neurons cultured by Harrison, cells in tissue-culture laboratories, remain living, actively dividing cells virtually forever, or as long as they are properly maintained. These cells have descended from cells derived from cancers or from cells immortalized *in vitro*—spontaneously immortalized mouse cells or cells treated with oncoviruses or transfected with oncogenes.[112] Some ES cells and GS cells are also immortal in tissue culture.[113]

On the other hand, *almost* invariably, cells freshly excised from adult tissue fail to divide after a period in culture and go into a state of replicative quiescence known as "crisis," "replicative senescence," or "mortality stage 1." Mammalian fibroblasts[5] "do not die after entering [replicative] senescence but remain viable for years if maintained with weekly changes of culture medium."[114] The cells enlarge, even forming giant cells with several enlarged nuclei, produce particular forms of enzymes (senescence associated [SA]ß-galactosidase), and go on living.

The number of divisions performed by freshly excised cells in tissue culture before entering "irreversible replicative senescence" is defined as the "Hayflick number" or "Hayflick limit." Beginning at about 50 in human-embryo fibroblasts, the Hayflick number decreases with age. Fibroblasts cultured from an elderly person might divide just a few times before entering replicative senescence.[115] The Hayflick number also decreases in parallel with the life expectancy of a species: from about 130 for the Galapagos tortoises to less than a dozen for rat- and mouse-embryo fibroblasts.

The Hayflick number posed a challenge to cloners of large mammals: Could a somatic nucleus be reset to the maximum Hayflick number by passing through the cytoplasm of an egg cell? If the answer were "no," then cloning was doomed to failure, since each generation of cloned animals would have a shorter lifetime. The fact that Dolly and other cloned mammals have given birth to normal offspring—exhibiting no signs of progeria and progeroid syndromes—suggests that cloners reset the Hayflick number in their clones. Moreover, the clones seem themselves capable of resetting the Hayflick number in their own progeny, since premature aging was not found after six generations of consecutively cloned mice.[116]

The Hayflick number posed a similar challenge to stem-cell researchers, but ES and GS cells (if not other stem or transit cells) seem to have extraordinarily high Hayflick numbers, possibly infinitely high. But ES- and GS-cell lines (one might add teratocarcinoma cell lines) are quite plastic. Although ES and GS cells *in vitro* are ordinarily capable of prolonged (infinite?) propagation, some lines are also available for tweaking into differentiation, at which time they cease cell division. In fact, unlimited self-renewal by cell division is one of ES-cell lines' main qualifications for replacement therapy.

The Telomere Story: Recent interest in Hayflick numbers has centered on the possibility that the ends of chromosomes, known as telomeres, shorten in successive divisions, thereby keeping track of cell divisions.[117] Telomeres are also thought to function in preventing chromosomes from sticking to each other, and their "capping status" was thought to be crucial to their function in carcinogenesis.[118]

The roles of telomeres in cell senility and carcinogenesis seem contradictory. Telomeres should be longer in cells that divide indefinitely, but "[t]elomeres in human cancer cells are often significantly shorter than their normal tissue counterparts."[119] The shortened telomeres of these cells account for some of the more bizarre chromosomes and karyotypes seen in these cancers (e.g., the carcinoma-*in situ*-stage of human breast cancer and the early adenoma or polyp stage of colorectal cancer). In some cancer cells (lymphoma), but not others (breast and colorectal), shortening of telomeres by successive divisions seems to send an apoptotic instruction.[120]

Unlike normal human cells, many immortalized cells maintain their telomeres with the aid of a complex holoenzyme known as telomerase. Similarly, human cells (from retinal pigmented epithelium to fibroblasts), normally lacking an active telomerase, produce the active holoenzyme when transfected with the gene encoding the catalytic subunit of telomerase (*hTRT* or *hTERT*). These cells then maintain their telomeres while undergoing cell divisions well beyond the expected Hayflick number.[121] Telomerase may even have therapeutic value, since transfection with the mouse telomere gene (*mTR*) in telomerase-deficient, cirrhotic mouse livers restores telomerase activity, cell division, liver regeneration, and improved liver function.[122]

Still, the relevance of Hayflick numbers and telomeres to cellular longevity is unclear. The Hayflick numbers may not be relevant at all to stem cells. According to the cell physiologists, Potten and Loeffler:

> [I]n a 70 year life-span the small intestinal crypt stem cells in man might divide 5000 times. Whether such a division capacity can be regarded as indicating immortality is debatable but the number of divisions that a normal stem cell is capable of is very large—1000 in the murine small intestine and several thousands in man.[123]

Hayflick numbers may still be relevant to the determination of senescence in fibroblasts, but, at the moment, a cell's history of divisions is not easily tied to its death, and no less to the death of the organisms. Cells generally, and stem cells in particular, simply have not run out of their prescribed number of cell divisions at the time the organism dies! Furthermore, some cells do not follow the fibroblast pattern of replicative senescence. Rat cells from the fetal optic[124] and sciatic nerves[125]—cells that would normally elaborate the myelin sheaths insulating nerve fibers—go right on dividing indefinitely in tissue culture as long as their medium is spiked with specific mitotic enhancers (mitogens) and cells are prevented from differentiating by the removal of factors present in serum. Moreover, these cells do not exhibit telomere shortening under conditions that cause replicative senescence and telomere shortening in freshly excised fibroblasts.

Belief in the "telomere story" faltered further with recognition of the fact that freshly excised rat fibroblasts undergo replicative senescence long before telomere shortening is significant.[126] What is more, mice have smaller Hayflick numbers than human beings even though mice have active telomerase throughout a lifetime and longer telomeres than human beings.[127] Moreover, yeast lack telomeres on their chromosomes, but yeast cells "undergo only a finite number of divisions, after which they die; thus their life-span is defined by the number of divisions each cell completes."[128]

At least two mechanisms for mitotic counting would seem to operate in mammals: a telomere/telomerase system, and a telomere-independent system. The normal operation of a telomere/telomerase system is suggested by cells from p53-mutant mice, which are deficient in telomerase activity and are abnormally susceptible to cellular oncogenes and immortalization in tissue culture.[129] A telomere-independent mechanism of mitotic counting might operate in some human epithelial cells (epidermal keratinocytes and mammary epithelium) which utilize the retinoblastoma/p16 cyclin-dependent kinase inhibitor pathway.[130] In contrast to fibroblasts, proliferative human mammary epithelial cells emerge from a transient growth plateau, suggesting that proliferative senescence is a cyclic phenomenon and not an insurmountable barrier to further growth.[131]

From yeast to human beings, aging may "superficially appear to be programmed," and be "genetically determined in the sense that the genetic constitution determines its course," but,

> [t]he genetic determination of life-span should not be equated with the action of a genetic program. The operation of such a program from birth to death is not likely, nor is it sustained by evolutionary theory.[132]

DISCONTINUITY

The life/death transition may be viewed as the foremost of life's discontinuities, possibly the most obvious, but actually only one among many. Life is, after all, dispersed in discontinuous, living things that also exhibit discontinuities within themselves: within organisms (between cells, tissues, organs, and organ systems), between organisms (age, sex, individual), and between taxa (species, genera, families, orders, class, phyla). Life, if anything, abounds with discontinuities. Next to flux, discontinuity may well be life's main characteristic, and bringing discontinuity into conformity with immortality will be as challenging as turning flux into equilibrium.

Differences within a Multicellular Animal

Colossal differences exist in multicellular animals. For example, in mammals, excluding cells of the lymphatic system, typical histology textbooks list about 250 different types of cells comprising tissues. The question, "Where do differences within living things come from?" is answered simply: from genes, or more precisely, from nuclear DNA, the DNA/gene. The question thus moves to "How do these genes create differences?"

The answer has not always been as simple as it is today. August Weismann was guilty, in this case, of muddying the waters considerably. Although he argued correctly that hereditary units impinge on cellular activity throughout the course of development, his proposal for a mechanism was complexity personified, requiring the cells to sort out developmental information through cell lineage. Ironically, the Nobelist, Thomas Hunt Morgan, who first trumpeted the virtues of Mendelian genetics in America, objected to August Weismann's version of how germplasm translated its influence to somatoplasm, and disavowed Weismann's physiological ideas of hereditary control over development. The arguments between Morgan's and Weismann's supporters became irrelevant following the accession of DNA to the throne of the biological gene and RNA to the role of Hermes, carrying messengers from genes to cytoplasm.

Francis Crick's "serial hypothesis" of 1958 anticipated the current consensus of how genes work.[133] Crick suggested that DNA performed its role as genes in cell-behavior through a variation of replication, namely by transcribing the nucleotide sequences of one DNA strand to a complementary strand of RNA.[134] The message in that RNA strand would then be translated to the sequence of amino acids (peptides) in a polypeptide and, hence, in a protein—the stuff most enzymes are made of.[135] Enzymes, in turn, did everything else that constituted life.

Rushing at break-neck speed, biologists filled in the many lacunae of Crick's serial hypothesis in the 1960s. Different types of RNA were discovered, each fulfilling a role in the serial hypothesis. Messenger RNA, or mRNA, contained the linear sequence of nitrogenous bases prescribing the assembly of amino acid into polypeptides; transfer RNA, or tRNA, carried amino acids to their respective places in a polypeptide chain; ribosomal RNA, or rRNA, in the company of specific proteins, formed a complex known as a ribosome and assembled the amino acids in the sequence dictated by the mRNA as interpreted by tRNAs. DNA serving as a template for RNA synthesis—DNA-dependent RNA synthesis—became known as "transcription," and RNA serving as a template for polypeptide synthesis—RNA-dependent polypeptide synthesis—became known as "translation."

At about the same time, theory and experimentation indicated that sequences of three nitrogenous bases in mRNA—soon to be known as "codons"—specified individual amino acids in polypeptides. By the mid-1960s, the genetic code was broken—each of the 61 or 62 codons was known for each of the 20 amino acids incorporated into polypeptides during translation. Two or three additional codons directed the translation process to stop, while a codon for one of the amino acids (methionine or a modified form of it) directed translation to start. The codons between the start and stop codons constituted an open reading frame or ORF. Surprisingly, the code for translating sequences of nitrogenous bases in mRNA into sequences of amino acid in polypeptides turned out to be virtually universal—almost the same in virtually all living things.[136]

Biologists had come to understand large parts of how DNA/genes operated—parts large enough for the biotech industry to perform some pretty neat tricks, such as making bacteria able to produce human insulin. But some large problems remained.

That the DNA threads of life alone did not determine life on their own became clear as techniques failed in the laboratory to mimic or match the processes of transcription and translation. In eukaryotes, such as ourselves, the DNA of some genes was found to undergo rearrangement before settling down into discrete genes. Moreover, the primary structure of polypeptide chains, or sequences of amino acids, was only prescribed in mRNA after a primary RNA transcript was cut and spliced—deleting portions known as introns while suturing together portions known as exons. Cutting and splicing is not an exception to the rule. Most of our genes engage in it, and about 35 percent of our genes are resolved into multiple mRNAs through alternate splicing. Indeed, multiple splicing seems to allow our 35,000 or so genes to create our amazing diversity.

Exons seem to correspond to portions of polypeptides with specific secondary structure—the shape of alpha helices and ß sheets—but a protein's activity also depends on how polypeptides are tailored and looped, phosphorylated and otherwise modified, molded to each other in macromolecules, and forged into super-macromolecules, such as ribosomes, with nucleic acids. Information for performing all these structuring processes resides in the wisdom of living cells, well beyond the encoded sequences of DNA.

Differences among Organisms

In modern DNA/gene-centered biology, genes are destiny, determining everything about us (including longevity, of course), which is to say, everything that is possibly different among organisms. Loosely speaking, a mean, average, or wild type trait is sometimes said to be inherited through the *gene*, and all the major variations thereof are considered *mutants*. However, in general, most genes, and even most of their variants, influence traits that are all roughly normal or, at least, functional. As a matter of fact, most genes are considered polymorphic and their variants are called alleles or allelomorphs capable of occupying the same locus on a chromosome.

Ironically, if not perversely, genes are named after their first demonstrably abnormal mutant (*white* eye in *Drosophila* identifies the locus typically occupied by the normal red-eye gene). Various conventions are then adopted to distinguish between mutant and normal genes. For example, if a gene determining schizophrenia exists, it might be called *schizo* and its normal counterpart *SCHIZO*. Presumably, *SCHIZO* would determine the complex and variable forms of human behavior operating within the confines of the "normal," while *schizo* would determine their "abnormal" counterparts.

Genes (not organisms or somatoplasm) are considered the replicators of life, the self-perpetuating units carried forward in the germ line and capable by themselves of determining somatoplasm and everything it does. Genes are filtered through the environment by natural selection. If the trait determined by the gene helps the organism reproduce, the gene has a shot at moving into the next generation; if not, it doesn't. From this point of view, organismic traits are mere signals that open or fail to open pores in the environmental filter through which genes enter the next generation.

Of course, genes are not individuals, such as ourselves, precisely because individuals change, while genes are the same, generation to generation. And even when genes change, or mutate, they continue unchanged in their mutant form in succeeding generations or until they mutate again.

Immortal human beings could take a lesson from genes. Like immortal replicators, immortal human beings will not change, or, when they do, will remain constant in their new form. But, immortal human beings will all be different from each other and must preserve their individual differences for the sake of their humanity.

Differences among Species

So, where do differences among species come from? Biologists would answer, without irony, "From genes, of course!" Species difference is explained in terms of different combinations of genes, and the evolution of these differences is explained with the help of a gambling metaphor.

- Genetically determined traits represent bets on the likelihood of successful breeding and prospects for leaving progeny—for projecting DNA/genes forward to the next generation.

- Some organisms will have a greater preponderance of good bets (traits) than other organisms and leave more progeny in the next generation than organisms with a preponderance of bad bets.

However,

- Odds change with the environment, and organisms with the "best of all possible bets" in one world at one time may not have the "best of all possible bets" in a different world at another time.

- In an ever-changing world, there may not even be a "best of all possible bets" and diversity, rather than any particular combination of traits, may represent the "best of all possible compromises."

The evolution of differences among species is also explained with the help of a business or competitive metaphor, rather than a gambling one. The object of the competition is not so much to win the game as to make the best deal and thereby leave the most possible progeny.

- The hereditary traits of some organisms will have a greater competitive advantage than those of other organisms, and organisms with those traits will leave more progeny in the next generation than organisms lacking this competitive edge.

However,

- Economics change from place to place and time to time, and organisms with all the advantages in one market may not have all the advantages in another market or at another time.

- In an ever-changing marketplace, there may not even be a set of optimum conditions providing advantages overall, and diversification as opposed to particular sets of traits may represent the best compromise available among hereditary traits.

Whether adopting a model of gambling or competition, geneticists direct their research to learning the odds on any trait and how it provides an adaptive advantage or pay off. Beating the odds is the name of the game whether one is playing with chips, capital, or Darwinian fitness, and only individuals with luck or particular sets of genes win, unless the game is fixed—which is always a possibility!

Species' differences, it would seem, result from compulsive gambling with DNA/genes in an environmental casino or from cut-throat *laissez-faire* capitalism in an organismic marketplace. Thus, everything in life that is truly different emerges as genes place their bets, wheel and deal, bargain, barter, bank their lucre and take their losses.

An Afterthought

Discontinuities, especially among individuals, are frequently prized, and individuality praised. But biology seems to take a different attitude, bordering on cynicism if not nihilism. Sameness, not difference, is valued and identified with the normal. This ambivalence toward the different haunts biology.

In eighteenth century Europe, life's discontinuities were rationalized in terms of everything having a place. Later, Ernst Haeckel (1834–1919), the nineteenth century successor to (and betrayer of) the German Romantics, devoted himself to answering "the question of all questions," the great enigma of "[t]he place of man in nature."[137] Haeckel claimed that his solution, a dictatorship of science heavily laden with fascist ideology, had "[t]he immortal merit of establishing the doctrine [of the eternal 'evolution of substance'] on an empirical basis,"[138] but his "eternal" solution hardly survived the first half of the twentieth century.[139]

Today, suggestions that cloning and immortality pose a threat to individuality are no more compelling than suggestions that man's place in nature is that of dictator. Clearly, a world occupied by immortal human beings—or, more likely, shared by mortal and immortal human beings—will be more homogeneous than a world occupied entirely by transient, mortal human beings. Indeed, were human beings to exist eternally at a particular physiological age, immortality would have erased one of the greatest sources of friction currently existing among human beings—aging. The consequent homogeneity would not threaten humankind with a loss of individual identity, since the superabundance of differences among and within organisms would compensate and preserve individuality among immortals. The consequent homogeneity would only reduce friction and create harmony.

WASTE

Life is prodigal! Since the time of Weismann, an organism, or somatoplasm, has been understood as a virtual waste-product from the moment it is conceived except as it functions as a receptacle for germplasm on its way between generations. Organisms are the wasteful links in the chain of life, and life would be far less wasteful were it left to germ lines. Selfish genes would still compete, but life would be more efficient.

Life's prodigality is prodigious. Just think about red blood cells that are replaced every 120 days or the lining of the small intestine that requires about 10^{11} cells per day for normal maintenance![140] And what about the invisible bacteria, algae, plankton, and protozoa disintegrating or sinking into oceanic sediments; and let us not forget so-called waste products, various excreta, and corpses. How ironic that we are taught to respect oxygen as the plant's gift to animals when it is photosynthesis' most toxic waste product! Waste products are so much a feature of life that probably the easiest way to search for signs of life on Mars is to look for detritus.[141]

Even the germ line is nothing to boast about. Think about an ejaculum of 3 ml with $60-100 \times 10^6$ spermatozoa per ml going to waste even if a single spermatozoon succeeds in fertilizing an egg! And what about the 400,000 potential eggs an average woman is born with, of which only 400 grow to maturity in a lifetime and 2.6 of these are fertilized. Still, selfish genes manage to reclaim something from all this waste, while somatoplasm loses everything.

Life is nowhere near as beautiful, efficient, efficacious, and economical as the theorists of DNA, God, or Natural Law would have you believe. Indeed, life should be spanked for its excreta, and for the corpses remaining after survival and reproduction. Immortality, on the other hand, is bound to make a dent in this enormous waste, if only because bodies will no longer be recycled through the chain of birth and death.

The Functions of Waste

Biology has yet to come to grips satisfactorily with life's prodigality. Today's molecular biologists find in DNA such a perfect repository of information that they cannot imagine any countervailing force limiting prodigality. Similarly, in the eighteenth century, natural theologists saw no limit to God's purpose in nature and to nature's probity. God had created nature for us, and whatever it lacked in efficacy (waste, including human waste), it made up in aesthetics (supporting human pleasure). This tradition underwent a sea turn but continued flowing unabated with the elevation of adaptation to a scientific principle by Charles Darwin. Later in the nineteenth century, Claude Bernard shifted the pillar of faith to the regulation of an internal environment, and, in the twentieth century, ecologists shifted the concept of biological efficiency further to a theory of allocation, the adaptive distribution of an organism's energy according to the various demands made upon its survival and reproduction.

Death is the unambiguous confirmation of waste in life. Grossly, life's footprints are found in the remains of organisms (in fossils, stromatolites, diatomaceous ooze, and the White Cliffs of Dover), while living tracks are seen in cellular debris (dandruff, hair, and menstrual flow). Indeed, waste products and death are not entirely separable. Those magnificent trees we admire and envy for their longevity are nothing more than thin veneers of living stuff over pillars of dead xylem. As for the human animal, our own dead cells and their breakdown products are abundant. Some are recycled internally, such as the breakdown products of red blood cells turned into bile by the liver; some are simply dumped, mixed with bacteria and indigestible food items in our excreta. Corpses are like excreta—just so much grist for the mill of decomposers.

Some biologists have come to appreciate that life itself depends on the recycling of wastes and corpses.[142] Daily recycling through the biosphere of water, carbon dioxide, and nitrogen, is a megaton enterprise without which life on Earth would long ago have become impossible. Recycling has made this Earth a fit place to live if not the best of all possible worlds. But recycling is a compromise with thermodynamic reality.

Charles Darwin was among the first to appreciate the necessity of waste. The appeal of natural selection was not merely an explanation for adaptation but an answer to the Malthusian dilemma: Where would all the organisms go, to say nothing of their waste products, if they all survived and reproduced? By concluding that only the fit survived (if only long enough to leave more descendants than the less fit), natural selection offered the solution to the worst of all possible possibilities (and everyone's idea of Hell): vast overpopulation and inundation in excreta.

Even after billions of years of evolution, life has not evolved anything as efficient as immortal organisms, and cellular human beings are not likely to evolve into immortal creatures left to their own devices. Even the most extraordinary efforts to cure disease, capped by organ transplantation, have not made any human being immortal.

Yet I wonder, why hasn't life organized itself around the immortality of at least some creatures (a few good species), while promoting the perishability of other, expendable creatures? Perhaps immortal human beings will be such an exceptional species!

The Waste of Selfish Genes versus the Waste of Altruistic Genes

Richard Dawkins is the chief popularizer of the selfish gene theory.[143] Basically, the DNA/genes, which determine virtually everything about us, are quintessentially selfish. Their objective or intention, like that of parasites, is merely to perpetuate themselves by moving from one adult host to the next (leaving the sinking [somatoplasmic] ship).

One might wonder why at least some DNA/genes (my own, for instance) would not be satisfied with replicating indefinitely through my own cells, without moving to another vessel in another generation? The answer may be that while some DNA/genes are happy within the organisms they have built, other genes are not, and, out of discontent or jealousy, unhappy genes develop counter-strategies for defeating happy DNA/genes. The accumulation of unhappy genes is frequently thought to explain, at least in part, the origins of cancers and other degenerative diseases.

The problem of selfish genes is so profound that one may wonder how life is possible in the first place. What is more, how did truly selfish genes create organisms which are capable of sacrificing their own lives to rescue a child drowning in an outdoor pool or writhing at the window of a burning house? The answer offered by sociobiologists is that by sacrificing oneself for the welfare of one's offspring, one is also promoting the chance of one's genes surviving and reproducing in the next generation. Once again, it is the selfish genes who rule even if their rule is not one of self-survival. The small problem of sacrificing oneself for an individual who is not one's offspring is pasted over as a mistake due to the gene's cloudy vision of its offspring.

To whatever degree altruism is influenced by genes, the immortals will share this trait with mortals. The immortals will have kin, albeit not offspring. The point is that waste, whether mediated by sacrifice or the run-of-the mill variety created by ordinary life, is no more incompatible with immortality than efficiency is solely the province of selfishness.

ACHIEVING IMMORTALITY THROUGH BIOTECHNOLOGY

Biological life boils down to three points: life is in flux because genes flow; life is discontinuous because different genes offer one advantage or another to individuals; and life is wasteful because somatoplasm is only the vehicle of selfish genes on their way to the next generation.

What then is needed to make human life immortal? Life's flux must be limited to individuals; genetic advantages must benefit individuals; waste and selfishness must be played out within individuals. All this is within reach! *Human beings can be made immortal through the simple device of replacing germ cells with stem cells.* Immortal human beings will be sterile, and their bodies will remain permanently in a prepubescent state, but stem cells will keep them perfectly balanced between development and aging, between growth and decay.

The combination of cloning and stem-cell therapy promises to make all this possible. The premise of both cloning and stem-cell replacement therapy is that everything biological can happen if the right things are brought together in the right places at the right time. The nucleus of an adult cell, placed in the cytoplasm of an oocyte in the midst (metaphase) of its second meiotic division, would seem to be all that is necessary to produce a clone following a brief period *in vitro* and embryo transfer. Likewise, stem cells, in the juvenile environments, are all that are necessary to maintain, repair, and regenerate functioning organs eternally.

Ordinarily, the embryo, fetus, and juvenile are way stations, on the road to making an adult. Development would seem unnecessary and these way stations dispensable if appropriate genetic messages can be given to stem cells in correct sequences and on time even by juvenile tissues and organs. Never mind that the normal unraveling of information engenders waste. Waste is unnecessary. The point is that at the end of the process, all the genes necessary for producing an individual can have their say, so to speak, and stem cells can be directed to differentiate without having wasted time in developing organs.

The device for achieving immortality proposed here, namely, replacing germ-line cells with somatic-line stem cells, utilizes a cloned blastocyst grafted to an embryo for the purpose of replacing its rudimentary gonads and providing a durable generator of embryonic stem cells in perpetuity. The absence of sex cells should stop the process of aging at prepubescence, at a point before any of the genes for aging and degeneracy have acted— or, at least, before they have become dominant. This is the perfect point to start immortalizing. It is also the point at which biotechnology can intervene most effectively.

BIOTECHNOLOGY

Biotechnology has many practical applications—conspicuously in the design of diagnostic tools and as sources of purified proteins produced by cells transfected with modified genes. It spawned the biotech industry and helped to build the present culture of optimism. All in all, faith in biotechnology is justified and will continue to be justified in the future.

Biotechnology has already performed miracles. Technicians routinely harvest the products of genes from secretions, and once mammalian cloning gets going, identical animals will produce precisely the same product in quantity. We can now literally milk cloned ewes for specific human blood clotting factors. Cells might be coupled to microchips and nano-motors used as DNA tweezers for controlling or altering genes. Biotechnology will also, no doubt, play a role in the cloning of large animals and designing stem cells. Beyond this scenario are the prospects for combining biotechnology and stem cells to produce tissues and organs for replacement therapy not requiring immunosuppression. Biotechnology may not be able to solve all life's problems, but it can certainly solve some, including the problems of making us immortal.

Historically, biotechnology began as the art of amplifying genes—actually, DNA—or at least parts of genes and collecting large amounts of bits and pieces of DNA. The chief technique was originally gene cloning. Recombinant DNA—DNA combined from two different sources—was produced by recombinant DNA technology. The DNA was then introduced into or merely taken up by bacteria or other cells which reproduced, thereby amplifying the recombinant DNA. Later, the polymerase chain reaction (PCR), which utilized enzymes and repetitive cycles of polymerization to replicate specific portions of DNA, allowed technicians to produce relatively specific pieces of genes without cloning.

Three applications for purified genes form the centerpiece of biotechnology: (1) harvesting specific proteins from transfected bacteria or other cells; (2) harvesting labeled (radioactive or fluorescent) probes of nucleic acid able to complement (hybridize or anneal) with and thereby detect unique forms of DNA *in utero,* in adults, and in the laboratory; and (3) producing the segments of DNA used in sequencing and mapping genomes (e.g., the Human Genome Project).

Under appropriate conditions, modified genes transferred to bacteria can result in the production of proteins useful to human beings. For example, moving a modified human insulin-gene to a bacterium made it possible, with the help of a lot of tricks added along the way, to harvest human insulin, thereby supplying hundreds of millions of human diabetics with a cheap, stable, effective, and nonimmunogenic lifesaving hormone. Likewise, would-be parents can now be tested for dreaded hereditary conditions (such as Tay Sachs disease) with the help of probes produced through biotechnology. The Human Genome Project, with all its promise for aiding research, was simply unthinkable prior to recombinant DNA technology. Another, as of yet theoretical application of biotechnology is the replacement of bad genes with good genes in human beings suffering from, or likely to suffer from, inherited disorders.

Many other applications for biotechnology are found in the interstices between these techniques and human needs. For example, human diseases are modeled in patented transgenic mice bearing foreign genes, or their opposite number, knockout mice missing specific genes as a result of gene targeting technology. Both sorts of mice are created experimentally by combining the techniques of gene transfer or gene targeting to cells *in vitro* with *in vitro* fertilization, embryo culture, embryo transfer, and breeding of chimeric mice.[144]

New forms of organisms are certainly created in the modern biotechnology laboratory, but most of these forms are more or less variants of living forms created over centuries by breeders of domesticated plants and animals, and the bakers and brewers of bread and beer. Present technology merely puts contemporary biologists in a position to alter the genes in organisms more easily and reliably than in the past, and large pharmaceutical firms as well as small biotechnology startups are fired up by venture capital to use this technology. The production of GM (genetically modified) plants is a case in point.

Will widespread rejection of GM foods, to say nothing of protests, civil disobedience, and vandalism, stop Monsanto and other plant breeders? Probably not, but consumer organizations are certainly promoting better communication, and large manufacturers have not proved entirely deaf to public concern. For example, the "terminator gene" (which would have required tillage and grain farmers to buy fresh seeds every year) was terminated as a result of popular outcry, even if farmers are obliged by contractual obligations to buy fresh seed every year. No doubt market forces, which determine commercial decisions in the first place, will play a major part in deciding issues apropos of GM food.

A great deal more than biotechnology is involved in decisions to introduce new forms of life, such as immortal animals. One may ask if there is a sufficient consensus among biologists on what sort of organisms should populate Earth? Are we currently in possession of enough biological wisdom to design new organisms, as opposed to succumbing to the indubitable laws of evolution and the market place? On the surface, the answer is emphatically "No!" Biologists currently cannot so much as say with confidence what organisms are, no less what organisms should be, but biological wisdom is not the only motivating force behind efforts to create immortal life forms.

The technology is compelling for a future of immortal organisms. The problem is that, presently, biologists are not able to connect their molecular knowledge with life's molar properties—their knowledge of minute details with the integrated and complex properties of living things. Even the most ardent supporters of the DNA/gene, including Francis Crick, acknowledge that gene-centered biological theory leaves unsolved problems, such as what drives adaptation and how organisms develop. How many more problems are unresolved regarding immortality?

Many biologists are prepared to acknowledge that a cell is not a bag of enzymes, but these same biologists maintain that the nucleus is a bag of transcription factors, promoters, receptors, enhancers, and silencers. In fact,

[o]ur inability to pass from the molecular-genetic level to the macroscopic-morphogenetic level involved in visible ontogeny (embryonic development) poses a serious obstacle for our acceptance of the neo-darwinistic explanation of phylogeny (evolution).[145]

Biology is suffering from a forest and trees problem. Before biologists have the knowledge required to control reproduction, no less the wisdom to control it, they will have to come to grips with all the dimensions and fractals between "dissipative structures," "dynamical instability," "biochemical chaos," "information processing," and "self-organization."

IMMORTALITY AS GOAL

Goals, like ideals, are notoriously fragile and easily confused. For example, selflessness and altruism applied to kin, community, or country are frequently easily confused with greed. This confusion thundered through the Great War, and flourished during and after World War II even when the great narratives of Western culture lost most of their edge for inspiring and mobilizing action. If anything, these narratives were turned against themselves, first as nihilism and then as postmodern *ennui,* but science, ever inventive, has posted on today's bulletin board a seemingly endless list of goals and ways of achieving them.

Immortality research has its own narratives, including cloning, and continuous stem-cell therapy, which have mobilized individuals from various constituencies. These narratives may not offer anything different from those already discredited in human history, or they may pose new ways of achieving human potential in the future. The question, "What must be sacrificed to achieve these goals?" is seldom asked and never answered.

What is crucial for understanding narratives is the relationship of their components to each other, both temporally and spatially. If the consequences flowing from a component are entirely a function of known causal relationships, one might be able to make a case for predictability and the containment of consequences. The scenarios presently available for achieving immortality are still shy of meeting the criteria for containment and predictability, but never mind—driven by our selfish genes, we will, no doubt, take care of the remaining problems!

PROBLEMS AND SOLUTIONS

Regrettably, neither evolution nor development has provided us with a way of circumventing mortality, but biotechnology, cloning, and stem-cell research may yet change us sufficiently to permit our immortality. Evolution and development suffer from a lack of sideways movement, of devices for reshuffling and mixing as opposed to an overweening insistence on progress and accumulation. Evolution and development are supposed to add up. Once the pieces are in place, they should fall into an upward trajectory.

> [T]his process of spontaneous and autonomous morphogenesis rests, at bottom, upon the stereospecific recognition properties of proteins; that it is primarily a microscopic process before manifesting itself in macroscopic structures.[146]

All that may change in the decades ahead.

Today, biologists claim that their knowledge of evolution and development (notwithstanding all the hiatuses in knowledge) is sufficient. The tools of biotechnology, cloning, and stem-cell research will soon be adequate to ward off threats posed by Malthusian expansion and to achieve benefits available through inherited traits. Biology, we are told, not only has within its power the intelligence to compute the proper shape of human populations but the ability to program reproduction to achieve that shape; not only to identify desirable hereditary traits but to advance and capture those traits for posterity. The question is not, "Is the status of human knowledge and the standard of knowledge required to justify human action met by current biology?" The question is, "Is the world ready to accept the dictatorship of biologists?"

Perhaps one cannot take issue with biotechnology producing better things for better living through cloning, but the idea that biology now has the wisdom to determine what constitutes human perfection should raise eyebrows. Beyond the actuarial arguments on behalf of a stable mix of human beings in the future, the cloning of human beings meets only the most dubious human need and has no incontrovertible social benefit. Arguably, the chief biological justification for cloning and continuous stem-cell therapy is that they are the natural extension of natural selection, the human control of human evolution through biotechnology. This justification ignores a host of problems.

As a social phenomenon, cloning and stem-cell therapy undoubtedly present problems unanticipated by biologists, problems that are best confronted by society at large. One of the hidden tenets of cloning and continuous stem-cell therapy is that every form of life is just a variation on a generalization. Individuals, on the other hand, created by sexual reproduction, embody difference. Life forms not created by sexual reproduction might ultimately lack the quality of difference, of different individuals and all that implies, including the social encumbrances of difference. Are we ready to sacrifice the soloist to the chorus?

Finally, contrary to popular and scientific belief, biological systems do not work according to the prescription of perfection: Life is not governed by the sort of linear equations describing close-to-equilibrium chemistry. Rather, life begins far-from-equilibrium, in the domain of the nonlinear and the brink of chaos. The elements of contingency, random events, unforeseen opportunity, death, and extinction dominate biological scenarios at all levels of integration, and none of these elements is consistent with the premise of perfection. As long as life is not linear, biological planning based on linear models of biological progress is not suitable. Hence, cloning and continuous stem-cell therapy would seem to fly in the face of human life rather than with it. But the apparent might not be reality, particularly since immortal human beings will still be human beings.

HAZARDS AND OPPORTUNITIES

What is a reasonable concept of immortality that can be achieved realistically? Certainly, nothing in life is absolute, not even immortality. Immortality cannot come with a guarantee, for example, against accident or suicide. Even immortal life cannot be insured against new zoonotic viral epidemics or even against infectious diseases presently defying the best efforts at cure. All that can be reasonably expected of immortality is the permanent suspension of degenerative diseases that would otherwise accompany aging and senescence. In other words, the immortals will not die of any of the diseases associated with old age (e.g., Alzheimer's disease, cancer, cirrhosis, congestive heart failure, diabetes, heart attacks, hepatitis, immunodeficiencies, inherited blood diseases, leukemias, multiple sclerosis, muscular dystrophy, osteoarthritis, osteoporosis, Parkinson's disease, and stroke), and, as long as nothing else kills them, they can expect to live indefinitely which may, with a lot of luck, be forever.

Ironically, diseases peculiar to the young might represent a particular hazard to the immortals. Regrettably, the forever-young immortals will be exposed for prolonged periods of time (to say the least) to childhood diseases. Childhood leukemia which seems to have a viral rather than a genetic etiology, may become the scourge of immortals. Moreover, and certainly in the early stages of generating immortals, genetic diversity among the immortals would represent only a minuscule proportion of the biodiversity of the species. Resistance to new diseases among the immortals might be severely limited, rendering the immortals peculiarly susceptible and vulnerable to ever-evolving pathogens.

Immortality is not the panacea but only a step in the direction of endless, healthy life. Many of the problems associated with mortal life will be exaggerated by immortality rather than solved by it, but the same ingenuity and creativity currently brought to bear against these problems by mortals will continue to be available to immortals. In other words, human beings will certainly have to continue struggling against threats to life even after removing the threat of death—or, at least, of aging and senescence.

But other problems associated with mortal life may be solved by immortality. Given that the forever young will be sexually immature, the immortals will be sterile, providing a natural control on excess human fecundity (i.e., defusing the human population explosion). Moreover, one can anticipate that, in response to the inevitable shrinking of human biodiversity in the immortal population (although I would hope reasonable efforts would be made to preserve as much biodiversity as possible), a high priority should be placed on manipulating genes, fulfilling biotechnology's potential for creating a healthier and happier humanity. Hopefully, the immortals would represent a concentration of the exemplary traits of the human species. Presently, biologists do not know how to go from the beginning of this immortal narrative to the end, but we can learn. When decisions are upon us, sufficient wisdom will prevail to help us make good choices.

Chapter 2

Why Immortality Cannot Evolve

ADMIT IT: our situation is difficult because it works too well, because it's going too fast. This paradox engages the critical essence, or ateleological sense, of genealogical and archaeological investigation.

—Éric Alliez, *Capital Times*

If there is originality in neoevolutionism, it is attributable in part to phenomena of this kind in which evolution does not go from something less differentiated to something more differentiated, in which it ceases to be a hereditary filiative evolution, becoming communicative or contagious. Accordingly, the term we would prefer for this form of evolution between heterogeneous terms is "involution," on the condition that involution is in no way confused with regression. Becoming is involutionary, involution is creative. To regress is to move in the direction of something less differentiated. but to involve is to form a block that runs its own line "between" the terms in play and beneath assignable relations.

—Gilles Deleuze and Felix Guattari, *A Thousand Plateaus.*

Man knows that he is changing, willy-nilly changing. Conforming with a type he is yet always as individual unique . . . The inorganic world is one stream of individuals. No following life is like the one it followed. That states perhaps the utter most poignancy of death.

—Charles Sherrington, *Man on his Nature*

The easiest solution to the problem of our becoming immortal would seem to be our evolving immortality, either via natural selection or, "with a little help from our friends," via eugenic selection and "Darwinian medicine."[1] But as powerful as it is, evolution cannot harness immortality and turn human beings from a species of mortal *Homo sapiens* forma *mortalis*, into one of immortal *Homo sapiens* forma *immortalis*. The problem is that evolution places a high premium on reproduction which immortality will not pay. Evolution also relies on the inheritance of genes, and there are no genes for immortality. Immortality cannot evolve because it does not pay obeisance to reproduction and lacks the genetic underpinnings that can be passed on through reproduction.[2] Nothing, from genetics to neo-Darwinism, from Mendel to the draft sequence of the human genome, offers any hope whatsoever for the evolution of immortality!

Evolution—descent with change or the transmutation of species—has, no doubt, shaped many of the adaptations that allow living things to make their living through interactions with each other and the rest of their environments. It is, as Charles Robert Darwin (1809–82) suggested in 1859, a first order assumption (only one step removed from empirical data) and biology's equivalent to physic's notion of gravity.[3] But evolution has shaped and consolidated the lives of eukaryotic life around mortality, probably for more than a billion years.[4] Evolution cannot now make a sea change and turn human beings into immortals.

Of course, science has often achieved the impossible, and, as a scientist, I should be loath to label anything unachievable. My purpose here is, nevertheless, to explain why the immortality of human beings, or any other complex, multicellular animal, cannot be achieved by evolution and why, therefore, we must go beyond the scope of evolution to achieve immortality.

WHERE DOES LONGEVITY COME FROM, AND WHY HAS EVOLUTION MADE US MORTAL RATHER THAN IMMORTAL?

I believe it was David Brinkley who described United States draft laws during the Vietnam War as "so complicated that if they did not exist, they couldn't be invented." The same is probably true of contemporary evolutionary theory, but in the first part of this chapter I attempt to describe how evolutionary law (lore?) has evolved, since it too "couldn't be invented." My hope is that the reader may thereby understand evolutionary theory's present state of existence, its potential as an explanatory doctrine, and its limitations.

THE EARLY YEARS

Charles Lyell (1797–1875), the geologist and evolution-skeptic, dictated evolution's fortune throughout much of the first half of the nineteenth century. Lyell fostered a version of uniformitarianism, a doctrine of what goes up will come down, arguing for a God-given equilibrium in nature, and, hence, arguing against evolution. Lyell's preeminence was so commanding and his influence so pervasive that he was at least partially responsible for Darwin's delaying for twenty years the publication of *On the origin of Species by means of Natural Selection or the Preservation of Favoured Races in the Struggle for Life* (herein referred to as *Origin*),[5] and for Darwin's publishing *Origin* only when encouraged by Lyell who finally "saw species appearing and becoming extinct as part of his overall uniform picture of the world."[6] Indeed, even when disagreeing with Lyell, Darwin was reputed to be "doubly Lyellian,"[7] "Lyellian through and through,"[8] and, ultimately, "ultra-Lyellian."[9]

Lyell might have had other less direct and unintended roles in nurturing Darwinian evolution. It was Lyell's *Principles of Geology* that introduced, however critically, the English reader (including Darwin[10]) to Lamarck's progressionist theses of use and disuse and the inheritance of acquired characteristics. Furthermore, Lyellian uniformitarianism epitomized Darwin's great dilemma: How could God's design in nature (adaptation) be reconciled with natural law, since, "if blind law is adequate for adaptation . . . the pressing need to infer a designer is much reduced."[11]

Adrian Desmond, the historian/biographer, and Michael Ruse, the philosopher/historian, trace Darwin's solution to Lyell's dilemma through a political/economic analysis of Darwin's ascendance.[12] Darwin is portrayed as keenly aware of the practical requirements for making evolution palatable to the middle class English taste for natural theology—everything suits God's purpose. Darwin, therefore, attempted to blunt evolution's materialistic and mechanistic edge with a gloss of Victorian transcendence, ending *Origin* with the immortal sentence:

> There is grandeur in this view of life, with its several powers, having been originally breathed by the Creator into a few forms or into one; and that, whilst this planet has gone cycling on according to the fixed law of gravity, from so simple a beginning endless forms most beautiful and most wonderful have been, and are being evolved.[13]

Ultimately, Darwin and company resolved Lyell's theological conundrum by installing progress surreptitiously into evolution. Competition—well known and highly acceptable in the burgeoning English entrepreneurial class—was substituted for "blind law" and "design" was reconfigured as the outcome of competition choosing among alternatives (i.e., natural selection). Whether Darwin and his minions were self-conscious about the deception or not, ascribing the creative power of free-market economics to evolution made evolution safe in the English-speaking world.[14]

Darwinism's success at explaining away design was followed by equally successful explanations for similarities and differences among organisms. Darwin appreciated that similarities ran in families, and defining species as genealogies explained similarities among their members. Homologies thereby became any similarity attributed to their presence in the *paterfamilias*. Differences between species were likewise explained by the sort of variation occurring between families, however exaggerated under the auspices of natural selection.

DARWIN'S RISING AND FALLING FORTUNES

Darwin had taken a commonsensical approach to laying out natural selection as the means for changing species. In *Origin*, Darwin argued that if artificial selection in the hands of plant and animal breeders brought about all the changes seen in domesticated breeds, certainly nature could do no less through natural selection. Indeed, nature (God?) could do more: it (She? He?) could make species out of varieties. To answer the question, "What criteria would nature use to select individuals for breeding (in the fashion of plant and animal breeders)?" Darwin took recourse to the Malthusian struggle for existence or survival in the wake of over-population.[15] What is more, Darwin elected a perfectly reasonable gradualism for the instrument of change, although gradualism did not explain the source of ruptures between forms of living things. For support, Darwin touched all the rhetorical bases available to "good science," arguing both from the immediately experienced (the empiricism of Herschel) to the remotely experienced (Whewellian consilience).[16] And, like a mystery writer, Darwin dropped clues in

> [h]omologies, behaviors, fossils, distributions, embryos, and more—
> . . . the footprints, the blood stains, the fingerprints. And they point[ed] uniquely to one culprit: evolution through natural selection![17]

Darwin was "highly sensitive to the fact that he had—to put it mildly—a job of selling to do" but he did not shy away from this job, as sometimes suggested, writing prodigiously, accounting for a massive correspondence, and constantly enlisting new recruits to his cause.[18] Indeed, before the end of his lifetime, "the message of evolution as *fact* was accepted quietly and completely."[19]

The road to acceptance had many bumps. Darwin was at pains to explain how evolution's qualitative changes could be accommodated in the time available during the tenure of life on Earth. Working backward, he estimated a rather long duration (by then current standards), only to find himself at loggerheads with the redoubtable Lord Kelvin. Darwin reluctantly acknowledged problems with duration, compromising his conviction progressively through the six editions of *Origin*.

The spread of evolutionary studies was also plagued by pragmatic problems.

> Most urgently, there were money problems. . . . But, more important than money problems, no doubt in part bringing on the money problems, the program [of natural selection] was conceptually and evidentially flawed.[20]

In fact, before the turn of the nineteenth century, natural selection had been all but abandoned, even by Darwin's supporters, including his "bull dog," Thomas Henry Huxley (1825–1895).[21]

Other bumps on the road to Darwinism turned out to be even greater obstacles. The very popularity of evolutionism discouraged serious academic study and prevented Darwinism from becoming a mature and professional science. Even today one rarely hears of academic departments of evolutionary studies and then only as offshoots of ecology departments. This attitude even prevailed in the United States where Edmund B. Wilson (1856–1939), a Hopkins-trained cytologist and professor at Columbia,

> regarded the study of evolution as beyond professional bounds. . . . Wilson's science simply presupposed evolution as the metaphysical background, and then he got on with what interested him. . . . Wilson assumed evolution as fact; he rather looked down upon efforts to discern evolution as path; and he was professionally uninterested in questions of evolution as cause.[22]

In hindsight, early Darwinism's major problem was its failure to come to grips with heredity, in particular with heredity's monumental intransigence in contrast to evolution's prodigious plasticity. Commentators on the history of evolutionary thought wring their hands endlessly over Darwin's version of blending inheritance and his reliance on gemmules to account for the inheritance of acquired traits. Darwin's apologists frequently speculate on what might have been had he known of and adopted at that time the particulate version of heredity discussed by plant breeders, known later as Mendelism.[23] What was to become genetics offered a viable solution to the problem of hereditary stability and evolutionary variation, but the unification of genetics with evolutionary theory was hardly smooth.

BIOMETRIC SOLUTIONS TO EVOLUTIONARY PROBLEMS

Early efforts to solve the problem of heredity's place in evolution led to more controversy than concord. Darwin's gradualism—the slow accumulation of small changes—and adaptationism—the goodness of fit between morphology and environmental constraints—were first taken up in earnest by the experimental systematist Walter Frank Raphael Weldon (1860–1906), professor, University College, London, and Linacre Professor at Oxford, and by his friend, the biometrician. (Briton) Karl Pearson (1857–1936), professor of applied mathematics and mechanics at University College, London. Weldon's measurements of the carapace of crabs in the Bay of Naples and the mathematical/statistical models worked out by Pearson to describe deviation from a normal distribution suggested that natural selection was acting to break up a population. Weldon moved his observation to the laboratory and showed that crabs with narrow carapaces (frontal breadth) fared better in water artificially polluted with sediment, while frontal breadth increased in crabs kept in clean water.[24]

Weldon did not spawn a school of post-Darwinian gradualists, however, and Pearson's sophisticated mathematical modeling would not become the standard for evolutionary ecology it might have been. Prior to the *fin de siècle,* they did not believe that the quantitative traits they studied were subject to the constraints of qualitative evolution, known as saltation or discontinuous evolution. In the early twentieth century, they rejected particulate heredity attributed to Mendelian factors.

Weldon is now considered a "fanatical pan-selectionist . . . [who saw] adaptation everywhere."[25] Moreover, he was devoted to the positivism of Pearson and divested evolutionary theory of its stock in "embryology, paleontology, biogeography, and more . . . [which] detract[ed] from the purity of one's central causal investigations."[26] Ultimately, the biometricians would be relegated by some historians to the role of counter-Mendelians in the coming age of Mendelism,[27] although

> [i]f the Mendelians had worked with, instead of against, the biometricians, the synthesis of Mendelian inheritance and Darwinian selection into a mathematical model, later accomplished by population genetics, might have occurred some fifteen years earlier.[28]

ENTER MENDELISM

Gregor Mendel (née Johann Mendel, 1822–1884) was a dedicated Czech nationalist, high school teacher, abbot of the Augustinian monastery at Brünn (Moravia, Austro-Hungarian Empire, or Brno, Czechoslovakia, and later The Czech Republic), and, without ever knowing it, founder of the future discipline of genetics. Mendel studied the inheritance of alternative traits—such as tall versus short stems—in garden peas by crossing pure lines and determining the frequencies of traits in successive generations of so-called hybrids. Reduced, roughly, by their lowest common denominator, the frequencies resembled coefficients in a binomial expansion—the algebraic expansion of pairs of units. Mendel, therefore, interpreted his calculated frequencies in terms of paired hereditary (elementary) units—one member of each pair received by an offspring from one parent and the other member from the other parent (Mendel's first principle, or law of segregation).[29] This is not to say that all traits appeared in each generation. In some combinations, the only traits to appear in offspring were those governed by so-called dominant hereditary units, while traits governed by so-called recessive units only appeared in offspring lacking the corresponding dominant unit. Furthermore, Mendel observed that multiple pairs of alternate traits were distributed to hybrids in all possible combinations (Mendel's second principle, or law of independent assortment).

Mendel presented his results and interpretation to the Brünn Society for the Study of Natural Science in 1865, and published them in the society's *Transactions,* appearing in 1866, which were circulated widely in both Europe and America. Various objections were raised to Mendel's work. The Swiss botanist and professor at the University of Munich, Karl Wilhelm von Nägeli (1817–1891), believing that the evolution of traits (for example, size) took place in great jumps (saltations), criticized Mendel for attempting to study evolution by looking at small differences among varieties. Although Mendel continued to work on plant breeding, bee culture, and meteorology, he never became a scientific celebrity during his lifetime

At the turn of the century, William Bateson (1861–1926) led the rediscovery of Mendel's laws and heralded the opening of a new age of hereditary studies known as Mendelism, later as genetics. Bateson also became the first Professor of Genetics at Cambridge, before becoming director of the Innes Horticultural Institute.[30] He was an important and influential figure at the time, and his firm belief in particulate heredity (discontinuous variation) set his course clearly against the London biometricians and apostles of continuous Darwinian variation.

But as a theory of evolution, Mendelism was muddled. Particulate heredity via Mendelian factors would ultimately be the key to neoDarwinian evolution, but they did not turn evolution's lock in the early years of the twentieth century. Part of the problem was personal: Bateson was brutal in his attacks upon the biometricians, and, moreover, could not abide his American counterpart, Columbia University's Thomas Hunt Morgan (1866–1945). Indeed, Bateson never fully embraced particulate, Mendelian factors, preferring to think of heredity as arising from physical "vibrations." Despite Bateson's having demonstrated (counter to Mendel's second principle) that some Mendelian factors were inherited together and could have been linked on chromosomes, Bateson rejected, as long as he could, Morgan's idea of chromosomes conveying the inheritance of physical traits to organisms. When Wilhelm Johannsen (1857–1927) rechristened Mendelian factors "genes,"[31] and Morgan literally mapped the hereditary "beads" on chromosomal strings, Morgan eclipsed Bateson as the dominant force in genetics.[32]

In the meantime, Hugo De Vries (1848–1935), one of the co-rediscoverers of Mendel's laws of heredity, had worked out his own theory of evolution by mutation from his original work on *Oenothera Lamarckiana* (the evening primrose).[33] De Vries's mutation theory was consistent with the preference of the great agnostic Thomas Huxley, the aging eugenicist Francis Galton, and most botanists who believed that evolution proceeded in large jumps (saltations) and that speciation could come about through the spontaneous appearance of nonadaptive change (independent of any environmental influence). Mutationists were, at the same time, critical of biometrics and of Darwinian adaptationists. Ironically, De Vries originally believed he was supporting Darwinism and even named his hereditary particles pangenes to correspond to Darwin's erstwhile hereditary factors, but the inconsistencies finally drove a wedge between mutation theory and Darwinism. For a time, Darwinism sank into the penumbra of legitimate science and verged on eclipse.

Ultimately, "De Vries's theory of evolution by mutation was refuted resoundingly, with arguments mobilized by Charles D. Darlington (1904–1981) and other early cytogeneticists."[34] Indeed, "the hybrid and mutating *Oenothera* fits in several fundamental respects with the ordinary workaday theory of heredity and variation."[35] The cytogeneticists attributed mutations to chromosomal breaks (a forerunner to errors in DNA replication) and, hence, reinforced Morgan's chromosomal theory of heredity.

Gradualism, as a feature of Darwinism, was rescued after genetics was amended to accommodate quantitative traits in addition to its classical, purely qualitative ones. W. E. Castle (1867–1962), Professor of Zoology at Harvard's Bussey (agricultural) Institution, working on quantitative variation in the pattern of pigmentation in hooded rats, demonstrated that factors influencing their heredity behaved like Mendelian factors. Thereafter, genes influencing quantitative traits would be known as multiple factors (à la Mendelian factors) or polygenes (à la Johannsen's genes).

Meanwhile, differences among the environments in which organisms developed were invoked to account for the continuous variation typically found in genetically "pure" populations, while other environmental effects were summoned to account for the smoothing out of differences between hybrids or genetically "impure" populations.[36] At least in theory, an organism's genotype consisted of all the genes inherited in a Mendelian fashion, whereas an organism's phenotype, or developed traits, implied a combination of environmental and genetic effects.[37]

Genetic/environmental interactions are by no means simple or even predictable, as illustrated by so-called "norms of reaction," or the phenotypic outcomes for organisms developing in different environments. According to Richard Lewontin,

> A genotype does not specify a unique outcome of development; rather it specifies a norm of reaction, a pattern of different developmental outcomes in different environments.[38]

Beyond the uncertainty of genetic/environmental interactions, moreover, are random uncertainties or stochastic error.

> [V]ariation is a consequence of neither genetic nor environmental variation. It is *developmental noise,* a consequence of random events within cells at the level of molecular interactions.[39]

Mendelian genetics and Darwinism were also hot items during the pre-Lysenko days of the Soviet Union. Distinguished work was taking place at the Institute of Applied Botany in Petrograd (Leningrad), led by Nikolai Vavilov (1887–1943), and the Institute of Experimental Biology in Moscow, headed by Nikolai K. Kol'tsov (also spelled Koltsov: 1872–1940), and the department of genetics at the University of Leningrad, led by Juri (Iurii) Philipchenko (also spelled Filipchenko: 1882–1930). Among the notable contributions coming out of these institutions was Sergei S. Chetverikov's (1880–1959) mutation-natural selection theory which laid the foundation for contemporary population genetics by synthesizing biometric, naturalist, and genetic approaches to Darwinian evolution. Others labored in the vineyards,[40] literally, studying wild populations of the fruit fly, *Drosophila,* obtaining empirical evidence on behalf of population genetics, and conceiving of the "gene pool" in which evolution would "sink or swim."[41]

Consequently, Ronald Aylmer Fisher (1890–1962), John Burdon Sanderson (JBS) Haldane (1892–1964), working at Bateson's Institute, and others, would reinvent quantitative theories of genetic evolution. They reannealed particulate heredity to infinitely continuous change (an act of legerdemain rivaling the fusion of particle and wave in quantum mechanics) in the decades of the 1930s and spawned the "modern synthesis."[42]

The Modern Synthesis

Eighty years after Charles Darwin and Alfred Russel Wallace (1829–1913) independently worked out and published the concept of natural selection, Ronald Fisher and JBS Haldane worked out its genetic formula and inaugurated a new age of evolutionary theory. By showing how changes in gene frequency could be brought about through population dynamics and selection, Fisher and Haldane interpolated Mendelian genetics into Darwinism, producing thereby the microevolutionary theory of evolution known as neo-Darwinism.[43]

Fisher and Haldane were giants on the new evolutionary landscape. But, according to Michael Ruse, Fisher's celebrity was rooted in his prodigious power as a mathematician rather than in any compelling insight:

> Not to be unduly cynical, there is nothing that scientists admire (and fear) more than unrestrained mathematical virtuosity—and Fisher showed that, and more. Therefore, he could not be ignored.[44]

On the other hand, Ruse credits Haldane with laying out the modern way of producing facts in evolutionary studies:

> In epistemological terms, it could be the foundation for mature science, satisfying epistemic norms—if it was but formal itself, it was formal in the right way, giving hope of an empirically informed, predictive, consistent, fertile (etc.) science.[45]

Fisher and Haldane also committed the occasional scientific *faux pas*. Haldane guessed that dominant genes, those capable of overwhelming the effects of recessive genes in determining traits, would also overwhelm recessive genes in terms of their frequency in populations. But Goddfrey Harold Hardy (1877–1947), the eminent English mathematician, and Wilhelm Weinberg (1862–1937), an obscure German physician, easily demonstrated that the frequency of genes generally (whether dominant or recessive genes) would not change in large randomly breeding populations of organisms, excluding immigration and emigration, mutation, and any sort of selection. The "Hardy Weinberg Law" showed that populations at genetic equilibrium were resistant to change.

Fisher reacted by agreeing that populations in Hardy/Weinberg equilibrium were only minimally affected by mutation, but he argued that natural selection in large populations could effect the changes in gene frequency necessary for evolution and speciation. Haldane drew the equally provocative conclusion that speciation could only take place by natural selection when an initial population was segregated into subpopulations (known today as allopatric speciation). Other bio/mathematicians, however, were to become more closely associated with the role of small populations in evolutionary change.

Sewall (Green) Wright (1898–1988) demonstrated, theoretically, how sampling error, or accidents of the draw, known as random or genetic drift, could move small populations of organisms between peaks on an adaptive landscape. In contrast, large populations already residing on adaptive peaks could not cross the valleys of reduced fitness to other peaks, no matter how great a "pay-off" might be available on other peaks or how shaky the ground under an occupied peak. Wright's mathematical formalism for genetic drift did not depend on natural selection for initial stages of evolution, but natural selection took over later to push the population up the slope to an adaptive peak.

Wright proposed that genes could be fixed (or become extinct) in an expanding population through superior phenotypes resulting from mixtures of genes (heterozygous advantage) especially where there was a degree of outbreeding. Finally, Wright advanced evolutionary theory by redefining fitness. Instead of a match between morphology and environment, Wright defined Darwinian fitness[46] as the likelihood of an organism passing on its genes to a future generation.

Nevertheless, the so-called "modern synthesis" was more like a sieve for evolutionary problems than a basin—they simply passed through without any hope of solution. Despite their best efforts, the work of Fisher, Haldane and Wright

> had a limited impact on contemporary biologists because it was formulated in a mathematical language that most biologists could not understand; because it was almost exclusively theoretical, with little empirical corroboration; and because it was limited in scope, largely omitting many issues, such as speciation, that were of great importance to evolutionists.[47]

The Synthetic Theory

All was not lost, however. A mesmerizing new star was rising. Theodosius Gregorievitch Dobzhansky (1900–1975) and his followers would soon replace the modern synthesis with a "New World" synthesis or "Synthetic Theory" of evolution.[48] The transformation began in 1936 when Dobzhansky welded the cytogenetics of individuals to the dynamics of variations in populations. Later, working experimentally, especially on his favorite breeds (species?) of fruit flies, he renewed interest in genetic reserves (recessive genes hidden by their dominant counterparts in heterozygotes) as a source of plasticity in species. His enthusiasm then spread to variation among genes (genetic polymorphism) comprising balanced gene systems where losses inherent to one genetic configuration were compensated for by gains in another configuration.

Ultimately, members of the Dobzhansky school and those influenced by it wrote the closing chapters on classical evolutionary theory prior to molecular genetics.[49] The paleontologist, George Gaylord Simpson (1902–1984), reconstructed horse phylogeny in a Wright-like adaptive landscape (projected back through the Tertiary), reintroducing paleontology to evolutionists. Ernst Mayr (b. 1904) redefined species as a group of interbreeding organisms, and characterized speciation as the irreversible sexual isolation of formerly breeding communities. He and other animal evolutionists advanced the concept of allopatric evolution in which sexual isolation arises when incipient species are geographically separated. The botanist, G. Ledyard Stebbins Jr. (1906–1993) added hybridization, polyploidization, and sympatric speciation (speciation without the requirement for geographical separation) as mechanisms that created new species of plants.

Classical evolutionary theory inevitably harks back to adaptation, but nothing guarantees that a trait which is clearly adaptive under prevailing conditions evolved under similar conditions in the past. The problem of matching traits to their past was confronted by Ivan Ivanovich Schmalhausen (1884–1963) who worked out how selection might anticipate present utility independently of the origin of a feature. Known today as preadaptation, aptation, or exaptation, Schmalhausen's idea was that, under cover of other adaptations, a feature at the extremes of a distribution curve provided the raw material for rapid evolution when that feature's time had come.[50] Instead of dismissing the apparent fits and starts of the paleontological record as the consequence of missing links, Schmalhausen imagined periods of environmental change promoting specific organisms at the extremes of an existing population's spread (directional selection). New environmental pressures might also work against the mean of a distribution, rapidly splitting one original species into two (diversifying selection). On the other hand, periods of more or less constant environmental pressures seemed likely sources of specific narrowness (stabilizing selection).

Non-Darwinian Evolution

Beginning in the 1970s, modifications of the synthetic theory were made in order to accommodate data that, by some accounts, fell outside Darwinian evolution via natural selection.[51] Leigh van Valen thought up the Red Queen hypothesis, a concept of evolutionary equilibria in which a balance arises among nondirectional forces and species' dynamics resulting in an appearance of species-sameness in the presence of fixed resources.[52] Ordinarily, new groups appeared at the same rate that old groups disappeared, but opportunities for expansion made available in new environments provided the conditions for rapid speciation. In addition, Ernst Mayr advanced Sewall Wright's concept of genetic drift to explain rapid evolution from small founder populations of colonizers and survivors of catastrophic bottlenecks.[53]

Other explanations for rapid evolution skirted the edges of Darwinian natural selection and may even have stepped into the abyss of non-Darwinian evolution. Conspicuously among these explanations was Niles Eldredge's and Stephen Jay Gould's concept of "punctuated equilibrium."[54] In contrast to the slow accumulation of small changes prescribed by Darwin to account for descent with modification, Eldredge and Gould contemplated "adaptive radiations," the sudden appearance in the paleontological record of numerous, new species.[55] Devised to explain the fits and starts of species-formation, punctuated equilibrium proposed that revolution instead of evolution occurred between calms or normal periods.[56]

Typically, adaptive radiations followed mass extinctions. These were also being studied vigorously following Luis and Walter Alvarez's demonstration that the impact of an asteroid or comet on Earth could explain both the massive extinction at the Cretaceous/Tertiary border (K/T, K from the German for Cretaceous, *Kreide*) and the high concentration of iridium (the iridium anomaly) at this border.[57] Soon thereafter, absolute geochronological dating—based on data for reversals of magnetic fields—allowed Vincent Courtillot and others to lay the blame for biological catastrophes on "rapid eruption of enormous continental basalt formations" following mantle plumes, sometimes in double doses ("double whammy").[58] Meanwhile, the consequences of movement among continental masses—recognized by Alfred Wegener (1880–1930) as continental displacement or drift, and later, by Leon Croizat (1894–1982) as plate tectonics—along with giant tsunami, added to the cacophony underlying extinctions.

The mass extinctions 250 million years ago and again 65 million years ago were survived by some species in refuges, and, following periods of healing, survivors seem to have been propelled into adaptive radiations. These radiations cannot be explained by the survivors occupying ecological niches abandoned during the mass extinctions, since the extinct species inevitably took their niches with them. Rather, the survivors evolved hand-in-glove with new niches, and thus life moved on without repeating itself.

Finally, a new wave of evolutionary theory, led by the sociobiologists, John Maynard Smith (b. 1920), shored up punctuated equilibrium and neo-catastrophe theory. Equilibria during periods of evolutionary quiescence was explained by "evolutionary stable strategies" (ESSs), ways of keeping at bay other species with competitive adaptations. A successful ESS implied that the species' behavior within its niche rendered it virtually invulnerable to invasion by related species.[59]

THE GAMES SOCIOBIOLOGISTS PLAY

Sociobiology began as a branch of ecology as it is known today—not the ecology of Weldon's ecological evolution. Ecologists began to theorize about evolution when G. Evelyn Hutchinson (1903–1991) became President of the American Society of Naturalists in 1958.[60] He used his post to popularize model systems in communities and food chains (webs) as the foundation of evolutionary change. His eco/behavioral brand of evolutionary thought was not reductionist to begin with; it only became that way under pressure for funding.

Reductionism in biology—the method of breaking life down into parts and studying their operations and interactions—is not the only way of generating biological facts, but it is a widely accepted (and frequently profitable) way. In terms of biology's largest systems, ecosystems, Alfred James Lotka (1880–1949) and Vito Volterra (1860–1940), utilizing a reductionist approach, developed the logistics of population dynamics into models of competition among parts of an environmental mosaic. Robert Helmer MacArthur (1930–1972), Edward Osborne Wilson (b. 1929), among others, then extended ecological modeling to island biogeography, which rapidly became the premier system for experimentation on speciation. Wilson and Maynard Smith, among others, then brought evolution full circle by bringing it back to one of Darwin's favorite concerns—behavior. But the difficulty of quantifying behavior led to the excesses of sociobiology—yet another "new synthesis" immortalized in the title of Wilson's best selling textbook.[61]

This reductionist approach to evolution was clinched when William Donald Hamilton (1936–2000), "the most innovative thinker in the field since Fisher," invented a chromosomal (hence genetic) selectionist model that successfully accounted for sterile female bees and other hymenopterans working indefatigably for the care and feeding of their sisters, all of whom had the same mother and, allegedly, the same father.[62] Hamilton calculated that given the hymenopteran type of sex determination—in which females have a double dose of chromosomes (they are diploid), while males, or drones, have a single dose (they are haploid)—sisters from the same mother and father shared 75% of their chromosomes, whereas mothers and daughters shared only half their chromosomes. The idea was simply that it paid, in terms of Darwinian fitness— called "inclusive fitness" in this context—to help raise your sisters, who shared this large proportion of genes with you, rather than to raise your own offspring. Sisters would have a greater chance of getting their genes into the next generation by helping each other rather than by breeding themselves.

But this high degree of shared chromosomes among sisters occurred only if the queen—and mother of all the working sisters—mated with only one drone, the father of all the sisters produced by that queen. Hamilton's concept is still taught as if it were gospel, although queens are now known to have multiple matings and sisters are not as closely related as originally assumed.

In this throwback to nineteenth century evolutionism of the "red in tooth and claw" variety, late twentieth century evolutionists began to see Darwinian fitness in terms of an arms race: For every offense there was an equal and opposite defense; for every strategy, there was a counter strategy. Recently, the metaphor switched from war games to video games with the mutually enhancing development of computer hardware and software.

One popular game, harking back to the Vietnam War, is the "prisoner's dilemma"—or "hawks versus doves" game—in which strategies of cooperation and betrayal are played off against strategies of noncooperation and "honor among thieves." The idea is to employ a strategy that gets more of one's genes into the next generation than someone else's genes. Most strategies are defeatable, however. For example, a strategy of "honesty is best" is defeated by a betrayer who says one thing and does another. Sociobiologists do not ordinarily bother to explain where players come from or how they invent new strategies, but, as a result of the entry into the game of a new player with a new strategy, possibilities for upsetting any ESS are endless—each possibility creating a new arms race or period of adaptive radiation until the victory of one ESS installs a new "establishment."

Today, the chief inventor of gene games is the premier reductionist and foremost hawk, Richard Dawkins.[63] Dawkins dispenses with ancestral organisms and traces genes back to tribal genes, even inventing intermediate genes where necessary. After all:

> There will be times when it is hard to think of what the gradual intermediates may have been. These will be challenges to our ingenuity, but if our ingenuity fails, so much the worse for our ingenuity. It does not constitute evidence that there were no gradual intermediates.[64]

THE REDUCTION OF GENES: GENOMICS AND MOLECULAR CLADISTICS

Beyond the dominions of behavioral ecology, reductionism required biologists to analyze life in terms of its molecular parts. Reductionism of this sort began in the first decades of the twentieth century when hereditary traits were reduced to particles, particles were reduced to genes (symbols for traits), genes were reduced to DNA, and, in the closing decades of the twentieth

century, DNA was reduced to sequences of nucleic acids. The point of no
return in this scenario is sometimes thought to be the discovery of base
pairing in DNA in 1953, but, more likely, the point came in the 1960s when
gel electrophoresis made it possible to measure variation in DNA within
species, first as molecular polymorphism and then as nucleotide sequences.
The subsequent development of ultrafast, automatic, "high throughput" se-
quencers turned the Human Genome Project from a dream into a reality.

The vast amounts of sequence data generated by the Project were (and
are) grist for the mills of computers, and powerful interactive programs were
quickly written for cataloguing, comparing, and computing with sequences.
Conveniently stored in databases and freely accessible to research labs through
the Internet, sequence data were translated into structures, annotated for functions, and quickly became the root and branch of molecular biology.

Ultimately, sequence data generated two new disciplines: genomics, which
promised to teach us something about how genes worked from the structure
of complete genomes, and molecular cladistics, which promised to teach us
something about evolution by adopting cladistic techniques to sequence data.
Sequence databases are cornucopias for genomics, and structures are sought
endlessly among sequences of varying length, of known or unknown functions, and of varying degrees of similarity. Likewise, cladistics is in the throes
of a renaissance as molecular biologists seek to identify branching points and
evolutionary scenarios for molecules. Together, genomics and molecular cladistics have utterly changed how evolution is studied, but they have also
spawned more problems than they have solved.

NEW TWISTS IN OLD THEORIES: RANDOMNESS AND CLOCKS

The first innovation in evolutionary theory introduced by molecular biologists
harks back to a problem introduced in the 1960s: the high degree of variation,
known as polymorphism, in genes, or, more precisely, in the alleles or varieties of particular genes from wild organisms.[65] If species evolved toward an
optimal fit with their environment, as predicted by then current evolutionary
theory, then wild populations should gravitate toward genetic homogeneity
rather than heterogeneity. Genes which do not act independently of other
genes—presumably most genes—may only achieve a maximum fitness with
regard to other genes, and polymorphisms may "form together a single physiological unit with . . . alternative forms, each with its own characteristic
fitness."[66] Polymorphism became an even more pressing challenge with the
advent of DNA sequencing and prospects for reading DNA sequences for
entire organisms. Large numbers of silent mutations in DNA seemed to have
no adaptive value but were preserved throughout the genome.

The second innovation in evolutionary theory introduced by molecular biologists was neutral mutations or random errors in DNA replication to explain polymorphism in the genome.[67] This apparent reversion to the old idea of random mutations had a new twist: Mutations were thought to occur regularly, like the "ticking" of a DNA clock.[68] Modeled on radioactive decay, mutations due to nucleotide substitutions, deletions, and additions were supposed to occur and accumulate in the endless stream of evolution. The problem is that the clock is imprecise.

> For example, substitution rates in histone or actin coding regions differ by as much as tenfold in separate evolutionary lineages . . . [Although o]ther coding regions such as ribosomal RNAs . . . and glycerol aldehyde dehydrogenase genes . . . display a more consistent clock-like behavior.[69]

Imprecision among clocks extends from molecules to species. When mutations are collated and deviation among species is visualized as the length of branches in rooted phylogenetic dendrograms, some species rest inexplicably at the tips of longer branches than other species.[70] Some viral clocks are notoriously unreliable. Influenza runs fast[71] or slow at different times,[72] while other clocks run desperately fast (HIV) all the time. Clocks in the fruit fly, *Drosophila melanogaster,* and in the round worm, *Caenorhabditis elegans,* run faster than those of most other eukaryotic species, and clocks tick at different rates along the length of mitochondrial DNA.[73] DNA clocks are no chronometers and need an overhaul if they are to remain in the evolutionary timetable.

Nevertheless, molecular biologists use DNA clocks to estimate the time before molecular changes took place in genes. Phrases such as "this gene has been preserved for one hundred million years" are expressed freely in lectures and journal articles. Ideally, the clock is calibrated from independent evidence for the time at which branches of a phylogenetic tree diverged. The number of mutations (particularly substitutions) accumulated in genes can then be seen to converge on a time at which these genes were identical and presumably present in a common ancestor. Surprisingly, some genes are estimated to be far older than other genes in the same organisms, and even to have diverged long before the branches on the species' phylogenetic map.

MOLECULES AS OBJECTS OF NATURAL SELECTION

Molecular biologists also went back to biology's history for their notion of genetic homology. The idea is simply that molecular evolution relies on gene duplication to create new genes, known as homologues, which then deviate from each other. Deviations may take place in different species (orthologous evolution) or among duplicates in the same species (paralogous evolution).

> Homologues are genes whose sequences often (but not always) share significant similarities and represent modern versions of an ancient gene that at some moment in its past underwent gene duplication . . . Gene homologues may arise from speciation or from gene duplication within a genome . . . Single homologues from different organisms that are most similar in sequence and therefore form a distinct branch of a phylogenetic tree are usually thought to have arisen from speciation events, and are termed "orthologues" . . . Homologues present in the same organism are thought to have arisen from past intra-genome gene duplication and are termed "paralogues" . . .[74]

In theory, gene duplication is thought to be spontaneous—which is to say a total enigma—due to the incorporation into the genome of complementary DNA (cDNA) made by the action of a reverse transcriptase from a messenger RNA (mRNA) template, or a consequence of horizontal gene transfer—the acquisition of genes from a foreign source.[75] In practice, orthologous and paralogous genes are simply identified by similarities in sequence data, either in DNA from different species or DNA of one species.

David M. Hillis extends the analogy of homology among molecules several steps, namely to "partial homology" of structural sub-units (modules, such as fibronectin and immunoglobin repeats, and even to repeat units in non-coding regions), and further still to "positional homology" which begins grossly with the position of introns relative to exons, and continues into the fine structure of particular nucleotides or amino acids in a sequence. Inevitably, as the units of comparison become smaller, the likelihood of finding similarity becomes larger.

Molecular biologists seem to assume "that high similarity of aligned sequences never arises by convergence."[76] Rather, similarities are attributed to genetic conservation (the molecular biologists equivalent to Newton's conservation of momentum) and the presence of similar sequences in hypothetical common ancestors or common genes (hence, homologies). However, "convergence at individual nucleotide sites is common, facilitated by mutational biases."[77] It would seem that labeling similarities as homologies is inappropriate when data are as likely to be explained by convergence as by descent from a common ancestor, but molecular biologists cling to their concept of genetic conservation in much the way some early twentieth century physicists clung to Newton's conservation of momentum, and rarely examine the skepticism others have about the rigor of conservative assumptions.

The success of molecular cladistics is, in no small part, a consequence of the ease with which old concepts of homology[78] and particulate genes[79] have been translated to sequences in DNA. All the problems Darwin and others had trying to figure out where new species come from are truncated for the molecule under the aegis of "gene duplication and deviation," and all the problems of how species change are explained by intracellular natural selection operating on paralogues and more traditional forms of natural selection (between species) operating on orthologues. After making these assumptions, molecular cladists apparently have no difficulty leaping over the distance from sequences in DNA to the development of genetically determined traits.

THE "WORKING DRAFT" OF THE HUMAN GENOME

Those hoping to find genes for immortality or even for prolonging longevity must be disappointed with the working draft of the human genome released on February 15, 2001.[80] The most up-beat analysis was that of Aravinda Chakravarti who emphasized that "For the first time, nearly every human gene and genomic region is marked by a sequence variation."[81] Just as soon as a few problems are solved and variation can be studied more efficiently, studies on sequence variations might make it possible to identify the underlying differences in susceptibility to or protection from all kinds of diseases, the age of onset, severity of illness, and responses to treatment. David Baltimore urges caution in evaluating the working draft, since "[o]nly 1.1% to 1.4% is sequence that actually encodes protein; that is just 5% of the 28% of the sequence that is transcribed into RNA."[82] In other words, the greatest amount of DNA found in the nucleus of human cells still represents a vast secret.

Most importantly, no matter how rough the working draft, only a third of the expected number of genes were found, and while the spin doctors immediately made a case for complexity emerging through the reshuffling of gene parts, the missing genes left biologists with a numbing doubt that genes control human destiny the way they were supposed to. The existing genes are simply too similar to genes from worms and flies to make us uniquely human.

> Of the human proteins that are predicted [by the draft human sequence] 60% have some sequence similarity to proteins from other species whose genomes have been sequenced. Just over 40% of the predicted human proteins share similarity with fruitfly or worm proteins. And 61% of fruitfly proteins, 43% of worm proteins and 46% of yeast proteins have sequence similarities to predicted human proteins.[83]

Furthermore, reshuffling does not create an infinite number of permutations. Claims for restructuring human genes through multiple splicing variants seem far tamer than the unbridled complexity generally attributed to human beings.

> In the current set of full-length reference mRNAs, 11,174 transcripts have been sequenced from 10,742 distinct genes (2.4% of the genes have multiple splicing variants). Alignments of expressed sequence tag (EST) sequences to the working draft sequence, however, suggest that about 60% of human genes have multiple splicing variants, which has important implications for the complexity of human gene expression.[84]

The released working draft was accompanied by a series of analyses, intended to help readers grapple with the immensity of the data now available. Several of these analyses were relevant to prospects for prolonging human life. Jason Bock et al., discovered that several families of molecular players involved in vesicle trafficking expanded in the human genome.[85] Other analysts reflected disappointments with the results of the latest permutation of the genome project. Without meaning to dim the luster of the remarkable achievement one scintilla, the analysts concerned most closely with disease and life's prolongation were the least up-beat.

Rather than providing anything new, the Salk Institute's Thomas Pollard finds that "[m]ost cytoskeletal and motility proteins were discovered previously by biochemical isolation, traditional cloning methods or random sequences of complementary DNAs."[86] While he acknowledges that "[t]he complete genetic inventory will advance our understanding of disease . . . [and] reveal useful targets for development of new therapies," he concludes, "I doubt that the inventory of genes will provide much insight into molecular mechanisms, as even the simplest protein is multifaceted and has a complex mechanism of action."[87] Harvard's Andrew Murray and Debora Marks concede that the draft human genome suggested that activation of cyclin-dependent kinases (Cdks) requires phosphorylation to a threonine as well as binding to cyclin, but the authors conclude, "Disappointingly, we discovered a few novel cyclins and no new Cdks or components of the spindle checkpoint, and could shed little light on the organization of the cell cycle."[88] The analysts from the Cancer Genome Project and Informatics Division of the Wellcome Trust Genome Campus at Cambridge and others reporting on cancer discovered, in contrast to approximately 30 recessive oncogenes (tumor suppressor genes) and more than 100 dominant oncogenes identified in the past, "[n]o novel [tumor suppressor] genes were identified . . . [and no] oncogenic sequence changes in cancer cells [were detected] by comparing cancer genome sequences against the draft genome."[89]

WHAT IS AN EVOLUTIONARY VIEW OF LONGEVITY, AND WHY ARE THE PROSPECTS SO BLEAK FOR ACHIEVING IMMORTALITY THROUGH EVOLUTION?

Different answers to these questions would have been forthcoming over the last two centuries had Lyellian uniformitarianism prevailed, since it was more congenial to immortality than was evolution. Despite perturbations, uniformitarianism held that everything remained eternally the way God made it. Since precisely the same mechanisms operating "once upon a time," also operated in the present, mortality should be comprehensible and come under the purview of science, and scientists interested in it would have made immortality scientifically legitimate.

But the biological sciences decided in favor of evolution as opposed to uniformitarianism as the way species were manufactured, and evolutionary theory and practice, while spreading out over a wide terrain, from Darwinism and neo-Darwinism to sociobiology and molecular reductionism, had no place for immortality.

DARWINISM: THE EVOLUTION OF MORTALITY

The problem posed by mortality and immortality for evolutionary theory reminds me of the problem of *potato* confronting contestants at a spelling bee—to *e* or not to *e*. Mortality and immortality do not follow the rules and easily fit into the spectrum of variety and difference found among living things as explained by Darwin's and Wallace's theory.

For Darwin and Wallace, descent with modification was not an abstract principle derived by mathematical rumination but an explanation for empirical data, specifically, the many observations made during their travels on the variety of traits found among species and the great number of different species found on Earth. In contrast, the qualities of immortality and mortality are absolute and opposite. Neither has different forms, nor do they grade into one another. Furthermore, immortality defies empirical observation, since we have not been and will not be around long enough to observe it.[90]

Mortality and immortality must be reconfigured if they are to be brought under the aegis of traits or species-characteristics explained by evolution. One might look for immortality genes, since mean lifetime is a species parameter, but such a search would seem ill-advised inasmuch as mortality genes, or even aging genes, do not seem to exist.

The simplest possibility would seem to be identifying immortality with a potential for immortal life, and mortality as the absence of that potential. Immortality then becomes an open-ended lifetime, an attribute of species whose members have not (or not yet) proven themselves mortal. Mortality then becomes a characteristic of species whose members have lifetimes with durations distributed in a bell-shaped curve with a mean equal to the average life expectancy.

Potential Immortality

Do some organisms have open-ended lifetimes as opposed to lifetimes doomed by the "mortal coil" (DNA)? The issue of making human beings immortal may hang in the balance, since if open-ended lifetimes evolved among multicellular eukaryotes, then the evolution of immortality might be an option available to human beings.

The question of open-ended lifetimes is more difficult to answer than one would hope, since, in the wild, animals generally do not live long enough to grow old. An open-ended lifetime might be attributed to organisms meeting either or both of two criteria: organisms showing no sign of aging during their lifetime, and/or organisms obtaining unthinkably long life spans. Both claims are made for different organisms.

Leonard Hayflick makes the point that organisms showing no sign of aging—or what he calls organisms with negligible aging—are still very much mortal.

> [These are] animals that do not reach a fixed size in adulthood, and age either undetectably slowly or not at all. Animals of this class include some tortoises, many sport and cold water deep-sea fish, some amphibians and the American lobster... [But t]hey are not immortal because, like animals that do age, there is a constant threat of disease, predation and accidents.[91]

This would seem a dubious argument if immortality were a potential and not a guarantee, but Hayflick's argument is actually more subtle. He acknowledges that negligible aging animals may have extraordinarily high levels of telomerase in cells, "a hallmark of immortal cells in tissue culture," but insists that "[a]ging is not a programmed process governed directly by genes."[92] High telomerase activity helps negligible aging animals reach a great number of years, but their lifetime is not infinitely long. Telomerase still determines a finite life expectancy.

The case for smaller animals showing no signs of aging has been made for members of the Cnidaria. Anemones (Anthozoa) are said to have remained in pristine condition in an aquarium in Britain for 80 years until they were killed during WWII.[93] A longer, but controversial, record for longevity is held by Gerardia, a colonial zoanthid anemone. It is estimated to be 1800 ±300 years based on radiocarbon measurements of the specimen or 250 ±70 years old based on (1) the difference in aspartic acid (Asp) racemization measured in the outermost (youngest) and innermost (oldest) layers of the trunk of the organic endoskeleton of the specimen and (2) the estimated rate of Asp racemization, as extrapolated from heating experiments.[94] In any case, cnidarian longevity, which is frequently debated at the cnidarian web site (CNIDARIA@UCI.EDU), is generally thought to be due chiefly to complete cellular turnover made possible by the surface-distribution of virtually all cells.

If meeting its needs and avoiding contingency were the only problems faced by cnidarians in the sea, they might indeed seem to have a potential for surviving forever, but cnidarians also contend with members of their own species, or conspecifics, and that is where their mortality shows up. Many anemones are well equipped for combat with each other and in their normal habitat wage fierce territorial battles from which none emerge unscathed. A species with the potential to kill conspecifics would also be a species with the potential to die, or why bother fighting?

What are the organisms with unthinkably long lifetimes? Bristlecone pines (*Pinus aristata*) take the prize for longevity. Although several bristlecones are only somewhat more than 3,000 years old, one, in Wheeler Peak eastern Nevada, is more than 4,900 years old. Next in line are the Patagonian cypresses (*Fitzroya cupressoides*), reaching heights of 45 m and ages of about 4,000 years, followed by the giant sequoia or Sierra redwoods (*Sequoidadendron giganteum*) of the western slopes of the Sierra Nevada Range, California, reaching heights of 90 m and ages something less than 4,000 years. Oaks, redwoods, and junipers may live for more than 1,000 years.

Clones too may have unthinkably long lifetimes. Creosote bushes in California's Mojave Desert have lived 12,000 years. Mosses have been estimated to be 2,800 years old, while massive growths of English ivy are known to have survived for hundreds of years, and the mycelia of the Basidiomycete (*Marasmius oreades*) may have survived 400 years, venturing forth as mushrooms and darkening the grass in fairy rings 365 m in diameter.[95]

Are these extremely long-lived plants and fungi potentially immortal? On the one hand, they presumably have the potential to live somewhat longer, if only because they have lived as long as they have already. On the other hand, the rarity of such antique individuals suggests that most of their kind die at younger ages. These botanic and fungal Methuselahs would not seem to be immortal so much as organisms at the extreme of a survivorship curve approaching the asymptote of longevity. Of course, the mean lifetimes for these species are sobering but they do not make the case for "open-ended" lifetimes. The best that can be said about the evolution of potential immortality is that "the case is not established."

Longevity as a Trait

No claims are generally made for immortality among mammals, vertebrates (other than turtles and tortoises), or most other multicellular animals for that matter, but longevity varies considerably among these organisms and offers many opportunities for contemplating how physiology and evolution collude in the imposition of limits.[96] This collusion is not simple or straightforward.

First of all, the correlation of size and longevity (exemplified by Sierra redwoods), is problematic when applied to animals. Centimeter-size snails, crayfish, and beetles may live up to 30 years, while the giant clam (*Tridacna gigas*) of the South Pacific coral reefs, reaching a length of 1.37 m and a weight of 264 kg, has a life span of only about 40 years. The largest living invertebrate, the giant squid, *Architeuthis,* at four to five years, reaches full size, with a body length of 8 m and tentacles and arms of 22 m when fully extended, at which time it mates and dies (assuming that it follows the pattern of other, smaller squids, and octopuses).

Vertebrates are sometimes thought to exhibit a positive correlation of size and longevity, but the record for longevity in extant vertebrates, 177 years, is held by the giant tortoise and not by the larger crocodiles or alligators. Surprisingly, the 115–150 year maximum life-expectancy of human beings makes us the longest living mammal, although we are hardly the largest.

The conservation of heat may be one factor governing the evolution of body size and longevity in warm blooded vertebrates. Since body volume increases as a cube function, while surface area increases as a square function, and heat dissipates with surface area and is retained with body volume, one can understand Bergmann's Rule that warm blooded vertebrates tend to be larger in colder as opposed to warmer regions. One can also understand Rensch's Law that populations with large distributions tend to have larger varieties in the more polar parts of their range. (One is hard pressed to explain the distribution of elephants by the same logic.)[97]

Another factor sometimes correlated with size and lifetime is metabolic rate, but here the correlation is inverse. Smaller animals may simply burn out faster than larger ones. But the correlation of longevity and metabolic rate is not simple. Bats and mice have comparable metabolic rates, but bats live more than ten times longer than mice. Birds have higher metabolic rates than mammals but tend to live longer. For example, the royal albatross has the highest average longevity among birds, living several decades after reaching breeding age (at five to six years); geese and swans (in captivity) live more than 30 years, and ducks live 20 years. In contrast, mammals of comparable size have much shorter life expectancies: dogs live a dozen years and the average rat succumbs in three.

Body size is presumably a complex variable, tailored by evolution through multiple interactions in addition to the conservation/dissipation of heat and metabolic rate. Gravity, for example, presumably plays a role in influencing body size. Indeed, two-footed organisms living in a nonsupporting medium (air) are influenced considerably by gravity (as demonstrated by the problems experienced by astronauts living in weightlessness), and gravity's constraints no doubt figure into setting the limits on body size. We might not yet have reached our greatest average size, but heart and lung failures among those with congenital giantism indicate that we cannot expect to grow indefinitely. Similarly, to whatever degree our body size is correlated with our longevity, we may not have reached our greatest average life expectancy, but we cannot expect to live indefinitely.

The Fossil Record

The tendency toward increasing size seen among dinosaur fossils from the Jurassic (the age of dinosaurs, as everyone knows, thanks to Michael Crichton and Stephen Spielberg) may have been correlated with a trend toward increasing longevity but the trend is not certain. The fossil record cannot support the possibility of a trend toward increased longevity. Indeed, not even "living fossils" (e.g., horseshoe crabs, coelacanths, and the ginkgo tree) sustain such an argument. None of these organisms is known to be especially long-lived, while the ebb and flow of species belonging to younger taxa hardly suggests a consistent trend in longevity.

All the average life spans of species, which is to say, their duration in the fossil record, fit a random distribution. Notwithstanding contraction of species longevity due to periods of mass extinctions and the dilations possible in periods of relative environmental calm, or normal periods, species-longevity is neither progressive nor regressive. Species-survival

> ranges from a few hundred thousand years to several million years; the average, depending on the group, lies between 2 and 10 Ma [million years]. Within a given set of species, the probability of extinction is essentially constant over long periods (and, therefore, does not depend on how ancient the species may be) . . .[98]

If the frequently quoted figure is to be trusted, 99.9% of all species are extinct, despite this being an age of unprecedented speciation. Extinction, like death, is presumably the fate of all species.

Darwinian Fitness, Longevity, and Menopause

Mortality seems to have worked very well as a characteristic of life—as witness mortality's presence in all categories of eukaryotic organisms—but one is hard pressed to think of any adaptive advantage death has for individuals (other than relief from pain).[99] Typically, biologists suggest that death helps the group by making room at the top where a new generation may have access to limited resources. Explanations of this sort raise the specter of group selection—positing a selective advantage for the group—and are generally thought to be flawed, since Darwinism requires a selective advantage for individuals rather than groups.

The trick frequently used to make group selection acceptable is simply to paraphrase an advantage for the group in terms of *inclusive* or *Darwinian fitness*. Inclusive fitness includes all the ways, no matter how indirect or devious, genes get into the next generation. One's reproduction is certainly the most obvious way, but even one's death can help one's genes survive in the next generation if one's personal sacrifice were to rescue one's offspring, or even one's near relatives, from the threat of death. Inclusive fitness, as opposed to group selection, thus offers an acceptable basis for death and its evolution.

Inclusive fitness offers explanations for still other features of longevity. Evolution's standard dependence on reproduction suggests that the addition of fecund years would offer an adaptive advantage to any lifetime, but, somewhere between 40 and 50 years of age, women become post-reproductive (post-menopausal), although they may live to a ripe old age.[100] Indeed, since the mid-twentieth century, the average woman in industrialized countries lives as long in her post-reproductive years as she lived in her fecund years, a rare feat among sexually reproducing animals and even a rare feat in endemic populations of human beings.

According to the doctrine of inclusive fitness, the prolongation of post-reproductive survival of women pays dividends for getting genes into the next generation by providing baby-sitters, transmitting survival skills, and dispensing wealth. One might wonder, nevertheless, why women gain additional post-reproductive years but not reproductive years while men remain fertile, despite declining sperm counts, more or less throughout their lifetime.[101]

The proffered explanation for this difference between women and men in terms of inclusive fitness is that females in general make a higher investment in any one offspring, while males distribute their investment over many offspring. Therefore, it pays for females to safeguard an investment already made in offspring rather than gamble on prolonged reproduction.

A more physiological explanation falls back on the fact that women, like other female mammals, have limited numbers of eggs available as a consequence of the early differentiation of stem cells, while men, like other male mammals, have an unlimited number of spermatozoa available as a consequence of proliferation in undifferentiated stem cells. Limits on the number of eggs available to any female are widespread among animals. In many species, from round worms to human beings, that number is set before birth, and fecundity (the number of offspring produced by any female) diminishes with age to zero. Prolonged fecundity would not be achieved unless women had higher numbers of eggs, lower rates of egg degeneration, or continued egg production following the fetal burst. Furthermore, eggs would have to be sustained over a prolonged period of time (in excess of the present 40 to 50 years), a dubious proposition at best given the excessive number of aneuploid-21 eggs produced by older women. Presumably, all the necessary adjustments would have to be made simultaneously, to one degree or another, rending the evolution of prolonged reproduction that much more unlikely.

In contrast to modern women, marine invertebrate animals, which struggle through a lifetime determined by contingency, do not generally live long enough to fulfill their reproductive potential. Shedding sex cells or asexual progeny lavishly into their environment—known as broadcast sexual or asexual reproduction—these animals would leave more progeny were they to live longer, but evolution has presumably already shaped their morphology and behavior to maximize getting genes into the next generation, and the strategy of self-sacrifice is likely to represent the strategy of maximal reproduction.

Darwinian or inclusive fitness has it limits. One can imagine that increased post-menopausal longevity might be bred into women like other desirable traits are bred into domesticated animals or strains of fruit flies, but even such a prolongation would be limited. Nothing about inclusive fitness suggests how longevity could be extended to anything approaching immortality.

The Domestication of Longevity

Darwin was deeply committed to domestication as a model for the origin of species and devoted a great deal of attention to it in *Origin*. But one cannot expect to breed prolonged longevity into animals in quite the same way that elevated milk production is bred into cows or the rate of weight gain is bred into pigs. In livestock, one has pedigrees and animals with known production qualities. Breeders merely try (against the odds) to capture these qualities in offspring. In the case of longevity, one has only pedigrees, since one cannot know in advance if a specific animal is going to have a prolonged lifetime. One must decide early whether to breed any particular animal or not, since fecundity is likely to be reduced with age.

Indirect methods may be effective in breeding prolonged longevity into some species. For example, fruit flies selected for delayed reproduction give rise to strains having prolonged longevity.[102] Regrettably, the same trick does not seem to work in human beings. The experiment is already being done, if unbeknownst to the participants.

In so-called developed nations, women who occupy slots in the work force during what would otherwise be their peak reproductive years tend to commence reproduction late in their own lifetimes. Like the strains of selected fruit flies, these working women might push upward the heritable limits of the average lifetime,[103] since,

> [f]or humans . . . there *is* a tendency for below-average fertility to be associated with above-average longevity. This was found . . . [in a study] of the births, deaths and marriages of British aristocrats. However, there is no evidence that those who simply elect not to have children live longer.[104]

Regrettably, women reproducing later in their lifetime are more likely to suffer from breast and intrauterine cancers, reducing whatever advantage in longevity they might otherwise have gained.

NEO-DARWINISM: IMMORTALITY ON THE CUSP OF THE SYNTHETIC THEORY

The heyday of the synthetic theory was also the heyday for eugenics. Eugenicists not only helped synthesize the synthesis but frequently lived according to its dictates.[105] For them, natural selection was the power behind organic evolution, and eugenics held out the promise of playing "an indirect, 'cultural' role" through advances in agriculture and miracles in medicine.[106] As it turned out, eugenics also played a role in the horrors of genocide[107] and gave entrée to what is, in some people's estimate, "[t]he sole remaining 'killing field' . . . therapeutic abortion."[108]

Broadly defined to include direct and indirect roles, the eugenics movement can count the extension of longevity among its most conspicuous successes. Actuarial statistics show that longevity increased among human beings in the twentieth century. The half life (average lifetime) of human beings in so-called developed nations is widely acknowledged to have doubled in the last century. On average, we can expect to live beyond the age at which our parents died, to say nothing of our average ancestors. Many of us who have grown up in and live in developed countries can expect to survive well into our eighties and even our nineties with more than a modicum of good health and intellectual well being.

Yet these trends toward greater life expectancy are not readily attributable to changes in our gene pool or the accumulation of quantitative genes (polygenes) for prolonged lifetimes. Maximum lifetime, the furthest approach to the asymptote on a survivorship curve, seems to rattle around 120 years (115 to 150) today much as it has in the past. Increasing the slope and pushing out the mean of the survivorship curve are changes attributed to the larger proportion of the human population "living to the limit." For the most part, these changes are attributable to the availability of adequate nutrition, provisions for rest and recuperation from work and injury, healthy life styles, and efficacious health care, especially in the treatment of diseases of the young.

In theory, one cannot determine how much of the change in longevity is attributed to environmental as opposed to genetic influences. The evolutionary theoretician, Fred Brookstein argues emphatically that "a mechanism for expressing biometric findings in terms of *characters* . . . is mathematically inaccessible."[109] What is more: "[i]n cladistic language: *morphometric shape variables cannot possibly form a hierarchy.*"[110]

> [In effect, t]here is no way to extend the methods of biometrics . . . to test assertions of homology by biometric methods, and no way, also, to incorporate more than the brute assertion of homology into biometric analyses of causes and effects of form.[111]

Longevity is undoubtedly the product of profound and long-evolving biological processes, including mechanisms of growth, development and maintenance, which, in turn, are products of interactions among polymorphic alleles. Therefore, the arithmetic of single character analysis would seem entirely inadequate, if not utterly inappropriate, for the analysis of longevity. Richard Lewontin makes the point this way:

> We should not expect that single drastic genetic changes produced either experimentally or by the bad luck of naturally occurring mutations will account in specific cases for most, or even any, of the normal variation we see in nature.[112]

Brian Goodwin makes a similar point:

> History is not explanatory of form because it does not describe the generative processes that make different forms possible. Natural selection is equally deficient because it addresses the question of persistence, of stability (including, of course, instability) of characters in relation to environments; it neither explains generative origins of characters nor why they are possible[113]

GAMES AND COMPETITION: LONGEVITY AND THE INDIVIDUAL

Genes are reputed to be immortal, and one can imagine our pursuing immortality by playing the game genes play. That game is replication, and genes are extraordinarily good replicators. Their evolutionary stable strategy (ESS) for winning and getting into new generations is unbeatable, but it has one characteristic that may put it out of contention from human immortality: The immortality of some genes is only achieved at the expense of vast numbers of other genes.

Sex is enormously wasteful of genes. The theory of sexual reproduction generally taught to biology students predicts that for every sex cell or gene getting into the next generation, three are wasted. In practice, the waste is vastly greater. Great numbers of sex cells (eggs as well as spermatozoa) are ordinarily produced and lost without contributing to reproduction. Sex pursues a saturation strategy for overcoming the difficulty sex cells have finding each other and developing into offspring following fertilization. Most sex cells never make it into the next generation but the waste and death are small sacrifices by the standards of the ones that do make it. The very idea of individual immortality flies in the face of sexual reproduction, and strategies for life involving sexual reproduction seem incompatible with strategies for immortal life.

The analogy of gene replication and immortality encounters still other problems for human immortality. Genes are more than DNA. Functionally, they include histones and nucleoproteins that give the DNA its opportunity for self expression. After all, DNA as a molecule is virtually inert without everything else supplied by the cell or added to test tubes. In addition, most DNA, certainly in human beings, is not genetic in the sense of dictating the development of a trait or even encoding an amino acid sequence in a polypeptide.[114] Furthermore, a cell contains more DNA than that located in its nucleus, the alleged site of genes. As a consequence, playing the gene game may miss the "big game in town."

Cytoplasmic DNA is present in episomes, plasmids, plastids, mitochondria, and chloroplasts, depending on cell type, to say nothing of endosymbiotic bacteria and viruses. Some DNA, may not come under the usual rules of Darwinian selection, and not everything coming under the rules of Darwinian selection may be genetic DNA. As a consequence, the alleged immortality of genes may not characterize all genes, while other entities in living things, not ordinarily considered genes, may yet be immortal or, at least, timeless. The problem is that we may very well pursue the wrong genes while pursuing immortality by way of genes.

Are genes really as immortal as they are cracked up to be? Some genes only acquire their genetic character epigenetically, as a consequence of methylation through the influence of specific cytoplasm (maternal, paternal, placental).[115] These genes are hardly immortal, changing as they do in every generation. In fact, many genes, including the rapidly mutating genes of viruses, are hardly immortal. The mutations that foreshorten the life expectancy of these genes are sometimes dismissed for a variety of canonical reasons, including definitions of species and the consensus of opinion on the quality of viral life as well as evolution.[116] One might not want to rest one's hopes for prolonged longevity on quite so shaky genes.

REDUCTIONISM

Reductionism for biologists is simply the analytical technique of treating a living thing as if it were a watch and breaking it down into its working parts in order to see what makes it tick. In the case of evolution, Darwin and Wallace identified the "watch" as the species and invoked genealogy to explain variety among species and the great number of different species present on Earth. Genealogy, in turn, requires populations of mating organisms, which boils down to organisms behaving, and, hence, to physiology, to the functions of organ system, organs, tissues, cells, organelles, subcellular particles, macromolecules, proteins, and all the biochemistry that makes the watch tick.

That is the theory. In practice, those studying the evolution of longevity frequently ignore intermediate levels of integration for lack of relevant information and hence neglect the consequences and complexities arising from interactions. Aging and even the death of organisms are simply blamed on something going wrong with cells or the molecules governing them.

Problems between Cells and Organisms

The temptation to analyze biological problems at one level while ignoring others was illustrated by D'Arcy Wentworth Thompson (1860–1948) in his epic *On Growth and Form* "Large numbers simplify many things; a million men are easier to understand than one man out of a million."[117] Populations of cells have many characteristics worthy of analysis, such as those illustrated in distribution curves (mean and standard deviation, skewness, and kurtosis), but these characteristics of populations are not the same as those of organisms.

Speaking of a composite of cells as if it were an ideal organism is a distortion, especially exacerbated when statistical treatments are extended over time. Likewise, the characteristics of cells do not add up simply to the characteristics of organisms. For instance, cancer cells celebrated for their immortality are rather less than salubrious for organisms. Cancer cells and immortalized cell lines carry on indefinitely *in vitro* but kill organisms *in vivo*.

In the course of evolution of large animals, it would seem, the environment beyond the body's surface and within the lumen of the gut have acted as sinks for the disposal of cells, and cells on surfaces and in linings proliferate indefinitely, refreshing their population without clogging channels or overgrowing their containment.[118] Similarly, motile cells, such as those of the blood vascular and lymphatic systems, grow in one place yet move to sites where they are destroyed and their waste products are funneled outside the organism. Even bone is constantly broken down and remodeled, its calcium returned to circulation and picked up again according to the dictates of hormones, tension, and stress.

On the other hand, endless growth is not accommodated in internal organs lacking active turnover mechanisms or access to the external environment, such as the brain and remainder of the nervous system, heart, liver, and lungs, and even most skeletal and smooth muscles. In these organs, a healthy accommodation, whether achieved during normal development or following transplantation, requires restraints on growth. Indeed, the evolution of organisms with internal organs would have to have depended on bringing cellular growth under control, and genes operating in the control of cellular growth are, presumably, old and well-established residents in the genomes of organisms with internal organs. The problem for longevity is that constraints on growth can hardly be set aside in fully grown adults, and precisely these constraints dictate the aging of cells!

Problems between Molecules and Cells

The growth of cell populations in eukaryotes occurs through a highly controlled division cycle, or cell cycle. Biologists divide this cycle into two periods, mitosis (M) and interphase (I). M has two parts, during the first of which (known as karyokinesis) duplicated chromosomes divide into identical singlet chromosomes, and these representatives of the original chromosomes move to opposite poles of the cell. In some species, the nucleus breaks down and reforms during this part of M as well. During the second part, the cytoplasm divides (known as "cytokinesis") usually more or less equally, but sometimes in a lopsided fashion. The remainder of the cell cycle, I, consists of three or four phases. The principle phase is S, or phase of DNA synthesis, which comes after a gap known as G_1 and before a gap known as G_2. The fourth phase, G_0, also known as the quiescent phase, is sometimes considered a departure from G_1 that takes a cell out of the cycle, and sometimes considered merely a prolonged G_1.

Each phase and the transition between phases has checkpoints, or restriction points, but those between G_1 and S are chiefly responsible for preventing abnormal patterns of division. The products of no fewer than thirty cellular oncogenes (*c-oncs*), or proto-oncogenes, control the cell's movement through these restriction points and hence through normal cell division.[119]

The study of division-controlling genes frequently depends on viruses, such as retroviruses which harbor variations of *c-oncs* known as *v-oncs*. Other oncogenes, unique to viral genomes, are conveyed by the DNA of cell-transforming oncoviruses. Learning how these genes control cell division is a major preoccupation of molecular biologists, especially those specializing in cancer research.

Control at cell-division checkpoints frequently involves enzymatic phosphorylation—especially by cyclin-dependent kinases—but oncogenes work in a variety of ways—transduction, *cis*-activation and *trans*-activation—including cooperative interactions. For example, the adenoviral *trans*-activating transcriptional regulators E1A and E1B (or the *ras* gene's cellular product), when present simultaneously, react with tumor suppressors RB1 (retinoblastoma) and p53 proteins, immortalizing cells and altering their shape and behavior *in vitro*, and turning them into invasive destructive cancer *in vivo*. Transfected mouse cells expressing E1B alone are not transformed, while those expressing E1A alone are immortalized, not altered *in vitro*, not cancerous *in vivo*, and may, as a bonus, undergo apoptosis, which is to say, commit cell suicide.[120]

Apoptosis is an important dimension of growth control, since it is responsible for eliminating cells that are already present, and proto-oncogenes are heavily invested in apoptotic controls.[121] Genes such as *p53*, which encodes the tumor suppressor protein, p53, operate on both sides of the aisle, so to speak, encoding a cell-cycle checkpoint protein that doubles as an apoptosis-inducing protein.[122] Other proteins, such as those encoded by the proto-oncogene *BCL2* and the family of similar genes, block apoptosis while other proteins (BAX and $BCLX_S$) counter these blocks. Thus, faults in the induction and suppression of apoptosis also contribute to the development of cancer.[123]

Inevitably, interactions rather than linearity and complexity rather than branching characterize the control of growth. For example, the tumor suppressor p53 is a transcriptional *trans*-activator or sequence specific transcriptional factor (TF), which also interacts with various viral antigens and proteins (SV40 T-antigen, oncoproteins of adenoviruses and papilloma viruses).

The point is that all of these interactions and the sheer complexity of controls strongly suggest that one will not be able to improve on matters and turn cells into useful, immortal entities by altering any one of the component elements. The opposite would seem more likely, especially if the experience with p53 is any indication: p53 is absent or mutated (altered) in the majority of human cancers—Barrett's, superficial bladder, sporadic breast, colorectal, esophageal (both squamous cell and adenocarcinomas), gastric, lung, ovarian, pancreatic cancers, prostatic, hematological malignancies (lymphoid, myeloid leukemias and lymphomas, including Burkitt's, high-grade B-cell, Hodgkin's, and MALT lymphomas), hepatocellular carcinoma, possibly cholangiocarcinomas, endometrial serous cancer and adenocarcinomas, and all the associated lymph node metastases![124]

Immortal Sequences: Homologies among Molecules

One might have thought that the last place one would look for immortality was in fragile molecules, but today the idea of homology has been extended from organisms to sequences of nitrogenous bases in DNA and amino acids in protein. Homologous, or conserved sequences, are simply similar sequences whose similarity is attributed, usually without independent evidence, to the sequences not having changed much from their originary form. The homologues may represent duplicates in the same species (paralogues), or they may represent related genes in different species (orthologues)—sometimes in species that are only distantly related, to say the least. For example, homologues of *ras (rat sarcoma sequence)* occur in all eukaryotes examined so far, from yeast to *C. elegans, Drosophila* to mammals, (although in human beings the homologue is a pseudogene, incapable of transcription). Even the prokaryote *E. coli,* has a *ras* homologue in the gene encoding the EF-Tu elongation factor.

Familial relationships do not necessarily extend across entire genes. Rather, the homology may occur in small, usually repeated sequences of nucleic acids known as domains (encoding portions of polypeptides with known secondary structure) and motifs (encoding functional sites).[125] Elsewhere, gaps and additions may be blamed for distorting the sequence-similarity, albeit not beyond recognition. Nevertheless, the argument that similar sequences form the basis of molecular families and beyond them, superfamilies, has been argued so persuasively that molecular biologists are more likely to ascribe structure and function to whole proteins by identifying motifs and domains than by determining what the protein actually is or what functions it performs.

Sequences are expected to remain constant through biological inertia until some improved version comes along, but that seems to be a rare event. Changes in nitrogenous bases may be as frequent as six percent (*Drosophila*), but these are silent mutations having no consequences for the amino-acid sequence of the encoded protein. But silent mutations are not without consequence for evolutionary theory. Survival of the best-fit model of sequences led to the invention of DNA "clocks" which tick off changes in DNA without regard to fitness. Consensus sequences are thus defined as the remnant of homologous sequences left over after the ticking of the DNA clock and the accumulation of silent mutations.

Hot changes in DNA sequences that result in amino-acid substitutions in a polypeptide, it would seem, are largely weeded out by natural selection. For example, the normal products of *ras* genes are universally membrane bound GTPases, signal transducing elements that play a role in the control of cell division and differentiation, but "any one of many single amino acid mutations [in codons 12, 13, 59 and 61] can give rise to highly oncogenic [cancer-causing] proteins."[126]

Once again, life seems to offer few opportunities to "improve on a good thing." This is not to say that gene therapy cannot improve on bad genes present in cells, turning them off and turning on good genes in their place. Nevertheless, molecular evolution holds little hope for producing superior genes for extending human longevity in general.

AFTERWORD: IMMORTALITY TRIUMPHANT!

Now, imagine longevity as a trait capable of evolving into immortality. Substitute the idea of performance advantage for anything resembling purpose or progress, and scale longevity for measurement and appropriate comparisons.[127] One might also propose a phylogenetic scenario from comparative data and tease apart an order of events, since a trait may originate with or before a performance advantage (an aptation).

What then are the performance advantages of prolonged longevity? As already mentioned, the prolongation of average life expectancy might well be paid for by altruistic behavior, including baby-sitting and the banking of cultural knowledge and wisdom.

Altruism might not however, seem quite as attractive to immortals. Would an immortal, let us say a 200-year old (the equivalent of a great, great, great, great, great, grandmother or grandfather), be happy as a baby-sitter for the umpteenth time, and would such a baby-sitter be a better baby-sitter than a mortal grandmother or grandfather, to say nothing of a trained child-care worker in a crèche? Would a 200-year old worker even want to work after the fifth or sixth run-through at a career? Could the immortal store more information than, say, a computer with a mega-giga hard drive supplied with the equivalent of a large number of CDs, and how many times can anyone tell the same joke and make it sound fresh? What is more, age is not necessarily a qualification for wisdom, and "gems" fall from the mouths of babes.

Performance advantages are difficult enough to attribute to structures in the present; they are almost impossible to anticipate in the future. If immortality offers any performance advantage, we may simply have to find out what it is when we get there. This is not to say that it will not; but whatever it is, it is not intuitively obvious or theoretically predictable.

The question might better be asked, "What would immortality look like shorn of performance advantages?" In other words, what is the down side of immortality? What losses might lurk in the supposed performance advantages of immortality, waiting to spring upon the unsuspecting immortals?

One possible drawback is of concern to the science writer and novelist, Ben Bova. He is worried that institutions such as marriage and family would be decimated by immortality, given recent experience with prolonged "good times":

> In the twentieth Century divorce rates have skyrocketed, in large part because people are living long enough to want to change partners. Death does not part these married couples; boredom or infidelity or simply a gradual estrangement over the years sunders their marriages.[128]

I cannot say that I am worried about social structures; church and country have found ways of adjusting to change in the past. That immortality might irreparably harm individuals is a serious concern. Boredom, for example, is the leading cause of suicide. Would self destruction become the leading cause of death among immortals?

What does immortality offer the individual? What good is the certainty of infinite life if it comes without the pleasures of living? What is individual stability worth without the dynamics of birth and death? It is one thing to say that infinite life is attractive when one faces uncertainty and death, but quite another to trade pleasure and wonder for stasis.

Another problem can be anticipated from the link between prolonged longevity and reduced fecundity: the sudden-death syndrome.[129] How would a species with reduced reproductive potential due to increased longevity be able to cope with an unanticipated population disaster? What were once long-lived birds, the moas of New Zealand, seem to have been driven to extinction in a very few years after the Maori arrived and began hunting adults.[130] Similarly, "blitzkrieg" hunting of long-lived adult mammals in the Americas and Australia seems to have driven many prey to extinction simply because low reproductive rates foreclosed recovery.[131] Were long-lived human beings with reduced reproductive potential victimized by similar hunting or exposed to new virulent viruses, our species, too, might be in jeopardy. Immortality might then be our formula for extinction.

Chapter 3

Why Immortality Cannot Develop

Today, the sciences of chaos and complexity theory are exposing the extent to which the real is no longer "rational", and vice versa, but rather the most probable, giving priority to chance, to singularity and phase-space transition, and to non-linear dynamical systems which thrive on positive feedback.

—Keith Ansell-Pearson, *Viroid Life*

If I succeed in opening some space for the imagination, then we are not forever stuck with the implausible myth of progress.

—Bruno Latour, *Pandora's Hope*

Now where is, precisely, the difference between the heterogeneous qualities which succeed each other in our concrete perception and the homogeneous changes which science puts at the back of these perceptions in space?

—Henri Bergson, *Matter and Memory*

Why don't organisms such as ourselves develop immortality? The short answer is that immortality cannot develop because development reproduces mortal human beings not immortal ones. The "eternal return" does not have an option. That said, the question is, "Can anything be done about it?" Here the answer is "Not as long as development is left to its own devices." What then must be done to develop immortal human beings? Now the answer gets a bit more complicated and lengthy—hence Chapter 3.

Today, development is viewed in one of two ways. It is a miracle that Romantics have always marveled at and viewed with awe. They see organisms develop near-perfect structures with a degree of accuracy and repeatability that defies imagination. Magically, organisms develop "in order to" meet future needs rather than "because of" some causal chain of prior events. Eyes, for example, develop in the darkness of the womb as if anticipating the light and their unbidden function in sight. What is more, "[t]hat done, and their organ complete, they abide by what they have accomplished. They lapse into relative quietude and change no more."[1]

Hard-nosed materialists, on the other hand, ignore miracles and argue that biological development is a process of replacement, not of consummation. It only seems to lead to a stable adult, while in reality, adults are unstable and development is merely a cog in the wheel of life, a moment in the general turnover of organisms. Development is the process through which a mortal biological machine makes a mortal copy of itself.

The different points of view have important implications for immortality. The romantic point of view suggests that development could lead to immortality, since the only truly perfect end to the perfection of life is an end without end. The materialist point of view suggests that immortality cannot possibly develop, since development has been crafted by evolution to make mortal biological machines copy themselves. No matter how perfect, the copy, like the original, is still mortal. Before immortal human beings can be made, materialists will have to adopt the romantics point of view and allow immortality into the realm of possibilities.

The task for Chapter 3 is to flesh out the materialist's point of view— to find its weaknesses as well as test its strengths—in order to see how an impossibility can be turned into a miracle. The chapter begins by making sense of development—describing development's "who, where, what, when, how, and why?" Armed with this knowledge of development, the chapter proceeds to examine how immortality can be engineered into human development.

Making human beings immortal depends on changing the biological machine's design and mode of production—its development. Rather than allowing development to run its course to completion, it will have to be stopped short of its end. An endless source of stem cells will have to be installed early enough in development to give the cells adequate experience with the organism's history, and gonads, the sources of germ cells, will have to be suppressed. These changes will not be accomplished easily, but neither are they impossible!

DEVELOPMENT'S "WHO, WHERE, WHAT, WHEN, HOW, AND WHY?"

Prior to reaching sexual maturity, or adolescence, organisms experience a preponderance of progressive changes and are said to be developing. The gains identified as development accrue to embryos, larvae or fetuses, and juveniles which acquire axes and planes of symmetry, undergo pattern formation, and morphogenesis as their rudimentary components give rise to organs, and organ systems, and these parts undergo growth, differentiation, and sculpturing. No stage of life is invulnerable to damage and death, and developing organisms are often overtaken by death, but the net gain associated with development equips adults to resist thermodynamic decay for a considerable period, although the ravages of aging will ultimately prevail.

WHO DEVELOPS?

The simple answer would seem to be, "Embryos, larvae, fetuses, and juveniles develop." In other words, organisms at certain stages of life share one or more qualities, which, in combination, are called development. These qualities are not present in organisms at other stages and are ordinarily absent in adults, the exception being when adults regenerate parts.

The simple answer would not provoke much argument from embryologists, although they might dispute its simplicity. Historically, Aristotle (384–322 BC) and Karl Ernst von Baer (1791–1876), in particular, attempted to characterize the qualities of developing organisms.[2] For Aristotle, developing organisms were continuously transformed by the addition of qualities until reaching their final, adult state—vegetative or animal properties, climaxing in an individual soul—whereas adults were equipped with all these qualities and could thus function reproductively, thereby starting a new cycle of development. Known as Aristotelian teleology, the developing organism was imagined to be extruded from previous stages by each consecutive stage and ultimately by the adult or telos in a linear process of becoming.

Aristotelian teleology seems incompatible with mechanistic causality as demanded by contemporary science, but Aristotle would probably have been comfortable with the contemporary DNA paradigm—DNA makes RNA; RNA makes protein—as a device for drawing out the development of organisms.[3] Similarly, later preformationists with a teleological bent (see below) might have been comfortable with the idea of coded information residing in DNA. The same sort of determinism and fixity of endpoint would seem to be implied by teleology, preformationism, and DNA blueprints, recipes, and programs. This determinism, the idea of an immutable endpoint, also implies that immortality is impossible, since it is not presently an endpoint.

Von Baer attributed a different quality to embryos, larvae or fetuses, and juveniles than to adults. He attributed progress to these developing organisms. Moreover, like contemporary embryologists and developmental biologists, von Baer believed he based his views on observation and, in the title of his masterpiece, relegated "reflection" to second place behind "observations."[4] Actually, von Baer followed the great Enlightenment tradition of ascribing progress to change. He attributed the ability to turn homogeneity into heterogeneity, generality into specificity, and simplicity into complexity to developing organisms. Influenced by the German Romantics and Idealists, von Baer turned embryos into the heroes of epic tales and development into the quest for the perfect form.[5] Embryologists and developmental biologists have imitated von Baer's style ever since. In today's argot, development is "responsible for the instability of the homogeneous state and the coupling of the resulting field to all downstream processes."[6]

Von Baer's views of developing organisms and development are no more sensible than making embryos the heroes of Hollywood Westerns. Embryos are extremely vulnerable creatures, more likely to succumb to challenges than overcome them. Indeed, if death in embryonic stages were included in com-

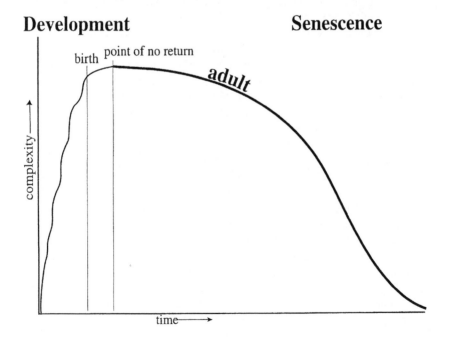

putations, the average life-expectancy of human beings would plummet and our survivorship curve would implode into a negative hyperbola resembling that of clams. Nevertheless, von Baer's view of developmental progress, ignoring death and heralding in the new, is the predominant view of contemporary developmental biologists. They have merely replaced the humble progress of embryos with progressive gene action.

WHERE DOES DEVELOPMENT OCCUR?

Answers to this question can be surprising. The easy answer is, "Wherever the embryo, larva or fetus, and juvenile happen to be." But embryos, larvae or fetuses, and juveniles consist of parts, and these develop in some strange places and even change residence during development. The more intriguing answer raises implications of the environment for development—both the external and the internal environment.

Environments are supposed to be neutral if development is to take place, but environments are hardly neutral, and sometimes development takes place at the behest of environments. For example, daphnia, the freshwater flea, changes the shape of its carapace in the presence of different predators; sex determination in reptiles is a function of temperature; and the axis of symmetry around which birds develop is determined by gravity as the fertilized egg passes through the bird's oviduct and into the uterus.

The most intriguing answers to the "Where?" question concern the development of tissues. Epithelial tissues such as the epidermis covering the body and the absorptive layer lining the gut begin their development in or about the place in the embryo corresponding to the place they end up in the adult. Other tissues such as nerve and muscle travel from their place in the embryo to different places in the adult, but their cells or cell processes remain in more or less coherent groups. The precursor, hematopoietic cells of blood and lymphatic tissues, and primordial germ cells travel from their place of origin to second and sometimes third and fourth sites which they invade and colonize before differentiating into functional cells. In each case, the cells presumably rely on each other and on their location for signals and support for differentiation, but these signals are largely unknown and would be different for each forming organ.

WHAT DEVELOPS?

Once again, one might answer simply, at the level of organisms, "Embryos, larvae or fetuses, and juveniles develop," but their parts also develop and add to the features of organisms. These parts would include cells, tissues, organs, and organ systems, since they are present in the developed organisms, but the parts of developing organisms also include sequentially developing components: germ layers, cell lines, and stem cells.

Developing the Parts of Embryos

Germ layers, cell lines, and stem cells become increasingly heterogeneous, specific, and complex in the course of development, and they emerge irreversibly from the branching points of nested, developmental hierarchies. Furthermore, germ layers, cell lines, and stem cells parallel each other, becoming progressively committed, then determined, and finally differentiated in the course of development. But germ layers, cell lines, and stem cells each represents a different answer to the question, "What develops?" and, notwithstanding their similarities, they may not be interchangeable.

Germ layers were Von Baer's answer to the question, "What develops?" He first identified a germ layer (*der Keimschicht*) in chick embryos but also found them elsewhere among vertebrate embryos. Generalizing from one germ layer to two and from some vertebrates to all vertebrates, von Baer concluded that germ layers were the only things made by fertilized eggs during early development and were the universal material out of which embryos were formed in later development. The formation of germ layers thereby became the point of departure in development, and the mechanical processes operating on these layers, such as folding and growth, became the means for producing embryos.

Today's germ layers, ectoderm, mesoderm, and endoderm, to which are sometimes added neural crest and germ cells, are not the same as those described by von Baer. First of all, he published on germ layers before the cell theory was promulgated, so his layers are not cellular, whereas ours are. Second, he employed chick embryos and observed the separation of the germ (*Keim*) in a region called the area pellucida where layers are tough enough to be dissected. There he found two layers: an inner germ layer (*das Schleimblatt*) now called the splanchnopleure and considered the fused endoderm and splanchnic mesoderm, and an outer layer (*das seröse Blatt*), now called the somatopleure and considered the fused ectoderm and somatic mesoderm. Von Baer's layers united in the embryo's midline, forming the tough notochord (*Rückensaite* [Chorda dorsalis], which von Baer also discovered), beneath the dorsal nerve tube (*Nervenröhre*).

Cells and nomenclature aside, von Baer's point is still well taken: "*Alle Virbelthiere bestehen aus heterogenen Schichten*" (All vertebrates come into being from differing layers).[7] Today, germ layers are defined as coherent layers of embryonic cells which give rise to all the tissues and cells found in the fetus or larva.

Ectoderm and endoderm are epithelial germ layers to begin with, consisting of closely connected cells mounted on an acellular membrane. Ectoderm and endoderm also have a penchant for remaining epithelial, although ectoderm produces neural tissue and neural crest, and endoderm produces the epithelial reticulum of the thymus.[8] Mesoderm and neural crest alternate between deepithelializing, or losing coherence, and reepithelializing, or gaining coherence, while they form most of the tissues separating the epidermis and absorptive gut lining. Neurons and their cognate neuroglial cells also deepithelialize from the embryonic neural epithelium to give rise to the central nervous system. Neural crest deepithelializes too, sending neurons, neurolemmacytes, neuroendocrine cells, pigment cells, as well as mesenchymal cells to the far reaches of the body. Mesenchyme, or embryonic connective tissue, does not constitute a germ layer because its cells are not connected and because it is derived from both neural crest and mesoderm.

Cell lines were August Weismann's answer to the question, "What develops?" Cell lines consist of all the "daughter cells" produced by mitosis, or lineages derived originally from the division of single cells. Weismann's emphasis on cell division was no doubt, in part, an historical accident resulting from his theorizing after the cell theory became popular, but his efforts to explain how cell division was instrumental in creating differences among developing tissues was purely speculative. Cell division via mitosis appealed to Weismann for its precision in dividing chromosomes which, he suggested, might also possess determinants of development. Were divisions to have been differential, mitosis might have explained how development unfolded so precisely, and why embryos resembled mosaics of predetermined cellular tesserae.

Weismann's theory of cell lines grew from the distinction he made between mortal somatic parts of organisms and immortal germ parts. According to Weismann, one of the earliest cell divisions, if not the very first one, separated the line of cells that would eventually become the germ line from the line of cells that would give rise to all the somatic lines. The soma, or body, was formed from somatic cell lines, whereas the immortal egg or sperm was formed exclusively from the germ cell line. In the course of embryonic cell division, Weismann's somatic cell lines increasingly lost their potential to form the organism as a whole, while the germ lines retained all their potential to form the entire organism.

Strictly speaking, Weismann's mortal somatic-cell lines and immortal germ-cell line have to coincide in the fertilized egg if only because it has one cytoplasm, if not quite one nucleus. The separation of germ and somatic lines

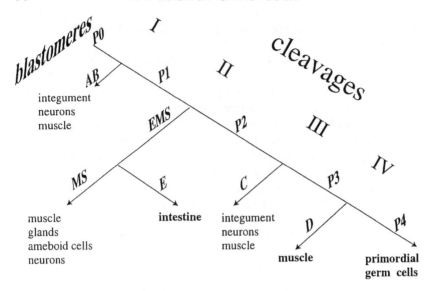

lineages

is also not as clean as Weismann and his interpreters sometimes suggest. This separation occurs at different cell divisions—known as cleavage divisions—or times of embryonic life in different species. In the round worm *Caenorhabditis elegans,* better known as *C. elegans,* careful analysis of cell division in embryos has shown that the separation of germ and somatic cell lines takes place at the fourth cleavage division. In vertebrates, primordial germ cells (PGCs) appear in embryos of several thousand cells, in human embryos, at about 16 days post ovulation (dpo). In Cnidaria, the separation of germ and somatic cell lines, if it can be considered a separation at all, takes place when somatic cells of adults differentiate as eggs or sperm in response to opportunities for reproduction.[9]

Weismann's cell lines and von Baer's germ layers may seem superficially similar, and cell lines might pass through germ layers in the course of their development. Of course, von Baer could not have suspected cell division as an instrument for creating difference, but the difference between germ layers and cell lines is not merely historical. Von Baer imagined development as a process of unfolding, something like a game of chess that unfolds as the pieces are moved, whereas Weismann saw development as rigidly determined, more like the operation of a machine. Von Baer's version became known as "epigenesis" or "regulative development," in which the moves made by embryonic parts, or their interactions, decided the outcome. Weismann's ver-

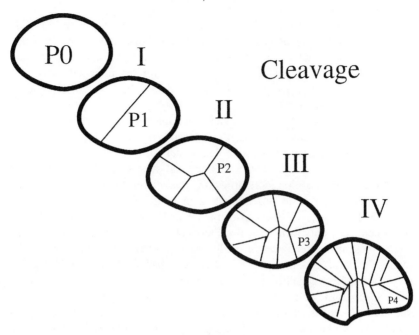

sion became known as "determinism" or "mosaic development," in which cells had little if any leeway once cell division determined their developmental fate.

Stem cells are a more recent answer to the question, "What develops?" Stem cells are, in theory, cells capable of self-renewal while turning out differentiating cells, but defining them in practice is not quite as easy. Some stem cells, such as embryonal stem (ES) cells and germ stem (GS) cells, are pluripotent, differentiating into a broad range of cell types when prompted. Other stem cells are already committed to one cell type of differentiation, and their ability to differentiate into other cell types becomes increasingly narrow. Still other stem cells may be capable of changing their commitment to differentiate in one direction—transdifferentiate—and move into a broader precursor population of stem cells capable of differentiating in several directions.[10]

GS and ES cells arise in embryos relatively early in development, while "most stem cells may arise late in development," although they may not be conspicuous in adults.[11] For example, hematopoietic stem cells isolated from adult mouse bone marrow constitute a "side population" (SP) of just 1–3 percent of the dividing cells.[12]

The gap between stem cells and differentiated cells is filled by "transit" progenitor cells already committed to a particular type of cellular differentiation and having limited self-renewing abilities.[13] Similarly, so-called "set-aside cells" in marine invertebrate larvae[14] and imaginal disc cells in insect instars which give rise to adult tissues, "[r]ather than being true stem cells . . . represent transient progenitor populations with functions limited to specific developmental stages."[15] Thus, everything that might seem to be a stem cell might not turn out to be a stem cell.

Concepts of germ layers and somatic cell lines are not easily unified with the idea of stem cells, although the concepts of layers, lines, and stems incorporate the idea of progressive determination, and cell division plays a prominent role in creating both cell lines and stem cells. Germ layers and somatic cell lines develop more or less *in situ*, whereas stem cells are mobile, taking their potential to differentiate with them wherever they go. Germ layers and somatic cell lines also mature and disappear as such, whereas some stem cells only form in adults. Stem cells take their cues from stem-cell niches present in already established tissues. Reserve stem cells, such as the satellite cells of skeletal muscle or dark spermatogonia of seminiferous tubules, are quiescent until stimulated to join the community of active stem-cells. In contrast, germ layers are continuously active, passing information via networks of embryonic induction, changing themselves and changing each other, while cell lines are progressively restricted by cell lineage to the narrowest lines of differentiation.

Developing the Parts of Adults

Organisms are generally said to consist of organ systems, organs, tissues, cells, and extracellular material or matrix (ECM). Organs are the working parts of organ systems, and, as such, perform similar, related or integrated functions while occupying discrete or continuous sites within organisms. Ten organ systems are generally recognized: cutaneous (or integumentary), skeletal (muscle and bone), gut (or alimentary), respiratory, circulatory and lymphatic, hematopoietic and immune, urinary, endocrine, female and male reproductive, and nervous and special senses. Four tissues are traditionally recognized, but six tissues are increasingly discussed in histology courses: (1) epithelium, (2) connective, (3) muscle, and (4) nerve, with the addition of (5) blood and lymphatic tissue and (6) germ (sex) cells. Hundreds if not thousands of cell types populate these tissues, and many produce or are embedded in complex extracellular materials.

Organs and Organ Systems are lumped into three categories depending on how they develop and the sources of their tissues: (1) indigenous, (2) melting-pot, and (3) colonized. The working and supportive cells of indigenous organs are all of local origin. Melting-pot organs consist of cells organized in more or less discrete layers arising from either local cells, foreign cells, or both. Colonized organs, are characterized by "foreigners" which originate outside the confines of the organ, enter it, and functionally overwhelm its indigenous inhabitants.

Indigenous organs develop generally *in situ* from local components, although these may then travel in embryos. These organs consist of a connective tissue capsule joined to connective tissue septa, in combination known as the "stroma," which supports the more conspicuous, functioning tissue which may be epithelial, known as the "parenchyma," muscle, or nerve.

Indigenous glands with an epithelial parenchyma include the secretory organs of the cutaneous system (sweat, sebaceous, and mammary glands), gut (liver and pancreas), and the portion of the respiratory system (lung) involved in gaseous exchange. Parts of the endocrine system that develop from the wall of the cutaneous system (adenohypophysis) and gut (thyroid gland) are indigenous, although these glands travel in embryos, and other parts of the endocrine system (infiltrated by neural crest cell) fall into the melting-pot category. The kidneys are also indigenous organs, although the remainder of the "plumbing" is melting-pot.

Discrete muscle masses—considered organs of the skeletal system—along with the heart, are indigenous organs. The stroma or connective tissue investing these organs comprises an epimycium (epicardium), perimycium (pericardium), and endomycium (endocardium). Layers of smooth muscle, on the other hand, are parts of melting-pot organs.

The brain and spinal cord, or central nervous system (CNS), invested in meninges, and special sensory organs (eye and inner ear) with their own thick investments of connective tissue, also fall in the indigenous category. Glial cells add to the supporting armature, or stroma, and nervous cells form the parenchyma.

The remainder of the nervous system, the peripheral nervous system (PNS), including the somatic sensory system and visceral sensory organs (proprioceptive, gustatory, and olfactory) and visceral motor or autonomic nervous system, is also indigenous, although cells or their processes may travel in embryos. In general, all these parts consist of and function through the interaction of neurons and their processes (dendrites and axons), specialized (sensory) receptor cells, and their supporting glial cells. Large and small peripheral nerves, encased in connective tissue (epineurium), consist of bundles of neural fibers encased in connective tissue (endoneurium) and surrounded by layers of myelin or embedded in neurolemmacytes. Fascicles of these bundles may also be encased in connective tissue (perineurium).

Melting-pot organs are characterized by one or more layers of cells and extracellular matrix. Typically, an epithelium and an adjacent layer of loose connective tissue containing small vessels of the circulatory and lymph drainage systems and nerves are covered or lined by a layer of dense connective tissue containing large vessels and occasionally skeletal elements, followed by additional layers of muscle, and ending with either loose connective tissue attached to the body wall or other organs or with a pavement epithelium bordering a body cavity. The layers of melting-pot organs fuse together after arriving at a site, but they may also form *in situ* from local cells and more-or-less invading foreign cells.

Organ systems residing on surfaces (cutaneous or integument) or organs surrounding cavities (bladder) or possessing a lumen, such as the conducting portions of the respiratory, urinary system, and gut or alimentary system, and vessels of the circulatory and lymph drainage system, are all melting-pots. Possibly the most curious feature of these melting-pot organs is the presence of foreign cells in different layers. For example, cells derived from the embryonic germ layer known as the neural crest enter and populate cutaneous epithelia with pigment and sensory cells, and infiltrate muscle layers and connective tissue with ganglion cells of the peripheral nervous system. In addition, the connective tissue of melting-pot organs is a reservoir of cells derived from the hematopoietic and immune systems.

In other melting-pot organs, the indigenous and foreign cells remain quite separate. Neural crest cells, for example, congregate in the dental papillae of teeth and the dermal papillae of cutaneous appendages (scales, feathers and hair follicles).[16] In the mammalian adrenal (or suprarenal) glands, cortical epithelial cells piled into zones (glomerulosum, fasicularis, and reticularis) represent the indigenous (mesodermal) portion of the gland and secrete steroid hormones (mineral corticoids, cortical steroids, and sexual steroids), while the central medullary cells represent the foreigners (neural crest) and are the source of catecholamines, especially norepinephrine and epinephrine. Cortical and medullary adrenal cells communicate through blood vessels (sinusoids) cascading down from the capsule to central veins.

Colonized organs—ovary and testis, and organs of the hematopoietic and immune systems—have parts of local origin and parts of foreign origin. The indigenous cells and the foreigners communicate with each other in various ways, but they always perform different functions. The ovary and testis have a hilus where they are attached to large circulatory vessels that take care of their bodily needs. Developmentally, these organs consist of indigenous (mesodermal) parts and colonizing germ cells. In human beings, primordial germ cells (PGCs), originating in the vicinity of the hind gut and allantoic vesicle at about 16 days post ovulation (dpo), begin to circulate at 24 ± 1 dpo, reach the mesonephric ridges at about 28 dpo, migrate into gonadal ridges at 32 dpo, and proliferating wildly. These are the cells which give rise to germ stem (GS) cells in tissue culture.

The hematopoietic and, hence, lymphopoietic systems are composed entirely of colonized organs. The first hematopoietic stem cells form *in situ* in splanchnic mesoderm of the embryonic yolk sac or splanchnopleure. Afterward, they appear as foreigners in the liver, spleen, and kidney of the fetus, before establishing definitive colonies in the bone marrow. The hematopoietic or red bone marrow would be defunct were it not for colonizing primary hematopoietic stem cells.[17] Likewise, the spleen, lymph nodes, tonsils, aggregated lymph nodes of the ileum, and diffuse lymphatic tissue would be incomplete and the thymus an empty sac without lymphocytes originating in the bone marrow (and bursa of Fabricius in the case of birds).[18]

Tissues represent the level of function where organs and organ systems perform their unique tasks as a consequence of cellular activities, and where diseases in organs result from cell faults and failures. Moreover, tissues represent the level where organs are formed by cellular activities.

Epithelial tissue consists of one or more layers of cells resting on a basement membrane. The cells are broadly in contact with each other, and the layer may be one or more cells thick. The cells are connected to each other at specialized junctional complexes which may form impermeable barriers or add to the tensile strength of the epithelium. The cells may also communicate with each other by passing small molecules through connexons or so-called gap junctions. The epithelia composing the secretory parts of glands are frequently surrounded by myoepithelial cells that respond to nervous or hormonal stimulation and contract, causing the gland to secrete its product.

Connective tissue consists of cells separated by an ECM containing one or another type of collagen, elastin, glycosaminoglycans (GAGs, formerly mucopolysaccharides), proteoglycans, and glycoproteins. In loose connective tissue, cells known as fibroblasts are widely separated by an ECM called ground substance. In addition to fibroblasts, loose connective tissue contains a variety of regulatory cells within the ground substance (macrophages, mast cells, plasma cells, and lymphocytes). In dense connective tissue, fibroblasts are enmeshed in an ECM of thick collagen bundles or layers, and elastin fibers or membranes. Cartilage and bone are skeletal or hard connective tissues. Cartilage, generally enclosed by a layer of fibroblast-like cells arranged in a dense periochondrium, consists of a dense ground substance with embedded chondrocytes. Bone consists of a calcified bony matrix with embedded osteocytes. Peripherally, fibroblast-like cells are arranged in a dense periosteum. Mature bone is formed first in flattened layers, then in cylinders (osteons) of concentric layers of bony matrix surrounding and penetrated by vascular canals. In marrow, a bony matrix without layers, arranged in spicules (cancellous bone) is covered by endosteum. In layered portions of bone, osteocytes communicate with each other through cytoplasmic extensions ending in gap junctions. Osteoclasts, also present in bone, resorb bone and function in the dynamics of calcium balance.

Muscle consists of contractile cells or myofibers surrounded by an external lamina—which resembles the basal lamina of epithelia but surrounds cells rather than supports them in a layer. Cardiac and smooth muscle cells contain intermediate fibers terminating on epithelial-like placodes, which, in cardiac muscle, juxtapose each other at intercalated disks. Visceral smooth muscle cells (but not circulatory smooth muscle cells) communicate with each other through gap (nexus) junctions which are also present in cardiac muscle at intercalated disks. Smooth and cardiac muscle cells may have their own source of stimulation (pace maker) but are also influenced by peripheral nerves. Skeletal muscle myofibers are composed of fused cells—known as syncytia—and are stimulated to contract by the electrochemical action of nerves operating through motor end plates.

Nervous tissue consists of electrochemical conductive cells, or neurons, accompanying glial cells, and neurosecretory cells. The neurons communicate with each other across gaps known as synapses where an impulse in one neuron results in the release of a neurotransmitter that stimulates (or inhibits) an impulse in another neuron. Sensory cells may also stimulate an impulse in sensory neurons. In addition, motor neurons stimulate the contraction of muscle fibers across motor end plates and the secretion of glands through their action on myoepithelial cells.

Blood and lymphatic tissue are related, since their lineages are traced back to primitive hematopoietic stem cells in bone marrow. These stem cells give rise to increasingly determined "blast-" and "colony-forming units" (BFUs and CFUs) that are gradually committed to one of three lineages: (1) a line of lymphocytes that give rise to T and B lymphocytes; (2) a myeloid stem cell line that gives rise to the unipotential erythroid line producing the progenitors of red blood cells, to two unipotential lines of granulocytes, forming eosinophils and basophils, and to a bipotential line that gives rise to neutrophils (also granulocytes) and monocytes (agranular leukocytes); (3) another line gives rise to cells such as osteoclasts and a variety of clean-up cells (macrophages and dust cells), some of which process antigens for the immune system (antigen presenting cells [APCs] or dendritic cells), and possibly other cells usually associated with connective tissue (mast cells). The volume of cells differentiating along these lines at any time is a function of circulating "hematopoietic growth factors" and the prior history of the cells.

Germ (sex) cells also constitute a discrete tissue, since all the germ cells in an organism are formed from PGCs and give rise to GS cells in tissue culture. In female human fetuses PGCs proliferate and populate the developing ovary with oogonia, reaching a peak population size of nearly seven million at about the fifth month of gestation. Nests of oogonia break up as oocytes enter meiosis and become surrounded by flattened follicle cells in primordial follicles. Arrested in meiosis as soon as it begins, some oocytes remain in this state for as many as fifty years, although most oocytes die leaving only about 400,000 at menarche. All else being normal and in the absence of pregnancy, from menarche until menopause, meiosis resumes in about twenty oocytes per month, although generally only one egg matures. Things are simpler in the male: germ-cell proliferation in the embryonic testis is modest and halts until puberty when it takes off along with the advent of meiosis.

Cells comprising each tissue constitute a host of tissue-specific cell types. Typically, histology textbooks describe some 200–300 of these cell types, but the number grows as surface proteins are identified and more is learned about how cells interact, for example, in the immune system. Several processes contribute to making cells of all these types, the most conspicuous of which is differentiation. Beyond differentiation, cells acquire both their unique and shared properties in a number of ways: through cell division, cell movement (en masse and individual), and communication (via circulating factors, hormones, and local interactions).

WHEN DOES DEVELOPMENT OCCUR?

This is a more challenging question than it might seem at first, because development, like evolution, is *not* observable. It takes place in the course of time and overwhelms our poor ability to identify it cognitively as an observation. Instead, memory or its literary cognate, history, integrates data and fixes them in narratives. Developmental narratives, like evolutionary scenarios or phylogenies, transform slide shows of disparate data into movies by interpolating movement and frequently introducing plots. Different answers to the question, "When does development occur?" flow from the different developmental narratives.

Development First
Even before the fourth century B.C., the notion of development was loosely tied to the early stages of events. Aristotle tightened the knot by equating the beginning of serial events with development (beginnings followed by middles and ends).[19] The temporal identification of development with beginnings works well for analyzing human constructions and as a principle for designing human enterprises, playing games, and getting jobs done but not for analyzing phenomena that human beings have neither designed nor created, such as evolution and organic development. As a result of applying the notion of development to the fossil record, some paleontologists erroneously interpreted early species as primitive and more recent species as advanced, and von Baer

and followers mistakenly ranked embryos as simple, homogeneous, and general, while judging adults complex, heterogeneous, and specific.

Historically, the requirement of development for beginnings led to dividing development into stages, each offering an opportunity for a new beginning. Moreover, stages were subdivided into phases and phases into periods. Sufficient beginnings ultimately accumulated to turn embryos into adults, but, at the same time, development was turned into a complicated staircase of both arbitrary and rational steps.

Development Last

The production of a sexually reproducing adult is the classical endpoint of development, the point at which development stops and yet may start all over again with the production of a new organism by reproduction. Indeed, the word mature, with its root in the Latin for ripe, refers not only to complete or full development but, traditionally, to the attainment of sexuality. For example, oocytes are considered mature only when they are capable of supporting the complete spectrum of developmental events upon fertilization.[20]

The idea that the production of an adult is the endpoint of development may explain some of the most egregious features of aging. Neo-Darwinism suggests that developing organisms would be provided with mechanisms for delaying degeneration if such mechanisms enhanced the success of offspring. In effect, reproductive adults, who themselves inherited these mechanisms, would pass them along to developing organisms in the next generation. But following sexual reproduction, adults could no longer relay messages to offspring. Degeneracy could develop without flashing an SOS.[21]

Maturation is also the climax of life in communities of unicellular organisms such as the ciliate *Paramecium*. By classical definitions, these organisms neither develop nor engage in sex, but they sometimes undergo conjugation—a form of reproduction strikingly similar to sexual reproduction in multicellular organisms—and their vegetative reproduction resembles development, at least as far as growth and cellular differentiation. When the vigor of growth[22] in a clone of *Paramecium* has begun to wane and its rate of cell division has dropped off, individual *Paramecium* conjugate[23] and exchange micronuclei reduced by a complex meiosis to half the usual load of DNA. Conjugation is the antidote for the community's decline. Its new cells, with nuclei reconstituted of a double dose of mixed chromosomes, begin a fresh round of vigorous vegetative growth.

Without stretching the comparison of unicellular and multicellular organisms too far, sex marks the end of vegetative decline and the beginning of vegetative development. In the case of *Paramecium,* conjugation signals the rejuvenation and renewal (a new "lease on life") of cells, while in the case of multicellular organisms, sexual maturity identifies the endpoint of development, and fertilization marks the beginning of development in eggs.[24]

Development Always

The problems for immortality implied by developmental endpoints may be tucked under the proverbial rug by substituting the phenotype for sexual maturity. Ordinarily, the phenotype includes all the qualities of an organism starting with the fertilized egg and ending with the death of the organism. Susan Oyama remarks,

> [W]hat is considered the "end" [of development] is somewhat arbitrary. Though the adult is traditionally seen to be the end of development, both in the sense of goal and in the sense of terminus, with everything else either an incomplete transition to, or a degeneration from, this basic form, a strong argument can be made that ontogenesis [development] is continuous with the life cycle. Every stage is thus equally the "end" of development. Unlike a machine, which is generally useless until it is completely assembled, an organism "works" at all points in its development.[25]

Ignoring contingency, development would then include all the processes as well as events linking the genotype of an organism with its phenotype, or, more generally, all the actions and interactions bridging DNA/genes in a species' genome with all the traits in a species' phenome.

Regrettably, the success of DNA as a prescription for protein synthesis has confounded thinking on phenotypic development. All too often, research on phenotypic development does not go beyond gene expression. What has been learned is nevertheless full of surprises. DNA/genes seem to operate in all sorts of different ways during the development of phenotype. Some control genes, for example, seem to operate qualitatively by throwing up blocks to the production of structural genes' products. Mutations in control genes may not influence the fundamental development of the trait (a leg is still a leg and an antenna is still an antenna) but alter its location (legs forming where antennae are normally formed). Old fashioned qualitative genes, determining entire traits, may now be considered control genes.

Other DNA/genes operate quantitatively and some, having the most profound effects on development such as those determining planes and axes of symmetry, segmentation, and segment identity, operate with the help of concentration gradients of secondary messengers.[26] Indeed, "many of the key genetic differences between organisms will be manifest as changes in gene expression during development."[27] Instead of a phenotype emerging from the expression of qualitative genes, the phenotype's emergence may depend on quantitatively differential gene action. The operating gene product may be present in different amounts in different places and at different times.

Of course, to the degree that a phenotype is a consequence of quantitative shifts in gene expression, it would seem all the more amenable to management, and even severe damage to an organ may yet be reversible by appealing to quantitative genes supporting regeneration. In many organisms, both multi-cellular and unicellular, growth is allied to asexual reproduction, or to a period in which potential germ cells are amplified prior to the onset and differentiation of sex cells.[28] Genes with a potential for supporting immortal-ity may be operative during asexual reproduction, growth, or even germ-cell proliferation.

DNA/genes that are not active during development—that may be useful for one or another effort to intervene in life—may also be discovered outside the normal course of development. For example, wound healing is a response to contingency, and the contingency-dependent DNA/genes kicking in during wound healing are not necessarily the same as constitutive genes operating in the course of routine development. Likewise, regeneration is contingency-dependent (liver regeneration) or physiologically induced (uterine myometrium and antler regeneration) but, in either case, is dependent on hormonal signals that may not operate at other times during development. Moreover, asexual reproduction, defined as reproduction from ordinary body (somatic) cells rather than from fertilized eggs (germ cells), may operate under rules having noth-ing whatsoever to do with rules operating in the production of a sexual adult.

Finally, phenotypic development includes processes or events with ab-normal endpoints. For example, cancer is perceived as destructive or anti-developmental, but many cancers undergo progressive change during the course of the disease. Ironically, in mice, cancers of testes sometimes produce embryocarcinoma cells, which can differentiate into adult tissues *in vitro* or contribute to the production of adults when transplanted to blastocysts.[29]

How Does Development Occur?

"How" questions invite answers which emphasize mechanisms or controls. These answers may be difficult to separate, since developmental mechanisms are generally under control and developmental controls impinge on mecha-nisms. Like a row of dominos, mechanisms and controls can fall either way.

Mechanisms of Development

Surprisingly, development results from only a few activities—differentiation, cell division and growth, cell movement, cell communication, and cell death. Collectively, these activities result in all the positive processes of develop-ment: embryogenesis, morphogenesis, growth, and sculpturing.

Differentiation is recognized by differences between cells of different types and among cells in the process of differentiation. It occurs both during the course of development and in developed organisms, especially in continuously developing tissues or sites of cellular turnover. In the canon of developmental biology, differentiation is due to differential gene expression, when genes are turned on and off or the rate of gene expression is tuned in and out, but the maintenance of a differentiated state is as much a part of the processes as the development of difference.

Stability is the most general property of differentiated cells and so-called "terminally differentiated cells," which have synthesized their last product, either remain ensconced in this condition within an organ (nerve cells within the CNS and skeletal muscle fibers within muscle masses) as they are, or they die and are removed from the organism (red blood cells in the circulatory system and intestinal absorptive cells lining villi).

The stability of the differentiated state does not seem to require the cooperation of the entire cell's genome except to turn most of it off and allow the small operating part to work uninterruptedly. The vast majority of genes in a typical, differentiated cell (up to 95%) are turned off, although turned-off genes are copied with precision prior to cell division. The massive efforts by cloners currently underway to "reprogram" genes for expression is mute testimony to the success of differentiated cells to operate on only a few genes, the most important of which would seem to be control genes.

By and large, developmental biologists ignore the possibility that the stability of differentiation in multicellular animals is due to cytoplasmic inheritance of the sort seen in *Paramecium* (see below).[30] Moreover, developmental biologists minimize the role of cytoplasm in neutralizing mutations. Nevertheless, cytoplasmic-mediated DNA methylation is increasingly recognized as a device for differential gene silencing if not expression.[31]

Differences among the tissue-specific cell types and among cells in the process of differentiating are considered evidence of different genes being transcribed and different transcripts being translated. Many additional processes influence transcription and translation, such as the differential splicing (eliminating different introns while attaching exons), transcript modification and editing, and other processes influencing the half-life of transcripts (whether they are translated or degraded). Furthermore, gene rearrangement is a major source of variation at least in the maturation of the immune system.

Cell division and growth adhere to one of two basic patterns: Cell division occurs in cells already part of the tissue or cell division occurs in a proliferative or stem cell population that is both self-renewing and capable of releasing cells to a tissue for subsequent differentiation.

Epithelial tissues exhibit both patterns. Cell division may be an option available to all cells (expanding cell populations) even if it is rarely taken, or proliferative cells may be restricted to a subpopulation of (germinal or proliferative) cells among a largely nonproliferative (differentiating) population.[32] The liver is the classic example of cells that can but usually don't divide. All liver cells (hepatocytes), or, at least those in the peribiliary area, may be capable of division but only divide when the liver is severely reduced, for example, by surgery. Subpopulations of proliferative cells are found in the innermost cells of the epidermis (the epithelium at the surface of the cutaneous system) and in the pits, crypts, and glands of the gut's lining. Dividing epidermal cells feed the outer layers with differentiating keratinocytes, while dividing gut-lining cells provide the differentiating absorptive cells and mucous cells constantly lost at the gut surface and tips of villi.[33]

The fibroblasts of connective tissue, similarly, do not ordinarily appear to be candidates for division, having dense nuclei. But, removed from the body and placed in tissue culture, some fibroblasts are easily provoked to proliferate, although the number of times they divide appears to be limited (see Hayflick limit in Chapter 1).

Smooth muscle of the uterus is capable of dividing, although it only does so during pregnancy. Other smooth and cardiac muscle cells seems to have lost the potential to divide. Skeletal muscle, consisting of a syncytium formed by the fusion of myoblasts, like other syncytia in multicellular organisms, is not proliferative. Embryonic skeletal muscle grows during the fetal period by the fusion of fetal myoblasts to muscle fibers, and, while post-natal skeletal muscle is static, myoblasts or satellite cells remain attached to myofibers and, following trauma, proliferate and fuse into new muscle fibers.[34] Skeletal muscle is thus serviced by a reserve stem cell population capable of self-renewal and differentiation.

The belief that nervous tissue was nonproliferative has shattered recently. Glial cells were known to be proliferative but were thought to give rise only to glial cells. However, when brain tissue in rats was shown to grow, glial cells (subventricular zone astrocytes) were seen to behave as neural stem cells and differentiate into neurons, adding neurons to the brain mass.[35] What is more, neural stem cells can also differentiate along hematopoietic lines and vice versa.[36]

Cell division among stem cells is at the root of all hematopoiesis. In adult mammals, red blood cells are enucleated and incapable of normal division, and white blood cells (leukocytes) do not normally divide after differentiating in the bone marrow. The presence of red-blood precursors in bone marrow is well established and readily promoted by the hormone erythropoietin, but hematopoietic stem cells are rare in adults or not easily transplanted.[37]

Sex cells frequently have a peculiar habit of failing to complete division (cytokinesis), remaining connected to each other by discrete intercellular bridges. In vertebrates, cells destined to form oocytes remain together in small nests until they become surrounded by follicle cells. Cells destined to form spermatozoa remain together until they release residual bodies and become free spermatozoa in the final stages of differentiation. With the exception of some prosimians, sex cells in female mammals only proliferate during the embryonic and fetal periods, while in males stem cells known as spermatogonia are self-renewing and differentiate throughout adulthood.

Cell movement en masse or individually is a feature of tissues in transition. Keratinocytes, for example, scale the layers of differentiation in the epidermis and absorptive cells climb to the tips of intestinal villi. Normoblasts squeeze through holes in bone marrow sinuses and spermatocytes translocate luminally in the pleats of supporting cells. These movements are not the passive consequences of pressure from below generated by cell division. Rather, they are due to active movement along or through a matrix of cells or extracellular material.

Cell movement is the hallmark of gastrulation in the embryo. The inward migration of the first two E cells marks the commencement of gastrulation in the round worm, *C. elegans*, while in vertebrates mass cell movements herald gastrulation and, with the exception of amphibians, establish extraembryonic membranes. In fish, vigorous and dramatic surface movements create the yolk sac, while in amniotes (reptiles, birds, and mammals) massive numbers of early embryonic cells move into position to form the chorion, amnion, and allantois as well as their own version of a yolk sac.

Cell movements also figure prominently in embryogenesis. In tetrapod vertebrates, raising the edges of the neural plate in neural folds and their convergence and dorsal fusion establish the neural tube, while convergent mass-cell movement elongates the embryo along its anterior-posterior axis.

Individual and mass cell movements may not be fundamentally different. Individual cell movement through the primitive streak and node in hens and mammals has the same consequence as mass cell movement in gastrulating reptiles.[38] Indeed, individual cell movement and movement en masse may rely on virtually the same mechanisms: cytoskeletal elongation and contraction. Furthermore, cells appearing to move en masse (e.g., the early hypoblast of chicks) may actually be individual cells moving along a basement membrane (commandeered, in the case of chicks, from the epiblast).

Communication is the essential element of organization and operates at all levels of organization. Local-acting substances of low molecular weight, especially products of ordinary metabolism, may pass from one cell to another (via gap junctions), possibly creating gradients as a function of distance from their source. Parahormones operate within organs (stomach) or organ systems (gut), while hormones, and circulating growth factors—from glycoproteins to small polypeptides and amino acids, steroids, and neurotransmitters—circulate systemically and locally (through portal vessels), helping to integrate organismic responses and regulate organismic homeostasis.

Communication of all these sorts also taking place in the embryo is likely to be spoken of as *induction*. This was the word that Hans Spemann (1869–1941) coined for the formation of a dorsal nerve cord from ventral embryonic tissue in the presence of a transplanted blastoporal lip. He intended induction to mean something like a change brought about by external conditions, such as the change a person experiences when inducted into the armed forces, but the metaphor of a communication network was less metaphysical and more useful for describing the changes observed under the new circumstances.[39]

Since Spemann's discovery, induction, has been one of the premier research topics of developmental biologists, and many new inductive systems have been studied (e.g., Nieuwkoop's signal model) and restudied.[40] The idea of induction now embraces cellular, tissue, and organismic communication, from deciding the fate of cells produced by asymmetric cell division to shepherding entire systems through the development of immanent properties.[41] Little else in developmental biology is quite as robust.

Cell Death is the fifth ingredient in development. Developmental death is not the death that follows traumatic injury, but the death prescribed by the developing organism's hereditary material. Programmed cell death (PCD) is genetically determined but not necessarily "hard-wired" or triggered by genes within the dying cell. Mitochondria play an essential role in inducing apoptosis, the sequence of morphological events followed by the moribund cell. PCD frequently plays a major part in sculpturing organs and organisms during embryogenesis, organ metamorphosis, and tissue homeostasis.

> PCD occurs throughout mammalian development, beginning with apoptosis of the initially solid embryonic ectoderm to generate the proamniotic cavity . . . [*In vitro,* t]he removal of cells of the inner core [of embryoid bodies] to form a cavitated or cystic EB is the first known wave of PCD during mouse morphogenesis.[42]

Controls over Development

Genes are more than DNA. They are the valves that regulate and control the flow of development. Thomas Hunt Morgan (1866–1945) bestowed posterity with the first coherent genetic plan of development.[43] Early in his monograph, *Experimental Embryology,* he placed genes squarely in command of embryonic development:

> The developmental changes that we see and try to explain are supposed not to be primarily due to changes in the chromosomes (for

the genes remain, we think, intact and perhaps unaltered throughout embryonic development), but in the cytoplasm of the egg. These changes in the cytoplasm are relatively gross processes in comparison with the minuteness of the genes that are the ultimate agents behind them. In the study of embryonic development we see only the gross events; the presence of other agents is inferred from a different kind of [genetic] evidence.[44]

Morgan goes on to ask, "How then, is the ordered sequence of events, that takes place in the cytoplasm, related to the activity of genes in the chromosomes . . . ?" He then speculates, "Is it due, for example, to the sequence in which the genes become active?"[45] Biologists have been trying ever since to find the evidence that would answer Morgan's question. Some of that evidence contradicts Morgan's basic assumption, but most validates it.

The old metaphor of a key-and-lock control mechanism of development is totally inadequate to describe the dazzling cascades, if not avalanches, of control activities discovered by cell and developmental biologists: Extracellular ligands bind to surface receptors; activated transmembrane proteins (G-proteins) congregate on cell surfaces; messages are transduced by transmembrane proteins through the plasmalemma; chains of phosphorylating and dephosphorylating enzymes stream from the cell surface all the way down to nuclear proteins and genes. In addition, small hormones move directly through membranes, complexing with nuclear proteins and binding directly to specific DNA elements. Thus, extracellular influences—hormones, parahormones, circulating factors—enter the cast of determinants, bringing information into embryonic cells and to their DNA/genes.

Cells were discovered in stages and their relevance for development was only slowly appreciated. Henri Dutrochet (1776–1847) first proposed that animal and plant tissues were constituted of cells, a view reiterated by many—notably, Jan Evangelista Purkynê (1787–1869), Johannes Müller (1801–1858), and Jacob Henle (1809–1885)—but cells became something more than microscopic billiard balls after Giovanni Battista Amici (1786–1863) introduced achromatic lenses in France in 1827 and Ernst Abbé (1840–1905) made the first apochromatic lenses and ultimately immersion objectives, allowing virtually optimal optical resolution.[46] Félix Dujardin (1801–1860) described cellular contents, Robert Brown (1773–1853) the nucleus, Max Schultz (1825–1874) the plasma membrane, and Gabriel Gustav Valentin (1810–1883) the nucleolus.[47]

Lorenz Oken (born Okenfuss, 1779–1851) was probably the first to suspect that cells were builders of organisms, but Matthias Schleiden's (1804–1881) and Theodor Schwann's (1810–1882) cell theory of 1839 popularized the idea of cells building organisms, although they were utterly confused about how cells pulled off this trick. Christian Gottfried Ehrenberg (1795–1876) described binary fission in infusorians, and Robert Remak (1815–1865) described it in the animal embryo, demolishing at the same time the notion of the intracellular origin of normal cells proposed by Schleiden and the extracellular origin of normal cells proposed by Schwann. Remak's evidence for cell division also overturned the notion that tumors originated from extracellular cytoblastems.

Rudolf Virchow (1821–1902) proceeded to replace tissues with cells as the dominant materialist monads of life and disease. According to his cell doctrine, all cells, and hence all life, came from cells: "No developed tissue can be traced back either to any large or small simple element, unless it be to a cell."[48] Virchow launched cells on a recognizably modern trajectory, but leading botanists, zoologists, and protozologists—including E. G. Balbiani (1825–1899), Otto Bütschli (1848–1920), Hermann Fol (1845–1892), Walter Flemming (1843–1915), Oscar Hertwig (1848–1922), and Edward Strasburger (1844–1912)—correctly described mitosis in the 1870s. Today, mitosis plays different roles in determinist, or mosaic, development as opposed to regulative, or indeterminate, development.

In the determinist, mosaic view of development, popularized by Weismann and others in the nineteenth century, cell division distributed determinants to the embryo's first cells, or blastomeres, and hence to cell lineages that thereby became determined themselves. Cell division, or cleavage in embryos, was portrayed as rigidly patterned, especially in marine annelids and mollusks, and in parasitic round worms. Considerably altered in the twentieth century, cleavage is now seen to distribute cytoplasmic determinants rather than nuclear ones, and determinism is extended from organisms exhibiting determinist development to all organisms, even those whose early cleavage seems to produce undetermined, interchangeable cells.[49]

In the case of mice, for example, cleavage furrows, perpendicular to the egg's surface, entrap surface determinants in blastomeres and fix the cells's fate. As cleavage turns the fertilized egg into a blastocyst, blastomeres on the surface retain a portion of the original egg's surface and become part of the trophectoderm and later the surface layer of the extra-embryonic membrane known as the chorion. In contrast, blastomeres cut off from the original egg's surface by cleavage furrows parallel to this surface become members of the inner cell mass that gives rise to all the other extra-embryonic membranes as well as the embryo proper.[50]

Similarly, in the fruit fly, *Drosophila melanogaster,* most of the cells produced during the insect's version of cleavage, known as cellularization, are determined by cytoplasmic factors. The first cells to form, the polar cells, appear at the posterior end of the embryo and are determined by polar cytoplasm as primary germ cells and possibly hind gut cells.[51] Elsewhere in the insect embryo, the anterior-posterior axis, the first axis of symmetry to be determined, develops under the guidance of other cytoplasmic determinants inherited from the egg.[52] In contrast to the mouse, surface-layer cells of the early insect embryo are incorporated into the embryo proper and extra-embryonic membranes are formed later.

Regulative, or indeterminate cleavage is the antithesis of determinant cleavage. Cell fate is left pending until it is settled by inductive signals. In general, cleavage resulting in relatively large numbers of cells (the vertebrate model) relies on global induction, whereas cleavage resulting in relatively small numbers of cells (the sea-urchin model) relies on local induction.[53] In vertebrates, inductive signals pass between layers of blastomeres (dorsal-ventral induction), between germ layers (neural induction), and tissues (tissue or secondary interactions), in short, where groups of cells make a choice between alternate developmental paths. Local induction is generally more specific but far more widespread. Even the free-living round worm, *C. elegans,* whose embryonic development was thought to be the paragon of hard-wired genetic programming, produces embryonic cells whose determination depends on local induction.[54]

Tissues antedate cells and were imagined to be the bio/naturalist's atoms long before that august position was usurped by cells. Michele Foucault traces the modern study of tissues to the morbid anatomist, Marie Francois Xavier Bichat (1771–1802), who applied the methods and instruments of chemistry to the remnants of normal and pathological tissues he obtained from cadavers in the hope of understanding how tissues gave organs their functions.[55] Applying the microscope to tissues cut into thin slices—known as sections, and stained to improve definition—fell to later microscopic anatomists—including Karl Wilhelm von Nägeli (1817–1891), Wilhelm His (1831–1904), and Francis Maitland Balfour (1851–1882)—who gave histology its modern mission.

The kind of tissue formed at any location in the embryo would seem to be influenced by a variety of conditions and forces: global and local induction, morphogenic gradients, a tissue's history, and cell lineage. As a result of this complexity, small changes in combinations of morphogenic substances may act differentially. For example, the cocktail of HOX proteins prepared by the differential action of *HOX* genes determines the morphogenesis of greatly different parts of the body along the anteroposterior axis of virtually all animals.

"Preparedness is all!" A tissue must be competent to respond to morphogenic signals before they reach it, and the timing of tissue interactions will influence the outcome. Tissue interactions do not develop when a tissue is unprepared to receive a signal, no matter how well broadcast, and morphogenic hormones,

[r]ather than acting on a system that is always prepared to
respond, . . . act during discrete windows of tissue sensitivity. The
time in and pattern of tissue sensitivity and the timing of hormone
secretion are regulated independently and form an interactive system
of great flexibility.[58]

A tissue's development of hormone-sensitive periods during specific developmental stages would seem to depend on progressive developmental events,
including prior exposure to hormones, and/or external synchronizing signals.

Organs and Organisms influence development spatially and temporally. On
the spatial side, Charles Manning Child (1869–1954) stands out as the most
persistent advocate of the organ's and organism's role in development.[59] His
concept of metabolic gradients placed axes and planes of symmetry into a
hierarchical structure that extended through every level of morphogenesis and
differentiation. Child influenced gradient theoreticians and experimentalists
who finally pulled their wavelengths, lateral inhibitors, and morphogens into
coherent, testable hypotheses.[60]

During tissue interactions, morphogenic messages released by cells of
an active tissue reach the receptive cells of a reactive tissue either through
direct cell contact or via an extracellular matrix. The signals are generally
qualitative, or "all-or-none," rather than quantitative, or "more-or-less."
Quantitative interactions are attributed to morphogenic gradients in which
a morphogenically significant substance is distributed over a range of inten-
sity. Yoram Schiffman has shown that gradients of cyclic adenosine monophosphate (cyclic-AMP) are morphogenically inhibitory, causing antiparallel
expression gradients in messenger RNA (mRNA) and/or protein (e.g., receptors for determinants of anteroposterior and dorsoventral axes of insect
eggs).[56]

Morphogenic gradients are sometimes equated to "morphogenic fields"
and to Lewis Wolpert's "positional information."

Positional information largely determines, with respect to the cell
genome and developmental history, the nature of the molecular differentiation that the cell will undergo . . . The specification of positional information in general precedes and is independent of molecular
differentiation.[57]

This equation is invalid, since morphogenic gradients are self-propagating
and can generate other related gradients, whereas morphogenic fields and
positional information require sinks as well as sources, and the morphogenesis they control requires additional gradients.

The temporal role of organs and organisms in development begins with evolution. Natural selection predicts that traits, not genes, are molded by environmental pressures. The question evolutionists have always confronted is how traits work backwards to genes. This question is especially difficult to answer since the central dogma, which has been more or less in force since the time of Weismann, precludes a direct effect of environments on genes. Various answers have been proposed which attempt to circumvent any direct environmental affect on genes.

The major instrument in the evolution of development seems to be changes in the timing of events. Time shifts go by a number of names: *heterochrony*, for changes in the timing or rate of developmental processes; *neoteny*, for the retardation or elimination of later developmental processes; *paedomorphosis* for the extension or fixation of earlier developmental processes. At the molecular level, control over timing seems to be exercised by control genes which either speed up and precipitate differentiation at early stages of morphogenesis or hold cellular differentiation in abeyance while embryos undergo morphogenic change.

Differences in the timing of histological and cellular differentiation are certainly the major theme in theories of evolutionary change in vertebrates. For example, no tetrapod vertebrate develops gills because differentiation in branchial arches is accelerated to the point where throat structures have emerged before gills could get a foot hold (so to speak). Similarly, heterochrony in the developing hearts of vertebrates illustrates delayed histological differentiation into successive morphogenic stages. It is not the differentiation of cardiac muscle that differs so much as the time at which differentiation begins. A fish heart did not evolve into an amphibian heart, the amphibian heart into a reptilian heart, or the reptilian heart into an avian or mammalian heart. What seems to have happened is that genes governing differentiation operated on equally undifferentiated tissue at early stages of development: Fish gear up to differentiation before amphibians, reptiles, birds, and mammals.

Other great evolutionary changes may be made through what appears to be rather simple transformations in the timing of events. For example, in amphibians re-patterning the evolution of larval reproduction is "marked by the reduction or elimination of metamorphic remodeling and the retention of larval features (usually including gills) through adulthood."[61] Even more dramatically, viviparity, or live-bearing following the retention of embryos by parents, in each of the three lissamphibian subgroups, seems to have evolved via heterochronic transformation. Functional changes in the corpus luteum play major roles in increasing "the duration of embryo retention, and . . . [altering the] specializations of the egg and maternal membranes to permit gas exchange and other forms of mother-embryo transfer or signaling."[62]

WHY DO ORGANISMS DEVELOP?

The Aristotelian answer is, "To make adults," or, more broadly, "To make embryos from eggs, larvae or fetuses from embryos, juveniles from larvae or fetuses, and adults from juveniles." These answers imply a teleological pull toward something more perfect—complex, heterogeneous, and specific. Today, developmental biologists substitute evolution for teleology and DNA/genes for pull with much the same effect. Both developing and developed organisms are said to have been shaped by natural selection in the interest of reproduction or inclusive fitness, but what is meant is that an organism develops because development has evolved, like everything else in an organism's phenotype.

It is a rare developmental biologist who can strip development of the last vestige of teleology, progress, and determinism. Most developmental biologists cling to remnants of the past and attribute development to abstractions based on evolution, such as hypothetical ancestors and nodes on cladograms, epitomized as stages of development—embryo (cleavage, blastula, gastrula, neurula, tail bud), fetus, neonate, juvenile, adult. Developmentalists will have to do better than that if they are to contribute to making human beings immortal.

The History of Modern Stages

The stages typically assigned to embryos in contemporary textbooks are not much more than a century old. Most of them were invented by Ernst Haeckel (1834–1919), who coined their names, characterized them, and established evolution as their principle *raison d'être*.

Haeckel placed the gastrula at center stage (pun intended) in embryonic development in order to vindicate the fictional gastrea, which he also created and placed at the hub of multicellular-animal evolution. Haeckel considered embryos at pre-gastrular stages too poorly constructed to support the rich evolution of metazoans. His blastula was nothing more than an undifferentiated, hollow ball—an epithelium containing a hole or blastocoel—corresponding to a sponge-like evolutionary stage. It lacked the specialization of a truly differentiated animal, a eumetazoan.[63] The structure of the gastrula, on the other hand, with germ layers falling into place, anticipated everything in the future larva or adult, at least by way of structures derived from germ layers. Likewise, the corresponding, hypothetical gastrea was supposed to have been the premier ancestral metazoan, having the potential to evolve into all metazoans along with everything present in them.

Haeckel took the word, *biogenesis*—meaning the biological origins of biological material—from Thomas Huxley and transformed it into the principle that living things evolve by additions to preexisting living things. He took the concept of homology—that a natural or genealogical relationship exists between parts exhibiting similar structural relationships—from French evolutionists, German Romantics, and English comparative anatomists, and turned it into the principle of recapitulation—that biological entities must first return to origins in order to develop. Woven together in a series of publications between 1872 and 1884, biogenesis and recapitulation became the famous biogenic law or law of recapitulation: "Ontogeny epitomizes phylogeny," or embryonic development recapitulates evolutionary progress in a truncated form.[64]

Historically, homology was attributed to structures when their relationships bore embryological, anatomical, and paleontological similarities. But following the promulgation of the biogenic law, embryological data became the most important evidence for attributing homology. The origin of structures from common embryonic rudiments was the very quintessence of Haeckelianism. By the *fin-de-siècle,* under Haeckel's influence, discovering evidence for evolution in conserved embryonic structures became the *raison d'être* of embryology, and sequences of evolutionary additions to lifetimes became the rationale of embryonic stages.

Haeckel was not breaking new ground here, since even before the advent of Darwinism in the nineteenth century, the embryo was viewed as the most conservative stage in a lifetime. Indeed, recapitulation or homology might even seem anti-evolutionary, since conserved structures are supposed to be preserved rather than altered. Haeckel convinced biologists that recapitulation was the quintessence of evolution through his power of persuasion—not his logic. He was biology's greatest publicist whose ability to promote his cause has rarely been approached and hardly ever matched.

Today, similarity in molecular sequences has replaced similarity in embryos as the chief argument on behalf of evolution. Sequences that Haeckelians would have characterized as "recapitulated," are now called "conserved."[65] Portions of molecules are said to be conserved when the sequences present in these portions are 20 percent or more identical. These molecules are also said to be homologous when elements, such as particular amino acids or nucleotides, appear at the same positions in the molecules.

Conserved and homologous sequences are thought to have been present in ancestral species. Presumably, these sequences are conserved as a consequence of some adaptive advantage provided by the original form. Adaptation need not be rigorously defined or tested to meet the requirements of developmental biologists. Adaptations can be mere biological inertia, or biological so so. Discovering homology would otherwise be quite difficult, since it requires finding similarity amidst the huge differences seen among embryos of species and among the vast changes taking place in embryos, literally before one's eyes—with the help of magnification. The selective blindness that allows one to ignore these differences is justified by the argument, however tautological, that embryos must share similarities, since any radical shift in embryonic development would bring about disastrous results for the adult.

The End of Stages

Today, molecular homologies have made stages appear all the more arbitrary. Sequence data suggest that some homologous molecules are phylogenetically older than others, although these molecules appear in embryos at the same stage of development.

Canonical monophylic notions of evolution do not justify placing anachronistic sequences at the same evolutionary horizon or developmental stage. Efforts were mounted, therefore, to replace morphological stages with molecular stages.[66] An early embryonic stage was thought to be dominated by "maternal" contributions to development or prezygotic products that came along with the egg. But even imprinted genes "are not controlled solely by epigenetic modifications established during gametogenesis ... [or] 'hardwired,' with embryonic cells only passively manifesting obligatory consequences of the gametic imprints."[67] Later, a postzygotic embryonic stage commenced, dominated by the activity of the paternal or zygotic genome, and in a third stage, "control genes" began operating.[68] These stages were clearly "up for epigenic grabs." The earliest stage corresponded to the period of axial development; the second stage corresponded to the period of pattern formation; and the third stage to segmentation of some sort.

The problem was that the expression of particular genes does not fall neatly into particular stages.[69] The reaction of molecular biologists was to conclude that all stages were arbitrarily precipitated out of fluid development.

Development is now said to be continuous, although some spectacular exceptions are admitted, such as metamorphic changes between pupa and adult insect or amphibian tadpole and frog. Staging is thought to distort development by turning its smooth progress into a staircase of beginnings and endings. The excuse for staging embryos is said to be convenience, but staging is not thought to be mandated by biological law and placing embryos in stages is considered arbitrary. Stages are thought to be concrete only in biology's literature.

Recently, an effort has been made to replace stages as an organizing principle with the notion of construction plans, or *Baupläne*.[70] What is attractive about *Baupläne* is that they are conceptually inclusive. They relate the familiar idea of a blueprint, written in nitrogenous bases of DNA, to Richard Owen's (1804–1892) concept of serial homology—a relationship among repeated structures, such as those occurring in segmental organisms. A variety of segments, or even parts of segments, form homologous structures if the right cocktail of determinants (e.g., products encoded by *HOX* genes) are present at the right time to trigger development. Homology is not in the structure so much as it is in the genes, and a *Bauplan*, is built from the bottom up—from the gene to organism.[71] Developmental instructions do not trickle down through stages so much as they lie in wait, or in suppressed states, capable of responding if and when called.

Baupläne-thinking has important consequences for animal taxonomy. The distinction between deuterostomes and protostomes, once based on descriptions of gastrulas, has now been seconded by molecular sequences in 18S rDNA and confirmed by sequences of *HOX* genes.[72] The molecular evidence even separates protostomes into Lophotrochozoa (brachiopods, mollusks, flatworms, nemerteans, leeches, and polychaete annelids) and Ecdysozoa (priapulids, nematodes, and arthropods, including onychophorans).[73]

Baupläne are not supported by the weight of evidence, however. The Burgess shale fossils of mid-Cambrian age demonstrate that life can be organized in vastly different ways than it is in extant organisms.[74] *Baupläne* are modern prototypes, derived more or less from Platonic archetypes and just as transcendental.

Development is still thought to occur because evolution and genes make it happen. Haeckel would be delighted to know that the products of a set of eleven conserved "dorsal-group" genes plus *cactus* are linked in a signal transduction pathway which, in turn, creates a concentration gradient of the conserved transcription factor Dorsal that allows the conserved Toll signal[75] to establish the conserved hedgehog signaling pathway triggering leg development in *Drosophila* and vertebrates![76]

DEVELOPMENT ACCORDING TO EMBRYOLOGISTS AND DEVELOPMENTAL BIOLOGISTS

The study of development, especially in animals, falls into two convenient categories—embryology and developmental biology. Embryology's greatest contributions are probably the concepts of induction (tissue interactions required for morphogenesis) and developmental homology (similarities in the course of development resulting from common ancestry), whereas developmental biology's greatest contributions are probably its exploration of genes and gene action, namely, how DNA directs the production of developmentally relevant proteins. What brings embryology and developmental biology together is the linkage of induction and evolution to DNA, not so much as a blueprint or recipe[77] for making an organism but as a series or cascade of interacting processes. These interactions resemble Maturana's and Varela's idea of triggers: "This interaction is not instructive, for it does not determine what its effects are going to be."[78]

Embryology and developmental biology are three-dimensional disciplines—each has data, subdisciplines, and paradigms. Embryology's data are typically organismal and trickle down to organs, tissues, and cells. Developmental biology's data are typically molecular and genetic, but cast their shadow upward toward cells, tissues, organs, and organisms. Embryology's subdisciplines are descriptive, comparative, experimental, and theoretical, while developmental biology's subdisciplines are molecular and cellular. Embryology's paradigms are epitomized by the terms *preformation* and *epigenesis*, while developmental biology's are *neopreformation* and *neoepigenics*. The two disciplines are easily distinguished historically and practically. For example, large animal cloners are typically embryologists, while stem-cell researchers are developmental biologists. The two disciplines offer complementary rather than contradictory insights for achieving immortality.

Embryologists

Embryology's descriptive data are generally organized in standardized stages. Its comparative data, whether descriptions or experimental results, are observations made repeatedly in some animals or experimental systems, and extrapolated to unexamined animals or experimental systems. Embryologists traditionally reach out, even to exotic species, for their comparative data. Experimental data are observations made after manipulating embryos, the results of which are thought to have relevance to normally developing organisms. Similarly, theoretical data, created by pencil and paper or computer and program, are expected to have relevance to other developmental data.

The tradition of describing embryos goes back to Aristotle, whose embryos included both household and exotic species, including snakes and a shark.[79] Developmental stages seem to have been added later and became fashionable in the Renaissance as part of the great shift away from description toward analysis. Descriptive embryology also narrowed during the Renaissance, gravitating toward a few species, notably the chick.

Comparative embryology was implicit in the Renaissance, although not rigorously delimited. Leonardo de Vinci, for example, took liberties with the comparative method, drawing a human fetus attached to a cow's placenta as if to say, "What is true in cows is true in humans."[80] A quantitative yardstick for comparisons was not recognized until the nineteenth century when von Baer discovered the notochord in twenty-eight different types of vertebrate embryos, from fish to dolphins and frogs to dogs, and predicted that the notochord would be present in any vertebrate embryo he had not yet examined.[81]

The parent of experimental embryology is generally considered Wilhelm Roux (1850–1924), who is credited with having the "perspicacity to appreciate that the embryo could be grappled with experimentally."[82] He also founded the *Archiv für Entwicklungsmechanik der Organismen* for the sole purpose of publishing the consequences of manipulations.[83] Alternatively, Hans Spemann might be nominated for the title of parent of experimental embryology since he became, in 1935, the only embryologist to ever receive the Nobel Prize in Physiology or Medicine, and he most certainly did experiments. But Spemann was the leading epigenicist of his day, while Roux was the leading preformationist, and experimental embryology is and was bound hand-and-foot with preformation.

As for theoretical embryology, Hans Driesch (1867–1941) generally gets the nod as founder, although his theory was based on the results of experiments with sea urchin embryos. Driesch's work led to both theoretical and practical consequences. Driesch had discovered that the blastomeres created by the first few cleavage divisions could form complete embryos if isolated from each other. His "harmonious equipotential system" explained how a blastomere could perform as part of an embryo or as a whole embryo depending on its circumstances, inspiring Charles Manning Child[84] to develop his theory of metabolic gradient, Alan Turing (1912–1954)[85] to work out his reaction/diffusion gradients and wavelength theory of pattern formation, and Yoram Schiffmann[86] to integrate Child's and Turing's theories into a comprehensive theory of polarity and form-regulation.

The practical consequence of Driesch's work lay with cloning livestock. Identical twins were known to develop naturally from single fertilized eggs, but it was Driesch's discovery that prompted livestock embryologists to separate blastomeres from cleaved bovine and ovine eggs and produce artificially identical calves and lambs.[87]

Embryology's paradigms are subsumed by the traditions of epigenics and preformation. In the epigenic tradition organisms and their parts are formed from unformed material, whereas in the preformation tradition they are formed from previously formed materials. These traditions are deeply rooted in historical, religious, and other cultural controversies, and, as might be expected, they took numerous turns with the times, ultimately moving toward synthesis in developmental biology's neoepigenics and neopreformation.

Epigenesis

Epigenesis is sometimes traced to Aristotle, especially because the celebrated William Harvey (1578–1657)—Yes! the Harvey of blood-circulation fame—

attributed the concept to Aristotle.[88] Anatomist and physician to Charles I, Harvey probably intended to give *epigenesis* a teleological ring.

Harvey had looked in vain for embryos in the uteri of does after rutting but only found long strings of mucus (presumably germinal vesicles) and nothing resembling embryos. He decided that the uterus was the mammalian egg, and mammalian embryos were no more present there prior to pregnancy than bird embryos were present in freshly laid avian eggs.[89] Concluding that "the egg comes before the chicken," Harvey's epigenesis decreed that there is no embryo in the uterus to begin with. Rather, the male and female elements arrive in the uterus through blood and develop there epigenically.

Actually, Harvey's argument on behalf of epigenesis is partially correct despite his erroneous identification of the mammalian egg with the uterus and his failure to appreciate the relationship of mucous strings to embryos. Mammals do not begin developing in the uterus, and embryos are not present during the earliest stages of mammalian development. In the first place, a fertilized egg in a uterine duct (oviduct or Fallopian tube) undergoes cell division into blastomeres, and these form a morula (a berry-like group of cells), and then a blastocyst—a hollow ball (cyst) with an asymmetric thickening called the inner cell mass (ICM). Even after arriving in the uterus and hatching from its membranes (the mammalian zona pellucida), the blastocyst still contains no embryo. Thus, as an "embryo" without an embryo, the blastocyst is properly called a preembryo.[90] Second, monozygotic twins (specifically, type 3), in which two separate embryonic axes form at 8–12 dpo, demonstrate that even the early embryo is still only a potential and not a presence.[91] Embryo-formation is generally said to commence at the "primitive streak phase" (13–15 dpo in human beings) when the position of the future embryo ahead of the streak would seem determined, if only potentially.

Despite Harvey's prestige, epigenesis found little support among the classical seventeenth century microscopists, and went into decline during the Enlightenment. Expanded and clarified by Caspar Friedrich Wolff's (1738–94) observations on granules—that turned out to be cell nuclei—epigenesis might have become a plausible mechanism of organismic development, but ferocious opposition mounted by preformationists left little room for dialogue.

> When microscopists began to look at the tissues of living forms they already had in their minds a view of matter as an aggregate of more or less uniform microscopic components. It is therefore understandable that when they saw everywhere agglomerations of more or less spherical halations, they concluded that these optical illusions were the fundamental subunits of animate matter; and when they actually saw cells they had no idea what they were.[92]

The turning point in epigenesis' fortune only came when it was endorsed by Karl Ernst von Baer following his codification of germ layers into a law of vertebrate development. But von Baer did not have his eye on *Insecten und Würmern,* or on generalities more sweeping than those he applied to verte-brates.[93] Reflections on that level were taken up by others, notably Ernst Haeckel, who named the outer and inner germ layers, borrowing the terms *ectoderm* and *endoderm* from the names previously given by the invertebrate zoologist, George Allman, to the outer and inner cellular layers of hydroid polyps. Thomas Henry Huxley followed through by naming a middle germ layer mesoderm, and by creating the great divide among animals—the schizocoels versus the enterocoels which became the protostomes versus the deuterostomes. Others joined the naming game. Ectoblast, mesoblast, and entoplast were coined by the descriptive embryologist Oscar Hertwig, while epiblast, and hypoblast were named by comparative embryologists Francis M. Balfour and Ray Lankaster. Robert Remak dubbed the inner and outer layers of gastrulas primary, on the grounds that they formed first, and he described the subdivision of the outer layer in vertebrates into an epidermal and neural plate, the latter subsequently giving rise to the brain and spinal cord.[94]

An entirely different tradition of epigenesis has remained outside the canon of Western embryology, a pariah frequently tarred with the brush of Lamarckism.[95] The "inheritance of acquired characteristics" is epigenesis's albatross even when the environment plays a legitimate role in development, as when gravity establishes planes of symmetry in hen eggs.

Otherwise, epigenesis is alive and well in embryology.[96] Germ layers provide the classic example of regimented epigenic scenarios, while epigenic effects on the differentiation of immune cells appear to be random, and dif-ferential gene splicing appears to be subtly controlled cellularly. In addition, environmentally induced epigenic effects are inherited in a nonMendelian fashion, such as the differential inheritance of traits from one parent or the other—methylation and allele silencing or imprinting DNA of the X chromo-some of males or the fragile X syndrome inherited from females.[97] The de-velopment of the placenta is epigenic, depending on interactions between maternal systems, embryo, and later, the fetus.[98] Even genetic diseases, such as Huntington's disease, ultimately have an epigenic parameter—the length of the problematic repeat.

Preformation

The preformation tradition was given biological expression by the seven-teenth century classical microscopists Marcello Malpighi of Bologna (1628–1694), and later by the entomologist Charles Bonnet (1720–1793) of Geneva and the physiologist (Viktor) Albrecht von Haller (1708–1777), the supreme if ambivalent preformationist of the Enlightenment. These Christian savants considered embryos no more capable of developing from unformed material than new species were capable of mutating or ascending from old ones. The doctrine of preformation was intended to explain development much the same way creationism explained variation among living things.[99]

Preformationists were committed to prefabricated structures, and preformationism rested on *emboîtement*, the encapsulation of structure within structure. Organisms developed from miniatures within the germ and only fleshed out their bodies over their period of development. The problem of reducing the size of embryos to accommodate their encapsulation was enormous. In the ultimate version of preformation, Bonnet approached the notion of encoded information and toned down preformationism to something more on the order of determinism.[100] Developing organisms henceforth contained a preexisting form, but something more like an organizational plan rather than a structure, and development as such acquired a fluidity, a quality of transformation from the virtual or potential. Determinism thereby admitted the possibility of error and contingency.[101]

Preformation continued to take shape in the late nineteenth and early twentieth centuries in the hands of August Weismann at Freiburg. Derived from germplasm in the nucleus,[102] developmental determinants were somehow transmitted to the cytoplasm (trophoplasm) where they determined somatoplasmic cell lineages.[103]

Weismann's doctrine was supported in grand style when Wilhelm Roux reported on a series of experiments in which blastomeres comprising halves or quarters of frog embryos were pierced by hot needles, and the remaining blastomeres developed into half and three-quarter embryos, failing to develop structures that would have developed from the pierced blastomeres.[104] Roux's results were so dramatic and so well illustrated that his report almost single-handedly launched the new field of experimental embryology, dedicated to unraveling predetermined influences on development.

The problem was that experiments with sea urchins performed by Driesch and with salamanders performed by Spemann, among others, demonstrated that isolated blastomeres could form whole embryos.[105] The development of partial embryos in Roux's experiments was due to influences emanating from the dead cells along with the living ones.[106] Indeed, the development of whole embryos from isolated blastomeres is the cornerstone of the cloning industry's effort to clone livestock.

Contemporary biology has been kind to Weismann,[107] despite inconsistencies in his theory and Morgan's rejection.[108] Weismann is broadly credited with the doctrine of nuclear control of development, and loosely credited with anticipating a role for ribonucleic acid as an intermediary in protein synthesis. Weismann and Roux had legitimized determinist or mosaic development both experimentally and theoretically. Determinants (tesserae) were somehow distributed differentially among the dividing blastomeres and filtered into the cytoplasm where they controlled differentiation utterly and irreversibly.

As the mid-twentieth century approached, deterministic concepts of development were still a long way from sequences of nucleotides in DNA and the transcription of messages for making embryos, but determined parts were no longer prefabricated. Encoded developmental information was just around the corner. Today's gene-centered notions of development are only partially the distillate of preformation. The replication of DNA from single strands, and the transcription of RNA from sense strands of DNA do not meet classical criteria of preformed parts, but they are the unmistakable heirs to Bonnet's vision and of Weismann's and Roux's mosaic determinism.

DEVELOPMENTAL BIOLOGISTS

Developmental biology is dedicated to figuring out how all DNA/genes are integrated across the time axes of development. Developmental biologists working at the molecular level are concerned with cascades of gene action leading to cellular differentiation, while those working at the cell level are concerned with gene action leading to pattern formation and morphogenesis, and all developmental biologists hope to discover homologies that leap across time and species. Data are abundant, much of them as nucleotide and amino-acid sequences, and these are stored in databases freely accessible at several sources including the National Institutes of Health web pages for the Human Genome Project: ncbi.nlm.nih.gov/.

The problem perceived by developmental biologists is figuring out how DNA operates as a "blueprint," "recipe," "formula," "prescription," or "software" for the developing organism. Blueprint is the most widely cited metaphor, but the linear sequence of nitrogenous bases in DNA does not reach the two-dimensional level of blue paper and white lines. Increasingly popular, ideas of recipes contain the elements of a plan but replace the precision of a blueprint with the arbitrariness of a cookbook ("season to taste"). And recipes always leave open the ineffable question: Who is cooking? In any case, no metaphor is sufficiently complex to encompass the four-dimensional space in which organisms develop. Biologists relying on metaphor will acknowledge, if forced to, that they are only trying to make a point and not solve the problem, but confessions notwithstanding, "How does DNA work?"

How Genes Work

Concrete ideas on how genes might work go back to Morgan. He began by suggesting that "[t]he arrangement of the genes in the chromosomes . . . [might be related] to the arrangement of the parts which the structures of the fully formed individual bear to each other." He concluded, prematurely, it would seem, that no such relationship existed. Recently, researchers in many laboratories, working with many animals, have discovered that the developmental genes known as *HOX* genes (encoding transcription factors with a DNA binding site known as the homeobox domain) are frequently present in clusters within which their position and order of expression parallel the embryo's anterior-posterior axis. A spate of scientific reports bearing on the arrangement of *HOX*-genes quickly spearheaded the study of organization in chromosomes and helped launched the new discipline of genomics.[109]

Morgan did not believe that genes changed during cell division as Weismann had suggested. Morgan suggested, instead, that genes worked through selective activation and inactivation (today's repression and derepression), and speeding up and slowing down (generally known as differential gene-expression). Negative feedback and checkpoints would operate not only in the control of physiological and biochemical pathways, but also in the operation of developmental pathways. Genes themselves might also operate in control or regulatory capacities, determining or influencing structural genes encoding the actual building blocks of structural proteins and enzymes. It would seem a good idea, but "very few gene networks known in development function in a truly hierarchical manner."[110]

Gene regulation consists of turning genes on and tuning them in. Direct regulation is widely attributed to various sorts of transcription factors—enhancers, regulator substances, and silencers. For example, "ligand-dependent transcription factors" include superfamilies of nuclear receptors such as androgen, estrogen, glucocorticoid, retinoic acid, and thyroid-hormone receptors. Upon binding their respective ligands, the receptors undergo a change in overall molecular shape (conformation), affecting their affinity for and binding to the hormone response elements in specific DNA-promoter regions. Consequently, the rate of transcription of genes regulated by these promoter regions is affected, either positively or negatively.

Indirect regulation of genes seems far more complex. Probably most reactions of cells to the arrival of a ligand—formerly considered a "tissue interaction process"—involve indirect regulation, especially reactions following the arrival of ligand reaching the receptive cell through an extracellular medium or coming from contiguous cells. For example, ligand-dependent cell-surface receptors, activate so-called G-proteins that bind guanine and transduce extracellular information to intracellular activity. Cascades of phosphorylating/dephosphorylating reactions are unleashed among signaling molecules and enzymes, and finally, particular genes are transcribed, and the cell is launched on a new pathway of development.

The direct and indirect regulation of genes encoding transcription factors, enzymes, signaling molecules, and structural proteins are presumed to be pre-

programmed in cells, depending on the presence or activation of receptor molecules at the time the ligand arrives at the target cells. "The readiness is all," and
cells react when they are pre-prepared with receptors. The expression of genes
encoding receptors is a prior condition for the differential activation of genes.

Cells may also be pre-programmed for "cell-autonomous processes"
or "cell-lineage autonomous processes" dependent upon a cell's history of
cell division. The effect of cell division may be mechanical, operating to
dilute or remove inhibitory nuclear-proteins that otherwise prevent specific
transcriptional activities. Alternatively, nuclear division may merely be a
source of undetermined nuclei, while cytoplasmic division may partition or
compartmentalize particular cytoplasmic determinants, thereby allowing them
to influence nuclei in the absence of competing signals. A lineage's fate or
prospective significance may then be determined as a consequence of interactions between cytoplasmic determinants and naive nuclei.

Repeated on a large scale, cell division seems to play a major role in
establishing compartments of gene expression. For example, during the early
development of insects, small groups of cells form "polyclones" when they
behave as a lineage compartment, even though they do not originate from a
recent common ancestral cell. The action of selector genes maintains a "stable
inheritance of discrete patterns of gene expression"[111] in the polyclone, and
cells do not generally move from one compartment to another.[112]

In all these mechanisms, determinism remains dominant, and developmental biologists are not likely to exhaust determinist premises in the foreseeable future. Cells respond at different times during development in different
ways, even to the same hormone, because of the expression of different
receptors or response pathway-elements and hence the transcription of different morphogenically-significant proteins.[113]

From cell-autonomous processes to tissue interaction processes, developmental biology's theories and concepts are distinctly determinist. Even where
processes are regulated and depend in one way or another on cues extrinsic
to the mechanism of activity, responsibility ultimately rests with genes. The
two terms used by developmental biologists to characterize this sort of regulation are neoepigenics, the unfolding of nuclear genes, and neopreformation,
the cueing of nuclear genes by regulating substances.

Neopreformation and Neoepigenics

In the last decades of the twentieth century, developmental biologists looked
backward for their inspiration and rediscovered epigenics and preformation,
renaming them neoepigenics and neopreformation to suit the underlying assumption of determinism. The essence of neopreformation is DNA undergoing replication and transcription, prescribing mRNA which enters the cytoplasm
and undergoes translation into protein. Similarly, the essence of neoepigenesis

is control over (epi-) genes and, hence, the prescription of protein synthesis. Neopreformation and neoepigenics are not oppositional but allied by DNA/ genes and the control of their expression.

The consolidation of preformation and epigenic narratives began at the advent of the twentieth century, although the determinists, who were about to become neopreformationists, and the indeterminists, who were about to become neoepigenecists, could hardly have known it. The forces of determinism, better known as *mosaicism* at the time, went to battle against the rival forces of indeterminism, better known as *regulation*. For the determinist, the embryo was a mosaic with each tessera already assigned a developmental fate, or significance. For the indeterminist, the embryo was constantly informing itself about its state of completeness and busily altering, adjusting, and fine tuning, or regulating, its ultimate differentiation.

Evidence for and against determinism and indeterminism was drawn from the results of experiments—the manipulation of spatial and temporal relationships among embryonic parts. Parts were separated completely or incompletely, moved from one place to another or between embryos at different stages, and labeled with dyes in order to trace lineages temporally and movements spatially. The results generally demonstrated that early embryos were not homogeneous, general, and simple!

Induction, the influence of cells or tissues in one position on cells or tissues in another position, became the hallmark of indeterminism, but induction inevitably depended upon preexisting differences between the inducer and the inductee. Likewise, cytoplasmic determinants, whether visualizable or not, epitomized determinism since these elements preexisted or emerged in specific positions in eggs and embryos where they exercised their power, including sending inductive messages that influenced other cells not previously determined.

What was conspicuously missing from these formulations was a role for nuclear genes. Morgan and others had resolutely resisted the efforts of Weismann, Roux, Richard Goldschmidt, and others to place genes at the peak of mosaic mountains and watch the avalanches of development. The early twentieth century sense of genes as hereditary units did not justify extravagant hypotheses concerning their action upon development. At a time when William Bateson could hardly stomach the chromosomal theory of inheritance, he could not be expected to digest genes escaping from the nucleus and triggering differentiation in the cytoplasm!

The Neopreformationist Offensive

The second great battle between determinists and indeterminists was fought in the twentieth century, coinciding with the era of World War II. It was fought over the role of nuclear genes and cytoplasmic determinants in development. Before the war, fundamental characteristics were defined as those determined by the cytoplasm, and superficial characteristics as those determined by nuclear genes. Development consisted of the unfolding of fundamental characteristics to which superficial characteristics were added. Geneticists of the Morgan school would have none of this and resisted every effort to legitimize the cytoplasm as the seat of developmental information.

Charles Manning Child was the leading epigenic theorist at this times.[114] His metabolic-gradient theory of development was supported by a wealth of experimental evidence from cnidarians to sea urchins. In addition, working mainly with sea-urchin embryos, John Runnström (1888–1972) developed a theory of antiparallel, morphogenic gradients and Swen Hörstadius (1898– 1996) showed how metabolic gradients developed in succession on perpendicular axes. In all the gradients, morphogenic control was fundamentally a function of cytoplasm, exercised superficially on nuclear genes.

At the end of the war, the relationship of cytoplasm and nucleus was about to shift 180 degrees. Despite the considerable momentum that had built up behind self-generating, cytoplasmic gradients, a momentum that would climax in 1952 with Alan Turing's reaction-diffusion model of morphogenic gradients (the Turing bifurcation of dissipative structures), the post-war period found the nuclear/gene/DNA poised to steamroller cytoplasmic determination and crush gradients utterly.[115]

The reversal followed James Watson's and Francis Crick's analysis of DNA's secondary structure, which suggested a testable, physico-chemical model for the replication of genes. As the epoch of molecular biology began, nuclear determinacy became triumphant. The march of the "nuclear-monopoly" had begun, and the ascendancy of the DNA paradigm ("DNA is destiny!") was assured.[116] By the late-twentieth century, with the poles reversed, DNA/ genes took the roles formerly reserved for cytoplasmic determinants. A nuclear mosaicism replaced a cytoplasmic mosaicism, and chromosomes overflowed with tessera of nuclear genes, while tessera of cytoplasmic determinants became the "has beens" of development.

The new determinism was not quite the same as Weismann's and Roux's mosaicism. Whereas Weismann and Roux proposed that development followed the irreversible distribution of genes during cleavage, the new determinism failed to solve the problem of how the nucleus and DNA/genes asserted their hegemony. That problem would be solved when both nuclear DNA/genes and cytoplasmic/nuclear proteins were shown to play mutually helpful roles as determinants and regulators. Neoepigenics and neopreformation would then emerge from the shadow of epigenics and preformation.

Thus, both DNA and its products are determinants, and the nucleus and cytoplasm play their own roles in the manufacture, distribution, activation, and inhibition of determinants. The details are still obscure, but molecular geneticists of the caliber of Nobelist Walter Gilbert assure us that confirmation will emerge clearly from the Human Genome Project.

CONCLUSIONS

So why aren't we immortal? A half billion years or so of developing mortal animals supplies an abundance of answers! We are not immortal because our development is determined by genes, inherited through genes, and constrained by natural selection around the poles of fertilization and death; because the components of our developing systems—germ layers, cell lines, and stem cells—rely in part on history to get their bearings and are generally eliminated or narrowed in scope with maturity; because our internal organs cannot dump effete cells as easily as surface organs can dump cells into external sinks; because internal organs have acquired controls over their growth that result in the accumulation of damaged DNA; because adults have insufficient supplies of stem cells to sustain adult life; because the stem cells they have are not sufficiently malleable to replace all the cells in an organism requiring replacement.

Can all the reasons we do not develop immortality be turned on their head and funneled into a plan for making us immortal? It will be difficult, even in theory, since ever since the Renaissance plans for the construction of organisms have been thought to be ingrained in organisms, rather than arising outside the organism. We are outside, but our knowledge of development, that began when Wilhelm Roux first tested our ability to manipulate development, has brought us to the brink of altering development in many ways— why not in immortal ways?

The physicality of organisms limits plans of development to one of two types: epigenesis and preformation. In epigenic models of development, a mortal adult lurking behind the plan for morphogenesis draws the organism outward. In preformation models, an equally mortal embryo drives morphogenesis from within. In either case, the developing organism acts upon itself with minimal environmental input and becomes what it was already programmed to be, namely, a mortal organism.

The epigenic and preformation concepts of embryology have now been transmuted to the neoepigenic and neopreformation concepts of developmental biology, and rewritten in the language of DNA/genes. Scenarios appealing to differential gene expression are the heart and soul of developmental biology. Other scenarios appeal to still more complex, and less understood, cytoplasmic regulatory mechanisms for the further integration of temporal sequences and gene activation. Displaced over time, these regulatory mechanisms are thought to account for pattern formation, segmentation, and specific morphogenic phenomena, including programmed cell-death and apoptosis. But no scenario for normal development leaves any room for human beings developing immortality.

Still, one may wonder if death is really the telos, the ultimate fate drawing out the embryo, larva or fetus, juvenile, and adult. Certainly programmed cell death is essential to embryogenesis, but is death as such the end of our development? Throwing off notions of progress would seem to exculpate development from the charge of leading organisms to death. The alternative would seem to be re-introducing stages into the notion of a lifetime and accepting development as the property of one such stage—from fertilized egg to early adult. One might also reexamine all the substages of development for what they may have to offer by way of building organisms.

One may also wonder what might be accomplished by intervening in development. Mosaicism was never more than half the story. One may grant that development is determined to the extent that every possible mode of development is anticipated by one or more determinant, but these determinants are frequently short-lived and dependent on the action of other determinants. After all, the results of manipulating cells spatially and temporally demonstrate that cells are subject to flux and regulation and can come under the influence of different determinants with different consequences. Development is also regulative to the extent that every possible mode of development is the consequence of coordinated interactions and, hence, subject to adjustment. All may not be lost, therefore, and immortality may be achievable through manipulating developing organisms, if not developed organisms.

The objective of manipulations on behalf of immortality is ultimately to allow the organism to maintain itself indefinitely. This objective is most easily met if the organism is in pristine condition to begin with. Immortality would then require only maintaining the organisms in this condition. Human beings, like most other animals, are in their most pristine condition at puberty, but, with the onset of sexuality, the organism rapidly moves beyond the pristine. *In order to maintain an organism as close to pristine as possible, it will have to be arrested in the prepubescent stage of development.* It will, in effect, be arrested in a developmental mode, a state of permanent self-maintenance and regeneration.

The perpetual preadolescent will have to produce a sufficient number and quality of stem cells to maintain itself in its condition and replace damaged organs when required. Indigenous organs, melting-pot organs, as well as colonized organs will have to accommodate to their complete replacement by stem cells. Even tissues that are indigenous must become replaceable by stem cells.

The three developmental components—germ layers, cell lines, and stem cells—will all have to be manipulated, since each contributes to making preadolescents. Germ layers, which determine the time and place of development, will have to permit the early introduction of stem cells, and cell lines, which determine the cast of cell types in the organism, will have to be rerouted to accommodate stem cells into unusual pathways. In addition, cells formerly directed toward germ cells will have to be destroyed.

It all boils down to this: Immortality can be developed by preventing prepubescent individuals from becoming adults and replacing their germ cells with sufficient numbers of stem cells to maintain the individual forever.

Chapter 4

Life's Fundamental Feature: Devolution

So at the base of ancient philosophy lies necessarily this postulate: that there is more in the motionless than in the moving, and that we pass from immutability to becoming by way of diminution or attenuation.

—Henri Bergson, *Creative Evolution*

If evolution includes any veritable becomings, it is in the domain of *symbiosis* that bring into play beings of totally different scales and kingdoms, with no possible filiation.

—Gilles Deleuze and Felix Guattari, *A Thousand Plateaus*

It [the cell] is far too complex to have arisen full-fledged as such. Further, the doings of this little individual life must somewhere and at some time have acquired the property of cohering in co-operative organization. Lesser lives thus have co-operated to make larger cooperative lives. Man is one of the latest of these latter.

—Charles Sherrington, *Man on his Nature*

The time has come to turn the tables on impossibilities. Chapter 4 shows how some of our fundamental biological features make immortality a doable goal.

Chapters 2 and 3 have only shown that immortality would not emerge in human beings left to the normal courses of evolution and development. But development and evolution are only two of life's key characteristics. Life has other characteristics, some of which would aid immortality and some would even abet it.

Life's key characteristics are those without which life, as we know it, would not exist. These are characteristics, such as autopoiesis and homeostasis, with self-evident adaptive value.[1] My object here is not to make a list of such characteristics, but to identify those most relevant to immortality and analyze them for their potential and problems in achieving immortality for human beings. In order to meet this objective, I have gone back to basics—to where it all began and to life's most fundamental features.

Life was different at its outset from what it is now, but life in extant species exhibits two fundamental features when stripped of modern appurtenances: fusion, or mixing, and fission, or fragmentation. I call the combination of fusion and fission *devolution* and devote Chapter 4 to tracing its history through life: its relevance to life's key characteristics in viruses and transposons, in prokaryotes and Eucarya, in sex and multicellular animals, in life histories and death. The chapter then concludes with a summary of the lessons of devolution for immortality.

GETTING DOWN TO BASICS: LIFE BEGINS

What was life like between 3.8 billion years ago, when it first appeared, and 0.54 billion years ago at the beginning of the Cambrian Period when animals with skeletons first left a substantial fossil record? In all likelihood, these steeled animals contended for their place in posterity and died much as we do. But what was life like earlier, before it was welded to sexual reproduction? Stretching the fossil record back to 2 billion years ago, by including the microfossils of bacteria, leaves 1.8 billion years, or nearly half the duration of life on Earth, during which time much, if not all, of life changed without benefit of Darwinian evolution. What sort of life prospered in this epoch, and did devolution play a role in changing it?

One cannot expect to examine primordial life today, but one may garner a glimpse of what it might have been like by taking a page out of physics and performing a "thought experiment." What characteristics of life would one encounter standing on a wave front as it moved through life's dimensions? What would life look like in one, two, and three dimensions rather than the familiar four—length, breadth, depth, and duration—physiological and evolutionary time?

How did life change when a point in biological life was stretched into a line? How did life change when a line was deflected into a circle or stretched into a biological plane—a primitive biofilm? How did life change when a plane was folded or pumped into a three dimensional compartment—a microsphere? What additional biological changes took place when life added duration and introduced sexual reproduction and generational change?

LIFE IN ONE AND TWO DIMENSIONS

Biology's literature provides sparse food for thought for imagining life in one and two dimensions, but the larder is not entirely bare. For example, Walter Gilbert has speculated on life in an RNA world—a far more linear world than our DNA/protein world[2]—where loose stretches of RNA, known as introns,[3] might have inserted themselves in coding regions, creating exons, and inducing mutations.[4] Shades of linearity might also be preserved in transposons whose insertion in some genes renders them hypermutable and even superhypermutable. Linearity is also exhibited where polynucleotides are added enzymatically to the ends of RNAs.

Two-dimensional polynucleotides might also have resided among the denizens of the ancient world. Mitochondrial DNA in Cnidaria is both linear and circular, raising the possibility that ancient prokaryotes may have had linear DNA as well as circular DNA (circular DNA prevailing in extant bacteria).[5] The rolling circle method of replication exhibited by bacteriophage, moreover, suggests an adaptive advantage for circularity in the amplification of specific genes. Vertebrates seem to utilize a similar method of replication for the amplification of nucleolar organizer genes during oogenesis.[6]

One might draw the picture of life in one and two dimensions more sharply by trying to imagine the life of a virus. Viruses seem to occupy a dimension below cellular organisms, since viruses contain either RNA or DNA, but cellular organisms contain RNA and DNA. In extant viruses, RNA replication (RNA to RNA) also requires smaller operating units than those involved in DNA replication (DNA to DNA) and transcription (DNA to RNA).

Viruses do not reproduce. Rather, they are made by cells. Replication, transcription, and reverse transcription (RNA to DNA), protein synthesis, scaffolding, self assembly, and envelope formation are physiological activities, performed by the cell, under the auspices of the viral genome but at the expense of the host cell's other properties, raw materials, and sources of energy. Moreover, extant viruses are quick to mutate, and may even be hypermutable, since their genome is virtually metabolic and up for grabs compared to the tightly regulated cellular genome.[7]

In summary, the fundamental quality of life in one and two dimensions is hijacked metabolism. Dominated by biochemistry, the descent of viruses, genes, and transposons seems to have been shaped by the effects of chance mutation and selection on physiology rather than on heredity.

LIFE IN THREE DIMENSIONS

What then is life like at the three-dimensional level of cells? Here, the life of prokaryotes is instructive. The most obvious difference between viral and prokaryotic life is the size of the prokaryotic compartment. Prokaryotes accumulate components of physiology within an external membrane and replace the metabolism of viral life with growth and division of cells. Moreover, additional hereditary material accumulates within the expanded prokaryotic boundary. As a consequence, heredity in prokaryotes is not restricted to changing what already exists. Prokaryotes have the potential for adding entirely new hereditary elements.

The movement of genes into bacteria was unthinkable prior to the discovery by Frederick Griffith (1877–1941) in the 1920s of the transforming factor, and the suggestion by Eugène and Elisabeth Wollman in the 1930s that bacteria obtained genes from each other. Regrettably, Griffith died in the Blitzkrieg of London, and the Wollmans died in a Nazi concentration camp, but work on transferable bacterial genes regained momentum after the war. Indeed, the rapid spread of the R factor—conveying resistance to antibiotics—across unrelated bacterial lines is now accounted for by the ability of bacteria to take up foreign DNA, and, until recently, the gene-cloning branch of the biotech industry added recombinant DNA exclusively to bacteria.

DNA is artificially introduced into bacteria through several portals and with the aid of many vectors: absorption from the environment, transposition, viral transduction, and parasexual copulation. New DNA may remain separate from the bacterial chromosomes (e.g., as plasmids or episomes), or the DNA may become incorporated into the bacterial chromosomes (e.g., as prophage).

The idea that genes are normally acquired by bacteria was first confirmed by Crawford and Milkman.[8] But prior to the recent spate of sequencing, few researchers suspected just how much of a bacterium's genome was due to DNA uptake. As much as 18% of the genome in the well-known coli bacterium, *Escherichia coli,* it seems, was acquired from related, if alien, sources![9]

Lawrence and Ochman described the dynamics governing genome organization in closely-related prokaryotes and apportioned roles to genome loading through the acquisition of exogenous DNA and to assimilation (amelioration) of transferred DNA-genes, as well as to genome decay through the loss of DNA (deletion).[10] W. Ford Doolittle, citing the current bandwagon of speculation on lateral gene transfer (LGT), drew the obvious conclusion:

> [T]he patterns of prokaryotic gene trees . . . can probably be accounted for by invoking LGT at the frequency inferred by Lawrence and Ochman . . . for *E. coli*'s past 100 million years, operating between

cells not radically different from modern bacteria and archaea over the past 3.5 billion years, which is the age of the earliest cellular fossils.[11]

Others are more sweeping: "[I]n most cases gene trees are likely to be the result of lateral transfer events between the primary domains of life."[12] This is not to say that skepticism is dead. Instead of their being attributed to LGT, hereditary subunits are said to "have arisen by a gene duplication that occurred prior to the last common ancestor of the eubacteria, eukaryotes, and *Sulfolobus.*"[13] But even Carl Woese, the grand master of prokaryotic genomics, acknowledges that the progenitors of his three great domains, Archaea, Bacteria, and Eucarya, might have exchanged genes.[14] Ancestral populations may have comprised something more like loose confederations of genetically open populations or broad circles of diversity rather than instantaneous branching points and unique nodes on phylogenetic trees.

Gene movement goes on among otherwise unrelated organisms, including bacteria and their sister prokaryote, archaeans, via horizontal gene transfer[15] or LGT.[16] The mechanisms of transfer involve transposons, transduction, and transformation. As much as a quarter of the nucleotide sequences in open reading frames (ORFs), or coding sequences, of the hyperthermophilic bacteria (*Aquifex aeolicus* and *Termotoga maritima*) resemble sequences in DNA-genes of archaeal thermophiles more nearly than sequences in bacteria.[17]

Advocates of monophylic evolution—all from one—continue to demand more data from the advocates of polyphylic evolution—one from all—since "vertical ancestry would become an increasingly untenable explanation for most cases [of gene similarity] if further evidence of extensive lateral gene transfer is found between additional diverse Bacteria and Archaea."[18] But percentage-similarity scores (identified by "best-hit" analysis) suggest that at least some genes arrived in Bacteria by horizontal gene transfer from Archaea, rather than by vertical transfer from a deep-branching bacterial ancestor.[19]

In summary, the potential for accumulating hereditary materials, made available by the enclosure of a volume, gives life in three dimensions more opportunities for complexity than it had in one and two dimensions. One would not say that life in one and two dimensions is entirely monotonous since it changes profoundly and constantly, and may even do so rapidly, but life in three dimensions can also take up and add hereditary information from its environment and other life. Even in the absence of sex and generational change, prokaryotes have the potential to evolve through the accretion as well as change in their genomes. But, in the absence of duration—a time dimension—there is only chemistry and physics. The products of replication are not new generations, and changes in the composition of populations is a consequence of statistics and mechanics. Transposons, genes, viruses, and bacteria have lines of descent but no pedigrees, and no death, although they may be killed.

LIFE IN FOUR DIMENSIONS

Life in one-, two-, and three-dimensional worlds thus begins to be recognizable, but it is also different from life in our world. Like the rising and falling of waves at sea, transposons, genes and viruses replicate and multiply, and bacteria grow and divide, but each of us has a beginning and an end. Their life is timeless; ours is calculable.

Identifying time's contribution to life is far less onerous than finding the contributions of the first, second, and third dimensions to life if only because we have ourselves as exemplars. Life in four dimensions consists of capsules of time, each with length, depth, and breadth, but measured by their duration: growth and development which climax in adulthood, maturity and competition which climax in procreation and the passage of generations, and aging and senescence which climax in deterioration and death. All together they constitute a lifetime.

Only eukaryotes seem to have mastered four-dimensional life.[20] They are the only organisms with a soma or body, consisting of one or more somatic-cell lines, which nurture a germ-cell line that moves from generation to generation. Strictly speaking, all adult organisms are eukaryotes and, although many eukaryotes do not reproduce sexually, eukaryotes are the only organisms that do.

It would seem that four dimensions are the minimum required to achieve the morphological complexity of eukaryotes, sexual reproduction, and death. Alternatively, the morphological complexity of eukaryotes, sexual reproduction, and death are the minimum requirements for four dimensional life. In either case, that is where we are at.

Eukaryotic cells are limited by a plasmalemma (a bimolecular phospholipid membrane or envelope studded with and penetrated by protein), have one or more nuclei containing chromosomes bearing genes and other DNA, surface organelles specialized in locomotion, a cytoskeleton capable of deforming cells, membranous organelles such as mitochondria (and chloroplasts in the case of plants and algae), a membranous system (including the endoplasmic reticulum, golgi apparatus, lysosomes, transport vesicles, and sometimes hydrogenosomes and peroxisomes), and an aqueous cytosol bathing everything else in the cell, and containing suspended ribosomal subunits, a host of proteinaceous enzymes, and other ingredients of metabolism.[21] These cellular constituents create a spatial division of labor which, in the case of multicellular eukaryotes, extends to cell types, tissues, organs, and organ systems, the separation of germ and somatic lines in organisms, and the separation of sexes or mating types among organisms. Furthermore, compartmentalization creates a temporal division of labor between generations.

In comparison to life in three dimensions, individuals living in four dimensions are generally large, although one might make an exception regarding size to accommodate prokaryotes living in the vicinity of volcanic vents or in layered stromatolites. Moreover, the amount of DNA in eukaryotes is generally orders of magnitude greater than in prokaryotes. Furthermore, genetic material in eukaryotes is far more stable than the genetic material of viruses and, in contrast to bacteria, extant eukaryotes resist the introduction and accumulation of foreign genes.

Multicellular eukaryotes, such as ourselves, devote vast amounts of energy and resources to accuracy in replication and transcription, especially via enzymatic proofreading of the synthesized nucleic-acid strands. Indeed, the widely accepted theory of nuclear equivalence—that virtually every cell in a multicellular eukaryote's body has an identical genome—is predicated on the belief that replication of DNA in eukaryotes is foolproof.[22]

In addition, stability in the eukaryotic genome is reinforced by resistance to gene transfer. With the exception of LGT, which seems once to have

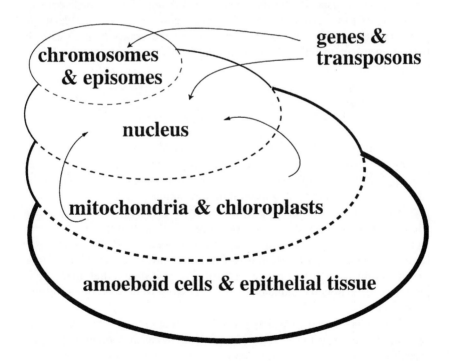

moved genes rampantly from organelles (mitochondria and chloroplasts) to the eukaryotic nucleus,[23] few cases of LGT, or of horizontal gene transfer, are recorded between prokaryotes and eukaryotes,[24] and fewer still among eukaryotes—the movement of *P* elements between *Drosophila* species via a mite intermediate being the only fully documented example.[25] Surprisingly, persistent membranes do not seem to interfere with LGT from chloroplasts obtained through secondary symbiogenesis (see below) and having different numbers of membranes.[26]

Thus, LGT among eukaryotes is generally considered a minor source of evolutionary pressure. Even W. Ford Doolittle adds, as a parenthetical afterthought:

> LGT is not expected to be common among or play the same role in the evolution of multicellular plants and animals [as it does in prokaryotes], especially those with sequestered germ lines, and there simply is no extensive data on LGT in unicellular eukaryotes.[27]

In summary, a great deal about eukaryotes is explained by their existence in a four-dimensional world. Having once achieved four-dimensionality, they were able to expand in the direction of a division of labor and temporal alteration of form leading to sexually reproducing organisms and death. At the same time, eukaryotes seemed to have put the brakes to the relatively simple forms of fusion and fission available to life in one, two, and three dimensions.

AN INTRODUCTION TO DEVOLUTION

The contributions to life played out in its various dimensions were integrated during life's evolution. Life's key features were both mixed and reassorted during its history, both fused and fragmented, and probably many times. I call the processes leading to this integration devolution.

Several roads led me to devolution: my studies of asexual reproduction,[28] speculations on the origins of cancer[29] and normal tissues,[30] and my search for the origins of Cnidaria.[31] Life seemed to create "order from order" rather than "order from disorder." Integration occurred by symmetry breaking as a consequence of fusion and fission rather than, or in addition to, symmetry enhancing by successive rounds of mutation and selection.

Fusion was already a widely accepted concept in the 1990s.[32] Symbiosis was the name given to the state of organisms living in permanent physical contact, and symbiogenesis was the name given to the formation of permanent bonds between originally separate organisms. Lynn Margulis, in particular, had successfully championed the notion of bacteria fusing with ancient, proto-eukaryotic cells and evolving into mitochondria, chloroplasts, and possibly other organelles present in extant eukaryotes.[33] Tom Cavalier-Smith, likewise, had popularized the idea of secondary symbiogenesis, in which a primary eukaryotic cell was taken up by a secondary eukaryotic cell, accounting for the origins of chloroplasts with three membranes in dinoflagellates and euglenoids, and plastids bound by four smooth membranes in sporozoans.[34] Other forms of fusion—commensalism, mutualism, and parasitism— also gave rise to permanent guests within and between organisms and cells. Fission, on the other hand, was rarely discussed, except as a possible source of parasites that sprang from their own hosts—adelphoparasites—or parasites that shared a common ancestor with their host—agastoparasites.[35]

I chose the term *devolution* to identify biological change brought about by fusion and fission and defined it as "The descent (collapse) of qualities upon successors through assimilation into chimeras and parsing out into fragments."[36] Enlarging on this definition, I claimed that

> [v]arieties of living things can be created, it would seem, either by starting from varieties or by acquiring various components in the course of time. The former idea is implied by the concept of life's multiple and separate origins, whereas the latter is implied by the concept of parsing out life into various forms. The two ideas are not mutually exclusive, since multiple origins could conceivably have been followed by mixing and sorting. In any case, the signature properties of present-day life may well have been represented by long-ago-lost elements and "strange bedfellows" in early Earthlife.[37]

Later, I enumerated devolution's difference with Darwinian evolution:

> Instead of ascendant evolution producing differences through intermediates, descendent devolution assimilates difference in chimeras and their fragmented products; in contrast to evolving samenesses stagnating in homology (biological inertia), devolving samenesses accumulate from redundant differences; whereas evolving differences emerge from mutations, devolving differences reassort into widespread samenesses.[38]

Possibly the best support for devolution in the evolutionary past is found in the recently published working drafts of the human genome by the International Human Genome Sequencing Consortium and the Celera entrepreneurs.[39] These drafts reveal numerous sequences of nucleotides that are similar in genes of human beings and those of the laboratory mouse, a fruit fly, a round worm, yeast, plants, archeans, and bacteria. The presence of similar sequences in diverse organisms may be explained as a result of fusion among the genomes of originally separate organisms. Furthermore, differences and gaps in sequences may have arisen by the fission of genomes and the loss of sequences.[40]

Fusion and fission may seem rare in contemporary organisms but they are hardly unknown in modern cells. Fusion occurs in fertilization, during which both spermatozoon and egg leave their stamp on the zygote; in syncytial trophoblast formation and implantation of the mammalian blastocyst, and in the formation of the mammalian placenta; in striated muscle formation by myoblasts in vertebrates; in conjugation among ciliates; in plasmodium formation of the true slim mold; and during infection by a variety of intracellular parasites. Fusion is also used in the production of tools for biological research, not only myeloma cells producing monoclonal antibodies, but as devices for testing dominance, recessiveness, and complementation among genes in different cell lines. Furthermore, cell fusion is one of the ways nuclear/cytoplasmic chimeras are formed for cloning.

Fission is sometimes displayed during metamorphosis, for example, in the starfish, *Luidia sarsi,* where the larva fragments into an epithelial ghost and a juvenile. Cytoplasmic fission is seen during the final differentiation of spermatozoa, when large amounts of cellular cortex—the stiff outer part of cells—and cytoplasm—the more fluid cellular contents—are discarded in residual bodies. Nuclear fission is commonly observed as chromosomal diminution during cleavage in nematodes, copepods, mites, and some insects—beetles, flies, butterflies, grasshoppers, and gall midges. In addition, fused cells *in vitro* undergoing cytokinesis throw off bits of chromatin and even whole chromosomes.

Fusion and fission represent transverse and asymmetrical biological change as opposed to the vertical and linear biological changes associated with sexual reproduction and Darwinian evolution. Fusion should be suspected wherever one discovers a mixture of genealogically unrelated hereditary material, whether nuclear, cytoplasmic, or cortical. New genes may appear against a background of old-genes due to transduction, LGT, horizontal gene transfer, and hybridization, coupled to ameliorative devices—such as autopolyploidization, endoreduplication, and reticulation—capable of rebalancing genomes or reducing the impact of strange genes on genomes.[41] Hybridization, especially xenohybridization, or hybridization among broadly unrelated organisms, may also result in the mixing of unrelated cytoplasmic or cortical units of inheritance. Fission, on the other hand, should be suspected wherever one detects gaps or defects in hereditary material, whether nuclear, cytoplasmic, or cortical. At bottom, fusion and fission should be suspected wherever canonical evolution is at pain to explain biological change.

THE DEVOLUTION OF EUCARYA

Devolution seems to have played several roles in the early evolution of eukaryotes. It seems to have provided eukaryotes with several adaptive advantages for life in four dimensions. As a result, eukaryotes were able to expand in different directions than prokaryotes and avoid competition with them in their three-dimensional space.

Among extant species, a superficial fusion occurs in lichens as a result of fortuitous encounters between fungi and either algae or cyanobacteria. These strange bedfellows may enjoy a mutualistic relationships, providing benefits to both partners, or a master/slave relationship of dubious value to the algae.

Other mutualistic relationships are more profound. In endosymbiotic relationships, algae and bacteria live within host cells, although they do not share their genomes. Aphids transmit their endosymbiotic bacteria through the egg's cytoplasm, albeit not through its nucleus, but, more generally, endosymbionts are not transmitted via sex cells. The host must acquire its endosymbiotic partner afresh in every generation.

> [T]he deep-sea worm *Riftia,* although it lacks a mouth as an adult, has a planktonic larva with a mouth, and acquires sulphur-metabolizing bacteria by swallowing them. The flatworm, *Convoluta* also has a mouth when young and swallows its symbiotic algae. Mycorrhizae in the soil must find plant roots, as must the nitrogen-fixing bacterium *Rhizobium.*[42]

In green hydra, many marine cnidarians (especially corals and anemones), other marine invertebrates, and ciliates, symbiotic algae retain cell walls. They are acquired by offspring from the detritus of parents (horizontal inheritance) or nonparents (diagonal inheritance).

In the long term, fusion may have accounted for the larger size of eukaryotes compared to prokaryotes and the greater amount of genetic material in eukaryotic cells compared to prokaryotic cells. Fusion may have occurred originally between representatives of the Bacteria (eubacteria) and Archaea (archebacteria), since eukaryotic genes encoding enzymes for fermentation are similar to those of Bacteria, while eukaryotic genes encoding enzymes for DNA replication and protein synthesis are similar to those of Archaea.[43]

Fusion may also account for the multiple compartments present in eukaryotic cells. The nucleus and cytosol represent the most conspicuous compartments, but organelles, membranous components, and the fibrous
cytoskeleton may represent compartments possibly acquired by fusion.

Fission, on the other hand, could have been adaptive for removing excess
material as well as smoothing out sticking points. For example, fission might
have removed genes doubled by fusion, especially genes that would have
caused a cell to crash like a computer were it to have two start-up programs
in its nucleus.

THE NUCLEUS

The nucleus is the most obvious candidate for a compartment created by
fusion. Today, it is the compartment most clearly associated with hereditary
stability, but it might have formed as a consequence of multiple prokaryotes
fusing within yet another cell. In this case, wrapping the internalized prokaryotes in a single envelope might have reduced the possibility of fission and
destabilization.

Once ensconced in a proto-nucleus, the prokaryotes's chromosomes might
have continued replicating, resulting in *polyploidization*—the multiplication
of chromosomes within a cell.[44] Fission would not then be destabilizing if at
least one representative of each chromosome were to enter every fragment of
the divided cell. Such a polyploid proto-nucleus might resemble the nucleus
of extant dinoflagellates (e.g., *Dissodinium,* Peridiniaceae) which have 5 to
10 times the usual amount of DNA found in eukaryotes and several hundred
chromosomes.[45]

The proto-nucleus might have formed a double-membraned nuclear envelope surrounding its chromosomes in any of several ways. The inner membrane of the nuclear envelope may have formed from the combined membranes
of fused prokaryotes; the outer membrane may have arisen from an invagi-
nation of the host-cell's membrane; both membranes may have evolved from
products of encystment, much the way cysts are formed by extant *Bacillus
subtilis.* In any case, an incipient nuclear envelope would have incorporated
the proto-chromosomes' attachment sites, or sites of nuclear-replication and
termination.[46]

Before the proto-nucleus could divide equally, the split terminus sites
that invaginate during binary fission of prokaryotes would have to have fused
and aligned themselves. Fusing these sites into a coherent and polarized
chromosomal attachment-site would have allowed the replicated chromosomes
to move equally and oppositely to the cell's poles and subsequently to the
cleaved cells. Cell division would resemble the closed mitosis of zooflagellates,

or Zoomastigina (so-called pleuromitoses found in trichomonads and hypermastigotes), where chromosomes attached to the nuclear envelope move simultaneously away from each other in two groups as the nucleus elongates.

Chromosomes in the proto-nucleus would have become members of an exclusive "club," stabilized by attachment sites on the inner nuclear membrane and secured against the encroachment of additional chromosomes by the outer nuclear membrane. Additional prokaryotes fusing with an incipient eukaryotic cell would be unable to add their chromosomes to those of the proto-nucleus, because its attachment-site would be inaccessible. Were the progenitors of the golgi apparatus and endoplasmic reticulum to have fused with proto-eukaryotic cells early, their chromosomes might have been incorporated in the proto-nucleus, while the progenitors of mitochondria and chloroplasts arriving later could only manage to transfer genes from their own chromosomes to the proto-nucleus.

At some point, the simple DNA helices of prokaryotic chromosomes inside the proto-nucleus might have fused with each other, giving rise to proto-eukaryotic chromosomes with massively more DNA and multiple origins of replication than typically found in prokaryotes. The transformation would have reduced the number of chromosomal attachment sites, facilitated chromosomal movement to nuclear poles during mitotic division, and paved the way for open mitosis. The transformation would also have created gene clusters, such as those found among *HOX* genes, stabilizing working relationships. The well-known prokaryotic operon would have been replaced by more sensitive single-gene promoters. The proto-eukaryotic chromosomes would have to have been linearized and telomeres added at their ends, thereby preventing adhesion of chromosomes to each other, and, finally, histones, nuclear proteins, and RNA would have to have been added to complete eukaryotic chromosomes.

ORGANELLES

Lynn Margulis's serial endosymbiotic theory (SET) broadly established current understanding of organelle-origins.[47] According to SET, bacteria living permanently as intracellular guests in early eukaryotic cells coevolved harmoniously with their hosts into mitochondria and chloroplasts.[5] This relationship of mitochondria and chloroplasts to eukaryotic cells would have to be the most successful relationship ever consummated through symbiogenesis. Not only did the purple endosymbiotic bacteria enhance the further evolution of eukaryotes but, as organelles, they became the most widespread and successful bacteria on Earth! The bluegreen bacteria that became chloroplasts come in second and far ahead of any other bacterium.

Historically, genetic approaches to inheritance by Ruth Sager and Nicholas Gillham left little doubt about the presence of genes in chloroplasts, and Boris Ephrussi (1901–1979) and coworkers demonstrated mitochondrial heredity through their analysis of the *petite* mutations in yeast. Recently, the complete genomic sequencing of *Rickettsia prowazekii*'s DNA has capped speculation that the rickettsial subdivision of purple bacteria is virtually a sibling ("sister") group of mitochondria.[48]

Ri. prowazekii's is a parasite, and, like other parasites, it has adapted to its life-style by reducing and tailoring its genome.[49] The 834 complete open reading frames (ORFs), or protein-encoding genes, of *Ri. prowazekii,* represent scarcely 20% of the ORFs found in the free-living purple bacterium, *E. coli.* Nevertheless, *Ri. prowazekii*'s ORFs account for ten times more genes than those in *Reclinomonas americana,* whose genome is the most mitochondrial-like of presently-sequenced bacteria.[50]

Mitochondrial DNA (mtDNA) and chloroplast DNA (cpDNA) present within these organelles would seem drastically "down-sized." A great deal of the missing DNA seems to have moved from mitochondrial and chloroplast chromosomes[51] to the eukaryotic nucleus and probably did so in more than one transport.[52] The presence of mitochondrial and chloroplast genes within the eukaryotic nucleus might seem like a trick played by eukaryotes on their guests for guaranteeing their continued presence—preventing their escape back into the environment—but other, less teleological, explanations are also available.

Ordinarily, one thinks of mitochondria and chloroplasts as trading partners with the rest of the eukaryotic cell. Mitochondria produce utilizable energy in the form of ATP; chloroplasts produce utilizable building blocks in the form of phosphoglyceraldehyde; and both acquire raw materials and nucleotides from the eukaryotic cytoplasm. But these exchanges might have been bonuses accompanying the capture of bacteria by host cells and the usurpation of their genes.

Eukaryotic cells evolved at a time of increasing concentrations of oxygen in the atmosphere, and oxygen is extremely cytotoxic to eukaryotic cells generally. Mitochondria and chloroplasts fit into eukaryotic metabolism as ways of handling oxygen. The hemes utilized by mitochondria and chloroplasts for handling oxygen would have been extremely attractive additions to the eukaryotic genome, and the lateral transfer of genes involved in their synthesis would have offered the eukaryotic cell an opportunity to control heme synthesis closely. But "There is no such thing as a free lunch."

Eukaryotic cells also have problems handling hemes.[53] Indeed, some eukaryotes living in the reduced-oxygen environment of a parasitized cell seem to have dealt with the burden of hemes by eliminating mitochondria, becoming the amitochondrial protozoa known anachronistically as Archaezoa.[54]

Most eukaryotic cells have worked out complex ways of coping with their problematic guests. Mitochondria play a role in programmed apoptosis and cell-death in tumor suppression, and in aging. "[S]ignalling from the mitochondria may [even] regulate life span in at least two organisms, *C. elegans* and yeast."[55] Mitochondria also play a role in cholesterol metabolism—regulating the plasticity of the eukaryotic plasmalemma—and in the production of steroid hormones, which are related to endocrine perturbations of aging, such as the reduced insulin levels in dwarf mice exhibiting delayed aging. Early eukaryotes, it would seem, thrived in part because they co-opted their endosymbionts' genes for managing oxygen. Extant eukaryotes, it would seem, thrive in part because some of these same genes operate in regulating cell death.

THE CYTOPLASM: PLASMAGENES

Cytoplasm is no longer cytoplasm. Once the eukaryotic cell's second great compartment, outside the nucleus, the cytoplasm is now several separate compartments: a fibrous endoskeleton, membranous systems, organelles, and a cytosol. Each of these may have originated as a consequence of one or more fusions and evolved as a function of one or more fissions. Many lines of evidence suggest that the cytoplasm, or its components, are responsible for their own heredity, but the idea of cytoplasmic inheritance is not widely accepted and has also generated fierce opposition.

Cytoplasmic units of inheritance have generally been subsumed under the generic term, *plasmagenes*.[56] Jan Sapp has described the history of the plasmagene concept in the twentieth century.[57] It is a history of internecine warfare between critics of plasmagenes, who believed in a "nuclear monopoly" (*Kernmonopol*) over heredity, and advocates of plasmagenes who defend cytoplasmic inheritance but cannot agree on what plasmagenes are in the first place.

The history of cytoplasmic inheritance begins in the late 1930s and early 1940s when viruses were coming into their own as conveyers of heredity. The inspiration for viral inheritance came first from Carl Lindegren (1896–1986) and Gertrude Lindegren (d. 1977), and soon thereafter from Max Delbrück's (1906–1981) and Salvador Luria's (1912–1991) "phage school." In 1944, Oswald Avery (1877–1955) and associates identified Frederick Griffith's transforming factor as deoxyribonucleic acid (DNA) and launched the search for the structural basis of hereditary material. James Watson and Francis Crick would solve this mystery for DNA, but their work ironically drove the analysis of hereditary materials away from plasmagenes and back to the nucleus.

Two lines of evidence initially supported some degree of cytoplasmic inheritance independent of the nucleus. First, by finding the right environmental conditions (nutrition, light, heat), cells could be made to outstrip the growth of organelles, such as chloroplasts in *Euglena* and of *Kappa* in *Paramecium,* indicating that cells had more than one mechanism of information storage and retrieval. Second, René Dubos (1901–1982) and others, using antibiotics such as streptomycin, could rid an algal cell such as *Euglena* of its chloroplast, suggesting that cells acted "as a symbiotic assembly of several independent genetic organelles which have become thoroughly integrated."[58]

Another form of nonDarwinian inheritance—in which the viruses of bacteria (bacteriophage) transport genes—was first demonstrated by Harriette Taylor (1918–1968), followed by Andre Lwoff (1902–1994),[59] and named transduction by Joshua Lederberg (b. 1925),[60] who also coined *plasmid* for any extrachromosomal conveyer of heredity. However, the discovery of lysogeny—the incorporation of a bacteriophage's genes into bacterial chromosomes as prophage—clouded the issue of viruses as cytoplasmic genes.[61]

Lederberg and Cyril Dean Darlington (1903–1981)

> began to develop a notion of "infective" heredity, claiming that viruses themselves were far more intimately and permanently associated with genetic material of their host cells than had ever been imagined. . . . [Lederberg and Darlington even] attempted to reconcile the attitudes that plasmagenes were symbiotic organisms and that they comprised part of the genetic constitution of the complex organism, playing important roles in development and somatic differentiation.[62]

At the time, a "purely gene-centered view might suffice for virus evolution but not for cell evolution."[63] Darlington was writing about plasmagenes made outside the nucleus and transmitted through eggs; Sewall Wright conceded the possibility of gene-initiated plasmagenes self-duplicating in the cytoplasm; and Sol Spiegelman (1914–1983) suggested that some plasmagenes were made in the nucleus and moved to the cytoplasm where they became self-reproducing agents of protein synthesis.

Spiegelman's plasmagenes should be considered antecedents to messenger RNAs, but they did not turn out to be self-replicating cytoplasmic conveyors of heredity. The issue upon which the fate of plasmagenes rose and fell was not nuclear control of protein synthesis but nonnuclear control of heredity. Did plasmagenes with reproducible biological consequence move between organisms in a horizontal direction?

Ultimately, the issue of plasmagenes was brought to a head over cortical inheritance—the nonnuclear transfer through fusion and fission of heritable patterns of cilia—specifically the "Siamese-twin" or double-bodied cells of *Paramecium.*[64]

Doubled-bodiness was inherited through hundreds of generations. Genetic studies completely rule out the possibility of nuclear gene control. Furthermore, because mitochondrial inheritance patterns of paramecia also can be manipulated by researchers, mitochondrial DNA control was excluded as the explanation for cytoplasmic inheritance of the doublet form. Other morphological mutants of paramecia ("swimmer," "snaky," etc.) also proved to be cytoplasmically—but not mitochondrially—inherited. Cortical inheritance is not under nuclear gene control.[65]

The idea of cortical inheritance was nurtured chiefly by Tracy Sonnonborn (1905–1981), but his work was clouded by association with Lamarckian inheritance.[66] In the end, the plasmagene-melodrama failed to climax but reached a denouement when Sonnonborn tied all the definitions of plasmagenes together in a Gordian knot that is yet to be untied.

THE DEVOLUTION OF SEX

Sex is fundamentally a balancing act between addition and subtraction of hereditary material. Addition is brought about by fusion, or fertilization, and subtraction is brought about by fission, or meiosis, making sex the quintessence of devolution and its evolution a paragon of devolutionary history. But sex is not a biological reminiscence, or vestige, of life in the primordial world. Rather, fertilization and meiosis are highly refined forms of fusion and fission, and sex's persistence and pervasiveness is a consequence of a variety of sex's adaptive advantages. Fusion and fission are remarkably pliable features of life, and sex's near-universality is a glaring confirmation of devolution's creative potential.

MEIOSIS

Meiosis occurs only in cells containing a double set of nuclear chromosomes—one set contributed by each of two parents at fertilization. The cells are diploid, since, with the exception of sex-determining chromosomes, all the chromosomes in each set are similar to, or homologous with, chromosomes in the other set.

Meiosis consists of one round of DNA synthesis, or replication, and two divisions. In animals, the single DNA synthesis occurs prior to the differentiation of sex cells. As a result of the synthesis, the cell's DNA content doubles. Later, pairs of homologous chromosomes emerge in the cell's nucleus as duplicated, or dyadic, chromosomes. Later still, the homologous chromosomes pair and fuse, forming tetradic chromosomes, and reducing the number of chromosomes per cell by half—from the original diploid number of homologous chromosomes to the haploid number of chromosomes in a single set.

Three different processes occur while the homologous chromosomes are paired. First, junctions—synaptonemal complexes—are formed between the replicated DNA of homologous chromosomes. The chromosomes become tenaciously bound, gene for gene, one to one. This configuration offers the meiotic cell's chromosomes a unique opportunity, not available to somatic cells' chromosomes, to correct double-stranded errors in replicated DNA. When the nuclear machinery detects double-stranded errors—by their pattern of DNA-methylation—a repair mechanism kicks in, and the sequences are replaced with correct sequences made by copying the homologous chromosome. Consequently, a repaired chromosome, rather than a damaged one is passed to the products of meiotic division and ultimately to sex cells.

Second, parts of homologous chromosomes are exchanged. Genes are swapped, and the homologous chromosomes are henceforth mixtures of the genes originally contributed by each parent.

Third, the homologous chromosomes are joined by pairs of crossed struts—chiasmata—which stiffen chromosomes and aid in orienting the members of each homologous pair in opposite direction on the division spindle. As a result, the first meiotic division separates homologous chromosomes, reducing the tetrad chromosomes to dyad chromosomes. The amount of nuclear-DNA per cell is also reduced by half. The second meiotic division then resolves the duplicated chromosomes into their unit members—monad chromosomes—and reduces the nuclear-DNA content again by half. Possibly nowhere else in the biological world is fission carried out with as great precision.

THE DIFFERENTIATION OF SEX CELLS

The familiar sex cells of animals—eggs and spermatozoa—are only two examples of *gametes*, or the ultimate products of meiosis capable of fusion. Gametes of different kinds occur throughout the Eucarya: isogametes, homogametes, heterogametes, and differentiated normal cells capable of conjugating (in ciliates and fungi). What is more, eggs are sometimes capable of undergoing parthenogenesis (virgin birth) as a result of some form of nuclear fusion without cellular fusion.[67]

The germ-line cells that differentiate as eggs or sperm are generally localized in adult organisms in gonads—eggs in the ovary and spermatozoa in the testis—or female and male gonophors. An egg is a sessile sex cell, sometimes chock-full of nutrients, such as the phospholipoglycoproteins comprising yolk, while a spermatozoon is a sex cell pared down to a nucleus mounted on a propeller. In addition, eggs and spermatozoa exhibit two physiological blocks: a block to interspecific fertilization, or hybridization between the egg and sperm of different species, and a block to multiple fertilizations or polyspermy. The interspecific block is dedicated to species-specificity, and is thrown primarily by the egg's extracellular membrane, the vitelline envelope—called the zona pellucida in mammals. The block works in different ways: Alien sperm fail to adhere to the envelope adequately; they do not respond appropriately to cues given by the envelope or an external jelly; sperm are unable to perforate the envelope. Still, the block to foreign sperm is not air tight. Human spermatozoa, for example, readily perforate the zona pellucida of gibbon eggs, and hamster sperm attach to guinea pig, mouse, and rat zonas, albeit without perforating them.

The block to polyspermy is also thrown in different ways. Ever since the early 1900s, when double and triple fertilizations in sea urchins were found to be deleterious to development, embryologists have assumed that multiple fusions between spermatozoa and an egg were unhealthy. In fact, the egg's nucleus must engage only one spermatozoon's nucleus, but the egg exerts discretion for choosing the fertilizing nucleus. Several spermatozoa generally fuse with large, yolky eggs—one spermatozoon providing the paternal nucleus, the others providing raw materials or "fuel for the fire" of development. In these eggs, the block to multiple fertilizations is thrown by the mitotic spindle surrounding the maternal nucleus which embraces only one paternal nucleus. In relatively small eggs, the block to polyspermy is generally thrown by the egg's vitelline envelope which hardens following perforation by the first spermatozoon.[68] In sea urchins, the egg's plasmalemma may throw an early block as a consequence of its depolarization. The sperm receptors in the mammalian zona pellucida also change their configuration, and large numbers of adhering spermatozoa are shed following penetration by the fertilizing spermatozoon.[69]

FERTILIZATION

Fertilization works counter to meiosis. Each parental sex cell contributes one set of homologous chromosomes, raising the number of chromosomes in the fertilized egg, or zygote, to the diploid number and the content of nuclear-DNA to two times that of sex cells.

Within the zygote, both the spermatozoon's and the egg's nucleus are reconstituted and transformed into male and female pronuclei. Their chromosomes are prepared for cleavage and undergo a round of DNA synthesis. Contrary to popu-lar mythology, the male and female pronuclei do not fuse in human beings or animals in general.[70] Pronuclei may interdigitate profoundly and their envelopes break down, but their chromosomes mingle for the first time on the division plane—the metaphase plate—of the first cleavage division.[71]

Synchronizing the pronuclei for division is probably the most profound task assigned to fertilization, and its failure results in botched development. In human beings, failures of synchronization may result in the formation of hydatidiform moles, characterized by swelling and cystic degeneration of the embryonic portion of the early placenta. True or complete hydatidiform moles are exclusively of male origin, presumably resulting from the expulsion of the egg's nucleus, and predisposed to malignant transformation. Partial hyda-tidiform moles appear normal in some portions of the placenta and may support the development of a malformed fetus. Their cells have half-again more DNA and chromosomes than the cells of normal embryos.

MITOSIS

An important exception to sex's ecumenicity occurs in the Phylum Acti-nopoda (former Radiolaria). "[S]exual processes . . . have never been observed" in the class Polycystina.[72] These floating, siliceous organisms which consti-tute a major source of radiolarian ooze are highly polyploid, having as many as 2000 chromosomes in their nuclei. They undergo multiple nuclear divi-sions followed by multiple cytoplasmic fissions, producing "swarmers" (mastigotes with two flagella or undulipodia).

Polycystina's sibling class, Phaeodaria, is also highly polyploid, but its chromosomes emerge at the nuclear envelope prior to division as dense, so-called "axial complexes," resembling meiotic chromosomes prior to the for-mation of synaptonemal complexes (see above).[73] Phaeodarians would seem to be poised at the threshold of meiosis but thwarted by excessive polyploidy from pairing homologous chromosomes and undergoing full-fledged meiosis. Alternatively, meiosis may have once existed in the class only to be lost as cells became excessively polyploid.

If polyploidy and swarmer formation represent the primitive condition of eukaryotes, one can imagine how sex might have devolved. Originally, poly-ploid nuclei could have divided repeatedly until nuclear contents reached a minimum. At that point, the cell applied the breaks and fragmented into swarmers. This process is reduced in extant eukaryans to the two meiotic divisions of diploid cells and the production of haploid cells with a single set of chromosomes. The cells differentiate into spermatozoa or into eggs and

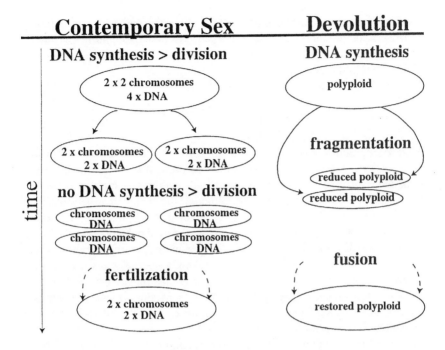

polar bodies. The proto-eukaryotic cells with reduced ploidy were presumably capable of fusion, restoring polyploidy, while extant eggs and spermatozoa undergo fertilization, restoring diploidy.

To whatever degree this scenario is correct, rudimentary meiosis and fertilization would already be exhibited by primitive eukaryotes. The sex cycle would then be an extension of serial fission and fusion, and Darwinian evolution would have been an accident waiting to happen. Furthermore, the primitive eukaryotes would not have been heterotrophic, or one of the potential partners to fusion would have become a meal instead of a mate.

This same scenario for the origin of sex from the hypothetical, eukaryotic ancestor suggests how mitosis might have been derived from meiosis. All that is required to derive mitosis is reducing meiosis from two divisions per act of DNA synthesis (two for one) to one division per act of DNA synthesis (one for one). Such a reduction might have evolved from the introduction of replication checkpoints which ensure that DNA is replicated before every cell division.[74] Mitosis would occur when all chromosomes have replicated completely and correctly, which, in the case of cells with pairs of homologous chromosomes, would allow the cell to retain diploidy, and, in the case of cells with single sets of chromosomes, would allow the cell to retain haploidy. Mitosis, in other words, may have originated as an *felix culpa* that promoted fission when all chromosomes in a cell were replicated, whether the cell was haploid, diploid, or polyploid.

THE DEVOLUTION OF METAZOA

Metazoa, or Eumetazoa, typically include all multicellular animals other than sponges, or Parazoa (= Porifera), and an assortment of "very small animals with few cell types."[75] Since the eighteenth century, metazoans have been separated into several main groups, although the boundaries between these groups have shifted. In 1809 Lamarck erected the Radiata, or radiarians, containing soft polyps, gelatinous medusas, and hard echinoderms.[76] In 1812, Cuvier corrupted the Radiata (*rayonnés*), expanding it into his ragbag fourth *embranchement*, or Class of zoophytes, including internal parasites, a miscellaneous assortment of aquatic Infusoria, and the remainder of Lamarck's invertebrates not belonging to the mollusks (= Mollusca), and articulates (= Arthropoda plus segmented animals and worms).[77] The Bilateria was later constructed by Berthold Hatschek (1854–1941) to contain every metazoan, or multicellular animal phylum except those belonging to the Protozoa, Porifera, and Lamarck's Radiata.

Later, in the nineteenth century, under the influence of Haeckel, radiates and bilaterians were reclassified according to the number of germ layers present in their gastrulas—radiates equaled diploblastic animals with gastrulas of two germ layers, and bilaterians equaled triploblastic animals with gastrulas of three germ layers. Recently, a prevailing prejudice against Haeckelian reminiscences has driven taxonomy back to Radiata and Bilateria, although "diploblastic" and "triploblastic" survive as "didermic" and "tridermic."

Devolution suggests that both these groups of metazoans emerged by the fusion of two or more types of cells or tissues. The fission and parsing out, or redistribution, of characteristics would then have given rise to all animal tissues and cell types in each group.

THE RADIATA

Radiates are chiefly comprised of living surfaces. They are often said to have not advanced to an organ-level of organization inasmuch as they virtually lack anything resembling indigenous organs, but their surface layers constitute melting pot organs and possibly colonized organs.[78] As a consequence, radiates are able to dispense with excess cells and generate replacement cells. The legendary immortality of some radiates would seem entirely attributable to their ability to regulate and renew their cell populations in this way.

The present Radiata consists of Cnidaria and two other phyla, Ctenophora, and Placozoa, of which only the placozoan *Tricoplax adhaerens*—representing the entire phylum—is truly radially symmetrical.[79] Ctenophores (the bioluminescent sea combs and sea walnuts) and many anthozoans are biradially symmetrical, having two planes of symmetry but no right/left sides. The appearance of radial symmetry in cnidarians is often only skin-deep, concealing an internal biradial or bilateral symmetry. Anemones with one siphonoglyph—a groove at one end of their gullet—have both right and left sides as well as dorsal/ventral and anterior/posterior planes. Despite the questionable appropriateness of their name, the radiates share sufficiently similar sequences in their 18S rDNA[80] and *HOX* genes[81] to place them on the same branch of the metazoan tree. A sibling (or "sister") branch contains all the bilaterally symmetrical, tridermic (triploblastic) metazoans.

Cnidarians and ctenophores resemble a thermos bottle, having a continuous inner and outer layer with a cellular vacuum between. The layers consist of supportive epithelial cells, comprising the epidermis, or ectoderm, and gastrodermis, or endoderm. Between the two layers is a mesoglea which may be a thin, acellular backing, a gelatinous bell-shaped body, or a thick, leathery framework. Another self-renewing and differentiating population of amoeboid cells is found in pockets between the supportive epithelial cells, near their bases. All non-epithelial cells are produced by amoeboid cells—in Cnidaria these include cnidocytes, nerves, sensory, gland, and sex cells. Other members of the Radiata lack cnidocytes, and Placozoa lacks nerves as well.

Developmentally, both epithelial cells and amoeboid cells segregate quickly from embryonic germ layers, while evolutionarily, they may have totally different sources. According to my

> evolutionary scenario for the "synthetic" origins of cnidarians . . . [epithelial and amoeboid cells arose from] two organisms on a co-evolutionary collision course. One of these hypothetical organisms [wa]s a member of the phylum Placozoa, an epithelial organism, resembling extant *Tricoplax,* a small flexible, globe-like organism consisting of a covering of conjoined cells (an epithelium) and a fluid-filled cavity having neither an entry nor exit pore. The other hypothetical ancestor [wa]s a protistan, already equipped with cnidocysts. It may [have] resemble[d] extant predatory dinoflagellates or a "sporozoan" capable of entering the placozoa's cells via a tube of its own making.[82]

Several other extant organisms can be nominated for the post of primitive epithelial-animal. For example, protobranch bivalves and aplacophorans form a primitive, epithelial test envelope, and insects form their cellular blastoderm by the superficial infolding of an egg's surface.[83] But these animals are representatives of the Bilateria, generally considered advanced metazoans. Furthermore, these epithelia are adapted to embryonic or larval life and are, therefore, more likely to be derived—coenogenic—structures than ancient—palingenic—structures. Presently, therefore, I return to *Tricoplax* as my nominee for an extant representative of an ancestral epithelial-animal.

My nominee for an extant representative of a primitive amoeba-like cell is the *Henneguya* sp, a member of the Myxozoa (Myxosporea and Actinosporea).[84] *Henneguya* is an obligate parasite, primarily of oligochaete worms and marine fish. *Henneguya* is highly compromised by reduction and secondary loss in accordance with the dictates of its parasitic lifestyle, but it still makes its way around hosts and develops only after choosing a site in which it can multiply and differentiate.

Myxozoans are ordinarily considered unicellular or oligonuclear (oligocellular) protozoans (protoctistans), but the analysis of their 18S (16S-like) rDNA suggests that they are more closely related to multicellular animals, even if the precise terms of this relationship are uncertain. Their 18S rDNA suggests a close sibling relationship with either bilateral (triploblastic) animals[85] or "robust evidence in support of the inclusion of the myxozoans within the phylum Cnidaria."[86] Myxozoan 18S rDNA is especially similar to that of the parasitic cnidarian *Polypodium hydriforme*—the infamous despoiler of sturgeon eggs. If this turns out to be the case, the parasitic myxozoans would seem to have evolved from a parasitic multicellular organism. The parasitic life style of myxozoans might then have been inherited along with its 18S rDNA.

The origin of myxozoans from a cnidarian ancestor and their return as parasites is not entirely novel and may even represent a common phenomenon in the origin of parasites. Adelphoparasites of plants, fungi, and algae[87] seem to originate from their own hosts, while many insects develop as parasitoids on related species—from the agastoparasites of bees and dulotic ants, to cannibalizing aphelinid wasps.[88]

Organisms capitalize on relationships in various ways, and what is a master-slave relationship from one point of view may be a slave-master relationship from another point of view. A parasite might seem to have the upper hand over its host, but a host that spawns its own parasite acquires a vector for its genome, and the possibility of spreading it to otherwise inaccessible venues. The parasite, on the other hand, rather than having merely another victim, gets a safe haven when infecting its organism-of-origin where it can expect to obtain most of its needs while freely mutating and acquiring new genes for testing elsewhere.

A similar argument can be made for dicyemids, or mesozoans—typically parasites of the renal sacs of squid and octopus. Sequences of *Dicyema orientale*'s 18S-rDNA, and its Hox-gene, *DoxC* "argue that dicyemids are members of the Lophotrochozoa and are related to phyla such as platyhelminths, molluscs [*sic*], nemerteans, brachiopods and annelids."[89] Because the sequence-similarities extend to multiple, unrelated genes, they are unlikely to have resulted from horizontal gene transfer.[90] Rather, the similarities suggest "that dicyemids are secondarily simplified from higher protostome animals" which they have "come back to haunt" as parasites.[91]

Assuming that parasites can arise by fission, and return to their host-of-origin, it would seem a small but portentous step for the "autoparasite/host" to become permanently fused. The autoparasite would then be a tissue within the erstwhile host. One can imagine that lateral gene transfer might account for integrating the genomes of autoparasite-cum-tissue with the host, and whatever tension that existed between disparate genetic components would be worked out by competition or assimilation. Resolving this tension would be the work of sympatric tissue-evolution within the new organism.

In the Radiata, the parsing out and redistributing of epithelial and amoeboid traits does not seem to have gone very far. The epithelial and amoeboid cell types have remained anatomically separate, for the most part, although their functional activities would seem admirably integrated. Indeed, among cnidarians, the experimental removal of amoeboid cells deprives the "epithelial-animal" of cnidocysts, nerve, gland, and sex cells, as expected, but it also deprives it of behavior and alters some features of morphological regulation, namely, the number of tentacles.[92] Still, some mixing seems to have occurred in the hat-like epitheliomuscular cells which possess a basal muscular "brim" and an apical epithelial "crown." Devolution suggests that more fusion and fission accounts for the greater assortment of tissue components found in the Bilateria.

The Bilateria

The presence of internal organs, removed from any convenient exit port, is the chief characteristic of the Bilateria. In addition to the layered melting pot organs residing on surfaces, the bilateria have a host of internal indigenous organs as well as colonized blood, lymphatic, and sex organs. Ironically, the evolution of these new organs introduced a host of disastrous diseases. Bilaterians did not invent death, inasmuch as death occurs in embryos before they reach the stage of bilaterian complexity, but by internalizing organs, bilaterian evolution created most of the familiar forms of death in adults.

In the bilaterians, the parsing out and redistributing of epithelial-like and amoeba-like traits seems to have gone about as far as they can go. Sorting out epithelial-like and amoeba-like traits is especially the job of the embryonic germ layers and cell lines, but it goes on for a lifetime in stem cells. There is no simple formula, and cells that produce mesoderm in indirectly developing species form ectodermal and endodermal in direct-developing species.[93] Probably no tissue in extant complex animals is purely epithelial-like or amoeba-like, and even those leaning heavily one way or the other exhibit some characteristics derived by competition. Nevertheless, epithelial-like cells form indigenous organs and parts of melting-pot organs, while amoeba-like cells provide the "exotic cells" of melting-pot and colonized organs (see Chapter 3).

The chief characteristics of vertebrate epithelia, muscle, and nerve would seem predominantly epithelial-like rather than amoeba-like. Epithelia derived from endoderm are the most conservative, exhibiting few amoeba-like characteristics and forming single layered tissue, or simple epithelia. Epithelia derived from ectoderm tend to pile up, or stratify amoeboid-fashion, as in the epidermis, and ectoderm also gives rise to the neural crest and nervous tissue of the central nervous system, both of which produce remarkably nomadic cells or cell processes. Epithelia derived from mesoderm are the most amoeba-like at times, going through one or more rounds of de-epithelialization and re-epithelialization.

Muscle forms from deepithelialized and reepithelialized cells. In the course of reepithelialization, pre-skeletal muscle myocytes fuse, although cellular integrity is retained by the other types of muscle cells. All muscle cells and fibers resemble epithelium by way of their surrounding basement membrane, or peripheral membrane, and cardiac muscle exhibits junctional complexes and desmosomes at intercalated disks, resembling structures found among epithelial cells.

Nervous tissue is remarkably plastic. Neurons of the central nervous system begin their migration from a neural epithelium in the embryo and may send out processes 3 meters long (in elephants and whales). The central nervous system's glial cells "hang back" but also exhibit some amoeba-like characteristics (forming "jelly-roll" myelin sheaths) as well as epithelial-like characteristics (the ependyma). But the neural crest gives rise to cells with the greatest range of plasticity for epithelial-derived cells, including epithelial-like neurosecretory cells (adrenal medulla, intestinal glands), neurons of the peripheral nervous system as well as satellite cells of ganglia and neurolemmacytes, myoepithelial cells in glands, the connective tissue of major blood vessels, and pigment cells.[94]

Mesoderm as well as ectoderm gives rise to connective tissue. The amoeba-like characteristics of its cells, such as the migration of fibroblasts in wound healing, overshadow its epithelial-like characteristics. Nonetheless, bone marrow cells (osteocytes) form junctions at the tips of cytoplasmic extensions, and even fibroblasts may exhibit an epithelial-like contact inhibition of mitosis and migration in tissue culture.

Blood, immune, and germ cells are the most amoeba-like. These cells are the colonists in colonized organs (see Chapter 3) and differentiate individually or in nests surrounded and supported by indigenous cells.

Regrettably, cells sometimes lose their identity as epithelial-like or amoeba-like. Possibly a tension remaining among epithelial-like and amoeba-like cellular traits is not always resolved. Cancers and autoimmune disease are the consequence. One cannot help but be impressed, if not depressed, by the spectacle of otherwise well-behaved epithelial-gland cells giving rise to malignant amoeba-like adenocarcinoma cells—among the most invasive and destructive of all cancer cells. In contrast, the more amoeba-like fibroblast, even transformed into fibrosarcoma cells, are likely to remain benign. Autoimmune disease, on the other hand, might be prompted by cells being in the wrong place at the wrong time as the result of migration or a failure of migration.

In summary, devolution proposes that at some ancient becoming, primordial cells fused and created new opportunities for the mixing and reassortment of cellular traits, launching multicellular organisms into new orbits of differentiation. The temporal regrouping of cellular characteristics occurring in extant organisms is called development, and the spatial grouping formed by cells having shared characteristics is called a tissue. The residue of conflict among characteristics still oppress us in the form of self-sabotaging disease.

THE DEVOLUTION OF LIFE HISTORIES

Life histories are usually defined linearly as a series of changes, or stages, between the fertilization of an egg and the maturation of an adult capable of producing eggs or spermatozoa. Tying the two ends of a life history together produces a life cycle in which eggs or spermatozoa are restored in adults who are themselves produced by eggs and spermatozoa.

Life histories, or cycles, confront biologists with two challenging problems. (1) Why should life change at all, in particular after delays by stages and over a protracted period of time? (2) Why does the life cycle roll generation after generation?

LIFE CHANGES

Life histories rarely follow straight paths. Approximately 80% of extant animal species pass through two or more phases of development, the transitions between which are anything but smooth.[95] Straight life histories do occur in species where an embryo and adult more-or-less share a common environment, and development is direct from an embryo into a juvenile or adult stage. Species in which portions of the life history are spent in different forms, living in different habitats, inevitably require a transition between structures adapted to one way of life and those adapted to another. Traditionally, the post-embryonic, or post-hatching, sexually immature form, not sharing a habitat with the adult for a prolonged period of time, is called a larva—or any of various synonyms. The pathway of development to such an adult is said to be "indirect," and the transition between the larva and adult is called "metamorphosis."

The presence or absence of a larval phase in development is strikingly plastic. A larval phase is suppressed, for example, by a mutation in a control gene, such as the *Manx* gene in urochordates.[96] In general, larval development is activated, or not, through unknown mechanisms, and "the duration of different stages, the timing of metamorphosis, and the concomitant niche shift can be modified without complete loss of a life cycle phase."[97] The presence of a larva in a former incarnation of the species can often be inferred even where embryos or juveniles are not appreciably distinguishable from adults. Larval phases may come and go. Indeed,

> the free-living tadpole stage may have reevolved independently from a direct-developing ancestor as many as four times in a specialized group of South American marsupial frogs in the genera *Fritziana, Flectonotus,* and *Gastrotheca.*[98]

On the other hand, larvae frequently differ from embryos and adults in so many ways that taxonomists may not suspect that particular larvae and adults belong to the same life history. Many larvae and adults have been assigned to different species before taxonomists discovered their developmental relationship. Responsibility for these oversights and errors falls in part on the hidden development of adult structures within larvae or on dormant, adult-forming cells in larvae that only become active and create a new organism virtually instantaneously at metamorphosis.

Metamorphosis is frequently a huge bump on the road of development. Very little in life is more dramatic than metamorphosis and several embryologists have used it to raise the alarm against Haeckelian views of terminal additions to life histories.[99] In echinoderms, amphibians, and endopterygote (holometabolic) insects, the metamorphosis of larvae to adults or juveniles is incredibly violent, and metamorphosis is frequently apocalyptic. Massive amounts of dedicated larval tissues undergo apoptosis, or in some starfish, virtually the whole larval skin is shed.

Contemporary, evolutionary theorists offer no explanation for how organisms reach these larval orbits far from adults. Theories generally run in mundane terms of recapitulation and Haeckelian accumulation. But one evolutionary experimentalist has offered an explanation for the massive shifts accompanying indirect development.

Donald Williamson asserts that the presence of a larva in a life history is due to the operation of a separate genome, and the presence of this separate genome is a consequence of an act of hybridization.[100] The embryo/adult genome and the larval genome operate separately because *two genomes cannot operate in the same animal at the same time.* Possibly, the point in embryonic development at which the larval genome "down loads" corresponds to the moment when the hybrid's paternal genes are first turned on, or are turned on with sufficient force to be felt.

According to Williamson, the more remote or distant the hybrid partners, the wider the larval swing outside of direct development. His experimental hybridizations between extant species are not intended so much to mimic originary events as to test possibilities for serial genomic interactions.[101] Results to date are ambiguous—some echinoderm/tunicate hybrids develop into whirling tops[102]—but Williamson has hardly exhausted the possibilities for hybridization.[103]

Don Williamson's novel notion of indirect development is a radical departure from gradualism and progressivism. Furthermore, he does not distinguish between embryonic and larval stages of development in his speculations on the origins of life-history stages. Rather, he embraces all stages of a life history under one rubric.[104] He can see no theoretical reason to privilege one life-history stage over another and imagines instead that all life-history stages resulted from hybridizations.

I dub Williamson's unconventional hybridization "illicit fusion" in order to bring it under the aegis of devolution. *Illicit fusion is hybridization among unrelated species that does not produce a chimera so much as distinct stages of development.* Furthermore, I dub Williamson's notion of development "nomadic development" in order to highlight its difference from canonical concepts of inflexible, or settled, development. *Nomadic development is the sequential development of stages in a life history arising from the activities of separate genomes having disparate origins.*

Illicit fusion boggles the minds of biologists, since "species" are supposed to mount barriers to interspecific breeding.[105] But genomes may well have been miscible at a time before species evolved self-recognition. In the first place, the existence of self-versus-nonself recognition in extant species is largely a matter of theory rather than empirical demonstration. Hybridization may yet be a major source of evolutionary novelty in the contemporary world. Conventional hybridization is also gaining recognition as an evolutionary force, largely as a consequence of Michael Arnold's work on the potential of hybrids to overcome fitness barriers and occupy fitness zones between species.[106] Secondly, the idea that foreign genes can live together in the same nucleus seems less alien, since the discoveries of assimilation or reticulation of foreign genes into the genomes of plants.

Nomadic development occurs when genomes fail to integrate or homogenize. Genes derived from one ancestor are then expressed predominantly in the larva, and those of another ancestor in the embryo and adult. This temporal separation would also be reflected in spatial separation— genes from one ancestor would be expressed predominantly in one somatic-cell line and genes from the another ancestor predominantly in another somatic-cell line.

Why, then, does life change? One answer is that life changes because illicit fusion and nomadic development have created plateaus in life histories which are called stages. Life is relatively stable at each plateau, but changes between plateaus are not.

LIFE CYCLES

Life cycles represent a unique instance where nature contradicts the laws of thermodynamics. A body is not supposed to return to an originary state once energy has been spent leaving that state, but that return is what happens when germ cells are produced by adults who are themselves produced by germ cells.[107]

The contradiction is widely recognized, by physicists—James Clerk Maxwell (1831–1879)—and philosophers—Friedrich Nietzsche (1844–1900)[108]—but, with conspicuous exceptions,[109] biologists dismiss it as a "cash-flow" problem. The return to an original state is said to incur a thermodynamic debt that is paid back in some way or other at some time or other.

Recently, emerging-order theorists, notably Stuart Kauffman, have suggested that the return of developing organisms is not a debt but an improbable state captured during the wide fluctuations characteristic of far-from-equilibrium thermodynamics.[110] Claims for the creative potential of far-from-equilibrium thermodynamics are based on nonlinear statistical theory and backed up by Belousov-Zhabotinsky reactions of nonlinear transport processes where beautiful wave-patterns are expressed in spreading cerium, a silvery metal. Calcium ions in cells oscillate with similar patterns, and, in theory, developmental patterns emerge the same way.[111]

Devolution offers another solution to the thermodynamic conundrum, or possibly an explanation for how life is catapulted to improbability far-from-equilibrium. Devolution suggests that the clash of different genomes brought about by illicit fusion may have produced a critical mass leading to explosive development.

The idea of explosive development is reflected in the cascade of events that trigger cleavage.[112] Like any explosion, these events cannot be called back once they have begun. Possibly, the interaction of female and male pronuclei following ordinary fertilization mimics the clash once brought about by illicit fusion, and the failure to produce such a clash accounts for the sparse distribution of parthenogenesis among animal species. *The difficulty cloners have inaugurating development from a single genome might rest on the requirement to recreate the chain reaction of development first brought about by illicit fusion.* Attention cloners: try blastomeres in place of eggs.

Life cycles, therefore, because in the history of life illicit fusions projected life into highly improbable states far-from equilibrium thermodynamics, and nomadic development proved to be life's way of negotiating its return to states of near-equilibrium thermodynamics. Likewise, in life histories, the initial cataclysm brought about by fertilization is followed by stages, or periods of relative stability between briefer periods of change, until, finally, egg and spermatozoon meet again.

THE DEVOLUTION OF DEATH

The advent of four-dimensional life coincides with the origin of death. Life in one, two, and three dimensions is timeless, if only because chemical reactions do not die; they merely reach their lowest free-energy point. In contrast, life in four dimensions has duration—the cornerstone of our temporal and spatial complexity—and life in four dimensions dies. One may speak of death in mechanical images—"The clock ticks . . . the bell tolls"—but death is not thereby conflated to chemistry and physics. In the four-dimensional world in which we live, death is not a metaphor. It is the climax of our duration.

Death requires complexity. In contrast to the endless life of prokaryotic cells, our cells are sufficiently complex to die.

> Contrary to bacterial cells possessing a relatively immortal reproduction potential, the majority of complex [eukaryotic] cells can be lost by programmed cell-death. Moreover, most of the physiological cell death in eukaryotes takes place, in part, through a mitochondrion-regulated active process.[113]

With the exception of biologists, few people appreciate death's fundamental relationship to biological complexity. Biologists also distinguish themselves by attaching great importance to death in theories of life's evolution. In the nineteenth century, death was cited as evolution's motor in theories of "survival of the fittest." In the twentieth century, death—while no longer evolution's motor—was still the most conspicuous block to reproduction in theories of evolution by natural selection. In virtually all theories of evolution, death is instrumental for shaping life, and, one way or another, evolution would not run without it.

Biologists might even place death among life's key characteristics, but unlike other key characteristics, death has no self-evident or redeeming adaptive advantage—no saving grace. Notions of group selection, such as "making room for offspring," are tautologies without explanatory value, and the modern synthesis (see Chapter 2) cannot explain death without "death genes" that would not survive in the gene pool. Inclusive (Darwinian) fitness may explain death's fine tuning, such as adjustments to the average life span or age when half a population is dead, but not the phenomenon of death itself, or its many varieties.

Despite the inadequacy of Darwinian and neoDarwinian theories to explain death, death has most certainly evolved. It comes in too many forms not to. It may even be absent in members of the Radiata with constantly renewing cell populations, but the presence of internal organs in bilaterians foreclosed that possibility. Moreover, the requirement to control cell division in internal organs means that death would result from the failure of these very controls.

Death comes to members of the Bilateria in three stages of their life cycle: early, middle, and late. Bilaterians are especially vulnerable to death while passing between developmental stages early in their life cycle. Later, juveniles and adults die when they encounter adverse conditions that they cannot escape or shape into a congenial environment. Finally, life leads inexorably to senescence and collapse. Nothing comes to the rescue except death.

Death at an Early Age

Contrary to widely held assumptions, the majority of human fertilized eggs fail to turn into blastocysts and implant in the uterus. Moreover, large numbers of implanting blastocysts do not survive gastrulation. As Lewis Wolpert, the embryologist and popular science writer, reminds us, "It is not birth, marriage or death, but gastrulation which is truly the most important time in your life."[114] Furthermore, a large number of embryos fail to negotiate the embryo-to-fetus metamorphosis.

Possibly because we are mammals who develop invisibly for a long period within a nurturing and protective womb, we have been unaware of the unseen deaths of eggs, blastocysts, gastrulas, embryos, and fetuses, but today, in the age of routine sonography, death in the womb is no longer shrouded. Fetuses are sonographed *in utero,* and the expectant mother is able to cherish the first photograph of her offspring months before she is able to take a newborn home. Surprisingly, sonography performed to aid the early diagnosis of twins has also revealed that the number of twins *in utero* is greater than the number of twins born. Even successfully implanted embryos are resorbed *in utero!*

Ordinarily, failures are chalked up to abnormalities in germ cells. The idea is that defective human eggs are produced due to errors made while eggs languish in the ovary for twelve to fifty years, and defective human spermatozoa are assembled due to errors made during their mass production. Certainly the frequency of trisomy in offspring increases with the age of mothers, while a quarter of ejaculated spermatozoa produced by fathers are immotile and another 20 percent are morphologically abnormal. But most of the germ cells that take part in fertilization are not certifiably abnormal. The death of blastocysts, gastrulas, embryos, and fetuses would seem to have causes other than overt abnormalities in gametes.

Haeckel offered no explanation whatsoever for the disequilibrium of animals in early developmental stages, simply asserting that the course of organismal development parallels the evolution of surviving species. He was enormously influential, and, ever since his time, biologists have struggled to understand how cells remembered branching patterns of evolution during organismal development while forgetting all the extinctions that happened along the way.[115] Possibly deaths occurring during early development are reminiscences of extinctions past.

Haeckelian biogenesis remains fashionable, especially in molecular cladistics and developmental biology, where "the search for the origin and evolution of larval forms is as alive and active as it was 150 years ago."[116] Haeckel's acolytes continue to believe "larvae may retain in their development many of the features that once existed in the adults of the ancestors but subsequently were lost in the adults of the descendants."[117] Haeckel's rudimentary concept of genetics probably would not have admitted genes for programmed cell death, but neither Haeckel nor modern geneticists would attribute death in embryos to evolutionary inertia.[118]

An intriguing explanation for deaths during early life is gleaned from the work of Walter Garstang (1868–1949): Early death occurs during transitions between stages of development. Garstang was a devoted larva-watcher who admired everything about larvae, their grace, beauty, and resourcefulness, as they struggled mightily with the elements despite their small size. What fascinated Garstang in particular was that each larva lived a "double life."

> [I]n each [larva] there is a compromise and adjustment between two rival needs—or, in other words, two competing selective advantages: on the one hand to grow up into the adult so as to reproduce the species, and on the other to remain floating as long as possible

so as to distribute the species far and wide in the ocean currents—
a particularly important matter for those forms with more sedentary
adults.[119]

Garstang was able to dent complacency about gradualism and progressivism
and make his most lasting contribution (beyond his verses) by making the
double life of larvae almost palpable and certainly inescapable.[120] The question is, "Does early death occur as life struggles with its 'rival needs'?"

Garstang would probably have been interested in devolution. The notions
of illegitimate fusion and nomadic development parallel his ideas on the
larva's "rival needs." Conflict between rival genomes might very well have
been ameliorated by the genomes operating separately, resulting in the segregation of traits into stages of a life history. Furthermore, the elevation of
egg and sperm to an improbable, far-from-equilibrium state by their fusion
might very well be resolved through small transitions between more probable
and less fluctuating near-equilibrium stages.

Certainly, without the plateaus represented by stages, life might crash in
one great fall from the highly improbable. Death in early life would still lurk
at transitions between stages, but the probability would rise that at least some
time, some organisms would pass successfully through the stages to a "soft
landing" in adulthood.

Prospects for immortality, on the other hand, would seem least likely at
transitions between stages. The lesson of death in early life would seem to be,
"Avoid transitions!" Certainly, early transitions would seem as inevitable as
they are deadly, but, the juvenile stage of life would seem a reasonable way
station at which to stop making transitions. At that stage, the organism is
equipped with all the appurtenances required for life and none of the liabili-
ties brought on by sex.

Death at Middle Age

Death cuts a broad swath across mid-life but not as deep a swath as that cut
in early and late life. Mid-age deaths take a toll in human productivity,
dampen our survivorship curve, and inspire our national health agencies,
nonprofits, and pharmaceutical companies to strenuous efforts. They are the
deaths of most interest to health-care researchers for obvious, selfish reasons.

Mid-life death follows myriad misadventures, some originating exter-
nally (contagious diseases and accidents), some originating internally (hereditary diseases), and some mixtures of the two. Even an animal's normal genes
(*c*-oncogenes) betray it, and genetic interactions that once supported growth
and differentiation turn into the triggers for killer cancers and crippling self-

destruction. These are the deaths due to the failure of organisms to cope with the fine points of regulating their own tissues, and to the inadequacy of organismic responses to challenges posed by the environment—especially products and wastes of civilization.

These are the deaths that, Claude Bernard's homeostatic mechanisms should prevent, in theory, and that enlightened health care should forestall, in practice. They are the deaths that should not occur according to Humberto Maturana's and Francisco Varela's conception of autopoiesis, or self-producing organization, that allows the organism to pull itself "up by its own bootstraps and . . . [rescue itself] from its environment through its own dynamics."[121] They are deaths that the best efforts of our physiology and the timely intervention of physicians should prevent. Why then, after millions of years of evolution, are organisms such as ourselves still succumbing to mid-life death?

John von Neumann's and Oskar Morgenstern's game theory offers some insight into death in mid-life but no hopeful solutions. Game theory proposes that the outcomes of competitive situations depend on the choices made by all the players in a game and by chance. Presumably, evolution has prepared us to anticipate the best possible outcomes of the probable choices available to the players, but who are the players?

An organism is not a 2-player game, like checkers, played with optimal strategic choices. Organisms are n-player games ($n > 2$), in which a multitude of players make strategic choices. What is more, players, such as cells, are capable of entering subsets, such as tissues, of forming coalitions, such as organs, and entering stable associations, such as organ systems, each of which becomes a player in the game along with the coalition of the whole. The players may not have a single goal, if they have goals at all, and the goals of cells, tissues, organs, and organ systems may not be entirely rational, utilitarian, or dedicated to the best interest of the organism as a whole. Obtaining a cell's, a tissue's, an organ's, or an organ system's goals may even result in a self-defeating strategy in the long run for the coalition of the whole.

Ordinarily, the cells, tissues, and organs do not play a zero-sum, or constant-sum, game of total conflict, with the payoff going to one winner and all other players losing everything. Rather, they play a nonzero-sum game, in which the players have some competitive and some cooperative goals. The game is played with variable sums, and all players may gain and lose simultaneously. They play a game with imperfect information, despite all the cells being dealt the same genes, since gene rearrangement prevents every cell, tissue, organ, and organ system from knowing everything in the hand or up the sleeve of other players. Furthermore, it is a game in which players communicate and constantly monitor each other's activities, aiding in achieving mutual goals, but it is not a determined game, like chess, in which all the moves are knowable, if not foreseeable. It is not a cooperative game with players making binding and enforceable agreements. It is a noncooperative game in which players will not violate agreements as long as other players do not, but there is hell to pay when agreements are violated.

Given the kind of game and the players, one cannot be surprised by mid-life death. Our manifold parts at all levels—our players, associations, coalitions, and subsets—cannot be relied upon, all the time, to set aside their disparate interests, strategies, and goals to work for their mutual benefit and for the triumph of the coalition of the whole. Our organ system, organs, tissues, and cells will not accommodate adequately all the time to each other and to organismic life, and, inevitably, a variable environment can be expected to throw a "curve" when a "straight ball" is expected. *There cannot be an adequate cure for all the problems of mid-life, and we would do well to avoid mid-life if we are to achieve immortality.*

DEATH IN OLD AGE

The most implacable forms of death are those forecast by thermodynamics. Thermodynamics might seem harmless enough as a set of formulas for getting useful work out of machines. Thermodynamics simply stipulates that in any physical system at equilibrium, lifting external constraints permits changes in properties.[122] How could "changes in properties" bring about ultimate doom in everyone who lives into old age?

The laws of thermodynamics are not about stable physical systems as such. The laws are about *dynamics,* about energy flow, energy changing places, and undergoing transformations, each of which is done at a cost. Entropy is the name of that cost, and, according to the second law of thermodynamics, this cost must be paid. Entropy is a working parameter reflecting the portion of energy in the system that cannot be harnessed for useful work. Entropy is also an index to the degree of disorderliness in a system The problem for any physical structure or organization is that molecular randomness or chaotic disruption on the microscopic level produces disruption and collapse at the macroscopic or statistical level.

Living things ultimately pay their debt of entropy at the expense of energy available for life. The organismic body has no alternative as long as it lives in a thermodynamic universe. Disorganization at the molecular and microscopic levels becomes incompatible with macroscopic life, and death becomes the increasingly probable alternative to life.

Young adult life is a state close to equilibrium—of least dissipation and minimal entropy production. However, the remainder of adult life is a period of continuous if not precipitous decline despite appearances. The steady state of overt characteristics—of extensive variables—is only achieved by a net flux in covert characteristics—of intensive variables.

Even in the best of times, entropy is increasing. Cellular housekeeping—intermediate metabolism, the absorption of oxygen by hemoglobin, anion, bi-ion, cation, and proton pumps, diffusion, the folding of polypeptides, translation, transcription, replication, etc.—all contribute to increasing disorderliness, running the body down even while holding it up. Add to these causes of disorderliness all the additional entropy-increasing acts of healing, physiological repair, regeneration, and recuperation—induced by wounding, wear and tear, molecular oxidative damage, and environmental insults—and the adult body acquires an insupportable amount of disorderliness. Useful work is no longer adequate to hold up the body, and it runs down.

Thermodynamic inevitability would seem to underlie many kinds of senescence. For example, increased entropy could reduce rates of cell division without any underlying genetic program and initiate all sorts of senescent consequences. Even a slight net decrease in the rate of cell division would cause the accumulation of more slowly dividing cells and, ultimately, the shutdown of division entirely. Thus, fibroblasts exhibiting attenuated rates of cell division would accumulate in the skin, and the characteristic increase in collagenase and fibronectin secretion by nondividing cells would contribute to thinning and loss of elasticity.[123] Likewise, the decline in T-cell proliferation with age might be a statistical consequence of entropy's effects on cell division, and "[m]uch of the decline in humoral immunity [in aging] is a result of changes in the activities of T cells needed to promote B cell activation and differentiation. . . ."[124]

Thermodynamic inevitability might seem to kill us when little things add up or when one or another mishap causes irreparable damage, but, actually, we are doomed because energy flows and disorderliness counts our days. *The solution would seem to be to avoid old age entirely!*

CONCLUSIONS

The lesson repeated throughout Chapter 4 is that life is not incompatible with immortality. Indeed, life has some fundamental features which would aid in achieving immortality and some which would even abet it. These features do not mean that immortality will be easy to achieve, but neither is it impossible.

Mortality is not a fundamental feature of life! Death exists only in the four-dimensional state in which eukaryotic life resides and functions. But life is also linear, even if it is more than linear in four dimensions; life is also planar, even if it is more than planar in four dimensions; life is volumetric, even if it is more than volumetric in four dimensions.

The addition of physiological, generational, and evolutionary time to life gave it duration, and duration raised the potential of life to otherwise inaccessible heights. It brought life to the state of complexity found in large, multicellular animals, including ourselves. But duration also introduced death, the climax of life.

Duration cannot be despised as the harbinger of death, since it also created life as we know it. Of course, life in one-, two-, and three-dimensional worlds contributes to our lives, but life for us does not reside in the endless worlds of transposons, viruses, and prokaryotes. We live in a four-dimensional world of extraordinary complexity where, so far, the duration of life is finite. However, no mind-bending tricks or metaphysical flip-flops are necessary to imagine immortal life. Immortal human beings will live in a four-dimensional world of extraordinary complexity where the duration of life is infinite. Immortal life will simply not climax in death.

The notion of devolution suggests how four-dimensional life was created, how duration was invented, and how temporal and spatial complexity was constructed. Devolution suggests that four-dimensional life was made by fusion and fission on a large scale. From molecules to prokaryotes—from RNA to proteins and DNA, from transposons and viruses to cells—life emerged by assortment and reassortment. From prokaryotes to eukaryotes—from nuclei and organelles to cell types, tissues, organs, and organ systems, from meiosis to fertilization, egg to sperm—life emerged by a blend of mixing and fragmentation. From radiates to bilaterians, life emerged by illicit fusion and nomadic development, and from gastrula to senior citizen, life emerged through the compromises it negotiated with rival needs, with the competing strategies of its many players, and with their thermodynamic loads.

Devolution also suggests why developing organisms are so threatened by death. Illicit fusion and fertilization project cells into a far-from-equilibrium, statistically improbable, state. The elementary processes of molecular events far-from-equilibrium occur at exponential rates, and, hence, small perturbations have large repercussions. Inasmuch as life is supported within a narrow range of fluctuations, molecular events far-from-equilibrium are likely to overshoot their mark. Perturbations are likely to result in instability, and the embryos that develop are likely to slip into a more probable state coeval with death. The high frequency of death among embryos, gastrulas, and larvae or fetuses would seem to be a consequence of molecular fluctuations conspiring with probability against the requirements of life.

What is more, devolution suggests how organisms negotiate a soft landing from the high fluctuations of their initial far-from-equilibrium state. Nomadic development prescribes that the genomes fused by illicit fusion or fertilization express themselves separately, both temporally and spatially. The stages of a life cycle thereby created allow organisms to break up the journey into small steps from far-from-equilibrium to near-equilibrium. At each step, the organism resides comfortably, if temporarily, in a near-equilibrium state.

Development proceeds as the organism descends from one steady-state to the next, until arriving at the pre-adolescent stage.

Turning mortal human beings into immortal human beings does not require turning them into living, perpetual-motion machines, defying the second law of thermodynamics. Any plan to do so would go against everything physics has to say about physical systems in a thermodynamic world. Likewise, turning mortal human beings into immortal human beings does not require playing the game of life against Darwinian evolution. Any plan to do so would go against everything biology has to say about living systems in a DNA/protein world. Turning mortal human beings into immortal human beings can be done by using physics and biology, not by trying to outsmart them.

The first task is to find a window of opportunity that can be pried open for creating immortal life. No stage of life is immune to death, but different sorts of death strike in different stages of life. Eukaryotes, in general, and large, multicellular animals such as ourselves, in particular, die young due to the failure to negotiate a transition between stages; they die in mid-life as sequelae to mishaps and the misfiring of genes; and they die old as consequences of breakdown and collapse.

We die because our stable heredity material has not smoothed out transitions during early development; because genetic stability does not prepare our tissues for every insult hurled at us by other tissues and the environment; because hereditary stability prevents our adjusting sufficiently to ward off the effects of thermodynamic decay; because evolution has no use for us following our opportunity to maximize Darwinian (inclusive) fitness. We die because the same genetic conservation that permits the production of a large, differentiated soma as complex and long-lived as we are relegates this soma (ourselves) to nature's junk heap ("the way of all flesh").

But life is not equally vulnerable at all stages, and prepubescence is probably the least vulnerable stage of all. At prepubescence, human beings hover at a nodal point in life's trajectory—a point at which the slope of the net-entropy curve changes. Before this point, life is vulnerable to transitional disaster, and beyond this point, increases in the entropic-load make the game of life unwinnable. But, at this point, the probability of macroscopic stability is relatively high, and molecular events fluctuate somewhere below far-from-equilibrium dynamics. This is the window of opportunity which, if handled judiciously, can be opened indefinitely.

Immortality can be achieved at the prepubescent stage of life by grabbing life at this point and preserving it there. This means preserving human beings at a stage before they are completely developed and mature but at which life is full of excitement, experience, learning, adventure, and, above all, meaning. Imagine a pre-adolescent, at the physiological age of about eleven, living forever! Such individuals would be close to adulthood and capable of living a relatively fulfilling life, enjoying life and contributing their creativity to it, albeit not reproducing. Immortal, these human beings would be forever young, never fully grown or sexually mature, but never aging.

Chapter 5

Making Immortals:
From Blastocyst to Generator

Men and women alive today may well be able to live for centuries, and if they survive that long, they will undoubtedly be able to live for millennia. We are reaching the point in our knowledge of biology and medicine where death from aging will no longer be inevitable.

—Ben Bova, *Immortality*

From my point of view the affirmation of dying seems absolutely fundamental. Affirmation not in the sense of glorifying death but in the sense—to put it bluntly—that without mortality, we're nothing. In other words the fantasy of transcending death is opposed to everything I care about.

—Donna Haraway, *How like a Leaf*

The concept of biological nature implies a hidden truth, rooted in the past and *already there,* though it may not always be evident in the phenomenal world. This past is usually the evolutionary past of the species, but sometimes it is more individual, as when the infant is thought to reveal the real nature of the particular person to come, a nature that is discernible because it is still largely untouched by nurture.

—Susan Oyama, *The Ontogeny of Information*

Becoming Immortal gets to the point in Chapter 5: Human beings can be made immortal despite their evolution, development, and inherent vulnerability! *Homo sapiens* forma *mortalis* can be converted into *Homo sapiens* forma *immortalis* by combining cloning with stem-cell therapy through prenatal biotechnology!

The means are remarkably short, simple, and straightforward. Human beings can be immortalized by providing them with a new organ, a *generator* of self-renewing stem-cells derived from a clone. Internalized as a blastocyst in the pre-gonadal tissue of an embryo, the generator will provide an eternal source of *exotic stem (es) cells* ("exotic" in the biological sense of not endemic). The immortalized person will be sterile and remain at a preadolescent physiological age forever but otherwise appear and be perfectly normal.

The reader will have noticed that I am not suggesting a way of immortalizing everyone. Indeed, I am not prescribing a way of immortalizing anyone alive today—including those reading these words. Immortalizing an adult is all but impossible, since so much degeneration has already occurred, even if hidden behind a screen of good health and vigor, while immortalizing a child would require surgical retrofitting bordering on the barbaric. My objective for Chapter 5 is merely to outline a method for installing a cloned generator of stem cells in an embryo, and to detail what the generator will devolve into in the immortalized human being.

TAKING ANOTHER LOOK AT CLONING

Clones are generally intended to reproduce organisms with particular heritable qualities, either present originally or introduced via recombinant DNA technology and gene transfer.[1] Clones can also serve as an internal, permanent source of stem cells in immortalized individuals.

WHAT IS A CLONE ANYWAY?

Clone has many definitions.[2] Originally, clones of organisms (animals, plants, and, later, bacteria) were the collective products of an organism's asexual or vegetative reproduction. Such organisms appeared identical when raised under the same circumstances, and their identity was assumed to be inherited. Thus, all the living things thought to be identical, and even their products, became identified with clones: organisms grown from isolated cells (carrots, tobacco, etc.); monoclonal antibodies produced by a hybridoma (lineages of lymphocytes fused to myeloma cells); cloned genes (fragments of DNA ligated to clonal vectors via recombinant DNA technology and inserted into or taken up by cells). Cloning quickly became a household word, and patented clones fired-up the biotech industry.

"Clone" had a different definition in the mid-1950s, when nuclear transfer was performed in amphibians. At that time, a "clone" designated all the tadpoles produced following the transfer of nuclei from a single frog embryo to enucleated frog eggs, usually from the same clutch.[3] Many of these tadpoles were morphologically different, however, and the word "clone" seemed inappropriate for a population of dissimilar organisms. The word was thus transferred to each individual organism in the population, since every tadpole was supposed to be made of cells with identical nuclei (see below).

This usage has been adopted for all animals generated by nuclear transfer, including mammals. "'Clone' no longer signifies a group of identical members; it signifies a single member of such a group."[4] "Clone" identifies an individual whose development was inaugurated in a nuclear/cytoplasmic chimera—an egg's cytoplasm from one source containing a nucleus generally from a different source.

Dolly, the cloned ewe and first large mammal cloned by the transfer of a nucleus from a differentiated adult cell thus "is not a 'true' clone of the original ewe at all. She is, rather, a 'DNA clone' or a 'genomic clone,'"[5] since the enucleated egg was from a Scottish Blackface mountain ewe, and the transferred nucleus was from a Finn-Dorset ewe. In the final analysis, a mammalian clone begins as a nuclear/cytoplasmic chimera, sharing its nuclear genes with the organism donating the original nucleus, but is otherwise unique, and certainly not a member of a population of identical individuals.

CLONING'S THEORETICAL FOUNDATIONS: UNDERLYING NUCLEAR BIAS

Ironically, the modern bio-engineering technique of cloning raises several questions whose roots can be traced to the Medieval Age if not to earlier times. Then the question would have been "What is the contribution of the father as opposed to the mother to the offspring?" Today we ask, "What rights do the nuclear and cytoplasmic parents have over the clone derived from a nuclear/cytoplasmic chimera?"[6] The notion of the female element providing the soil or being the vessel for the male element (phallus) and generating "his" crop, crops up again in concerns over the conflicting interests of cytoplasm and nucleus in a clone. Medieval rules of primogeniture might assign legitimacy and allocate inheritance to the nuclear parent, while the cytoplasmic parent would not even have recognized "property" rights! As male dominance was justified by God's law, nuclear supremacy would seem justified by gene-centered biological law, the same law that provided the rationale for cloning in the first place.[7]

Cloning rests upon two great theoretical pillars of modern biology. The first is the theory of nuclear equivalence, according to which all cells produced by mitosis, or mitotic cell division, have exactly the same nuclear genes as the dividing cell at the beginning of the lineage. This theory is vindicated by a long history of experimental results, but to say that it has been exhaustively tested is a vast exaggeration. The second great pillar of modern biology supporting cloning is the notion of nuclear hegemony or the nuclear monopoly of controls over all processes in living things, including all the instructions for developing and maintaining the organism. This idea is also vindicated by experience, but it too has never been tested rigorously.

Tested or not, the combination of nuclear equivalence and nuclear hegemony is overpowering. It provides the principle justification for the Human Genome Project, and its wide acceptance explains the approach taken by modern biotechnology to most biological problems, including approaches to human longevity: *chercher le gene*.

Nuclear Equivalence

How reliable is the idea of nuclear equivalence? Today, the greatest support for it comes from the results of cloning even if the logic of the argument is convoluted. Actually, a major leap of faith is required to argue from clones to normal organisms and from the equivalence of nuclei used in transplants to nuclei in all cells.

All the cell divisions and differentiation that came before the extraction of a particular nucleus for transplantation are thought to be neutral in their impact on nuclear potential if that nucleus can support the development of a clone. Moreover, if the successfully transplanted nucleus was chosen virtually at random, that nucleus would be like other nuclei, and any or every nucleus must be equally capable of supporting the complete spectrum of developmental events.

One might argue that the failure of the vast majority of nuclear transplants to support development makes just the opposite point, but considering all the problems of nuclear transfer, even the modest successes achieved so far are surely the exceptions that prove the rule. The possibility that the nuclear-transplanting procedure or the cytoplasm of the enucleated oocyte receiving the transplanted nucleus may have reversed effects of cell division and differentiation is simply dismissed. Stability is a far easier explanation to invoke than reversibility. Furthermore, the idea that clones develop the same way as normal organisms is taken for granted, since it would seem too much to expect clones to develop any other way than the normal.

Historically, the argument for nuclear equivalence has been even more convoluted. The history of nuclear equivalence begins a century ago when Hans Driesch separated sea urchin blastomeres by vigorous shaking and discovered that they developed into complete, albeit small, larvae.[8] Driesch was primarily interested in how the presence or absence of neighboring cells influenced a blastomere's development, but his results also illustrated that, despite cell division, blastomeres retained all the developmental determinants required to support the full spectrum of subsequent developmental events.[9]

At about the same time, August Weismann was developing his ideas on how germplasm influenced somatoplasm in the course of development.[10] Weismann hypothesized that portions of the germplasm were mechanically distributed by cell division and initiated differentiation when sufficiently rarefied in terminal cells. Consequently, blastomeres derived from cleaving eggs should progressively lose nuclear determinants. Wilhelm Roux seemed to have demonstrated precisely this sort of dilution of nuclear contents when he showed that blastomeres of two- and four-cell frog embryos developed into corresponding halves and quarters of embryos in the presence of sibling blastomeres killed by puncture with a hot needle.[11]

The conflicts between Driesch's and Roux's results were hotly debated (see Chapter 3) until Hans Spemann, among others, divided salamander embryos with the help of a noose made of baby hair and broadly confirmed Driesch's result.[12] Moreover, Spemann and his students discovered that amphibian blastomeres deprived of nuclei (merogons) began developing after acquiring a nucleus from an attached embryo of eight to sixteen cells. Even after undergoing three and four divisions, the resultant nuclei retained the potential of nuclei in the fertilized egg.[13]

In the 1950s, the results of nuclear transplantation experiments in frogs demonstrated that nuclei remained equivalent after undergoing ten divisions, despite coming from cells of late blastulas and early gastrulas. Moreover, some nuclei could still support the complete spectrum of development events even after fourteen divisions, but the number of such competent nuclei decreased precipitously during gastrulation. After much tinkering, a few tadpoles and an occasional frog developed from enucleated eggs that had received nuclei of red blood or intestinal epithelial cells. At least some amphibian nuclei of differentiated cells seemed equivalent to the pronuclei of fertilized eggs and the nuclei of early blastomeres.[14] Finally, after nearly 300 attempts, with the birth of Dolly, the single lamb produced from the combination of a cultured udder cell's nucleus and an enucleated egg, the idea of nuclear equivalence was extended to differentiated adult, mammalian cells.[15] Clearly, the ability of a rare nucleus to support the development of a clone is suggestive of universal nuclear equivalence, but, equally clearly, equivalence has not been demonstrated in all nuclei in an organism.

Nuclear equivalence is thus a circular idea garnered from the results of nuclear transplantation and a justification for nuclear transplantation. All nuclei in an organism, and hence a cloned organism, are thought to be equivalent to each other, and to the hypothetical zygotic nucleus or original donor nucleus, because a rare nucleus, transplanted from the cell of a differentiated tissue to an enucleated egg, is capable of supporting the full spectrum of developmental events.[16] Thus, genes are thought to be unchanged, or at least not irreversibly changed by cell division occurring during cleavage, blastula or blastocyst formation, gastrulation, embryogenesis, and differentiation in tissues.[17]

The idea of nuclear equivalence is reinforced by systems for replication *in vitro*. These systems seem to show that the enzymes of DNA replication are entirely indifferent to the genes being replicated. Thus, genes in cells would also be replicated exactly as they are and, working backward, exactly as they were in cells at the beginning of the organism's cellular lineage. Consistency may not be proof, but it is certainly seductive.

Nuclear Hegemony: Synchronization and Reprogramming

All vertebrates, including mammals, are "regulative" in the sense of the word used by Driesch—blastomeres adjust to suit their neighbors, adapting to their presence by contracting developmental potential, and to their absence by expanding developmental potential. The simplest method of cloning is to follow Driesch's lead and divide a vertebrate embryo in half, producing a clone of two (see below for the application of such clones to immortalization).[18] In this case, the clone members have begun with identical cytoplasm as well as identical nuclei and are thus artificial monozygotic (identical) twins.

Nuclear transplantation also taps Driesch's principle of regulation. Creating nuclear clones from nuclear/cytoplasmic chimeras depends on regulation in a nucleus, rather than in a blastomere, and on regulation in response to new cytoplasmic surroundings, rather than neighboring blastomeres. Moreover, the regulation of performance rises on a grand scale. Remarkably, "the magic works" at least some of the time, and development is complete and normal in almost 2 percent of the mammalian clones created with transferred nuclei (such as nuclei from undifferentiated fibroblasts).

Two percent would seem miraculous, given the sheer brutality of the processes involved in enucleation and nuclear transfer, but the future of cloning will depend on improving the odds. Possibly the low success rate is due to lapses in replication, in effect revoking nuclear equivalence, but most researchers seem to think that the failures are due to problems with nuclear regulation, specifically, with synchronization and/or reprogramming. *Synchronization* refers to bringing the nucleus and cytoplasm into the same phase of the cell cycle. *Reprogramming* is the process that allows all the genes required for development to start up, including those that have been turned on or off and tuned in or out during the prior passage of the donor cell through one or another state of differentiation.

Research on synchronization and reprogramming centers on the states of the egg cytoplasm, on the donor cell at the time of the nuclear transfer, and on how the new nucleus changes when placed in the medium of an egg's cytoplasm. In amphibians, a good match seems to be between embryonic nuclei and ovulated egg cytoplasm. Nuclei are far more likely to support development when their source is a young (but not too young) embryo, rather than an older embryo. In frogs, the best nuclei come from blastulas of about 1,000 cells, while nuclei from gastrulas increasingly lose their potency—their ability to support development completely—suggesting that nuclei from blastulas are more easily synchronized and reprogrammed with enucleated ovulated eggs than nuclei of gastrulas. On the other hand, the first successful cloning of cows by nuclear transfer was performed with nuclei from 60 to 120 day old bovine fetal cells.[19]

Some of the requirements for integrating the nucleus and cytoplasm may be general, but some seems to be species-specific. In mice, nuclear genes begin transcription by the two-cell stage, whereas in cows, genes become transcriptionally active only at the 16-cell stage. These differences may account for the major discrepancy in success with different techniques of nuclear transfer (e.g., culturing cells with or without plasma proteins).

Embryo stem (ES) or germ stem (GS) cells may also serve as a possible source of nuclei for clones. This possibility was first suggested as a criticism of John Gurdon's claim to have cloned tadpoles with nuclei from tadpole intestinal epithelium. Had he inadvertently used germ-line stem cells (primordial germ cells present in the intestine at the time) for nuclei?[20] The abundance of ES cells in mice is sometimes used to explain the relative ease with which mice are cloned, while the absence of ES cells in sheep and cows may explain why cloning them is so difficult.

And What about Cytoplasm?

A battery of sophisticated molecular tests performed at the end of 1999 demonstrated that Dolly,[21] several calves, and some Hawaiian mice[22] were pure nuclear clones. No equally rigorous tests are available for the purity of cytoplasm, even if, as everyone agrees, cytoplasm should not be discounted as a factor in development and heredity. Indeed, Wilmut et al emphasize how sheep cloned from the same nuclear source differ, presumably due to differences in the enucleated eggs used for cloning, although differences might also be traced to paternal cytoplasm and to the prenatal foster mothers incubating the transferred embryos.[23]

Cytoplasm is the source of a variety of nonnuclear determinants of development and heredity—otherwise known as cytoplasmic inheritance. A variety of mutant bioenergetic pathways, especially cholesterol metabolism, are inherited cytoplasmically, and the phenomenon of imprinting, through which nuclear genes acquire nonMendelian qualities of inheritance, is rooted in cytoplasm. Cytoplasm will have to be brought more sharply into the cloning picture if one is to avoid inadvertently introducing undesirable qualities in a clone through cytoplasm.

Success in combining a nucleus from one source with cytoplasm from another requires synchronizing nucleus and cytoplasm. In general, nuclei are sensitive to cytoplasmic cues and adjust activity rapidly when confronted with new cytoplasm.[24] One might imagine that adjusting to the oocyte's cytoplasm should be a small problem for the transplanted nucleus, especially since the preponderance of early influences on development are one way—from cytoplasm to nucleus. Nuclei of early frog embryos are not even transcribing mRNA, no less influencing cytoplasm.

The problem of synchronicity seems to be more one of chromosomal physiology than gene action. A nucleus, ripped out of a nondividing, differentiated cell's cytoplasm seems to find it difficult to adapt its chromosomes for repeated divisions in the rapidly cleaving blastomeres. Following nuclear transplantation, chromosomes sometimes throw up their hands and form bizarre and malfunctioning rings and cross structures. The meshing of gene action with cytoplasmic determinants in early development may remain a cytoplasmic prerogative, but figuring out how to mesh nuclear and cytoplasmic physiology is still a matter of guessing by cloning researchers.[25]

DOLLY ET AL.: THE SPECIFICS

Dolly was created at the Roslin Institute from a freshly ovulated oocyte treated with cytochalasin B to soften the cytoplasm and prevent chromosomal loss during mechanical enucleation.[26] Keith Campbell and Ian Wilmut, Dolly's chief creators, kept cultured cells in a nutrient-depleted medium for several days, forcing the cells generally into G_0, prior to using them as nuclear donors. The enucleated egg—a merogon or cytoplast—was "impregnated" with a transfer-nucleus—a karyoplast—by fusion aided by an electric current. This process—electrofusion—also activated the constructed zygote, initiating cleavage and development.

Alternate techniques abound for mammalian cloning. Beyond raising nuclear donor cells in different culture media, eggs are utilized at different stages—e.g., advanced, post-fertilization eggs no longer in need of activation—and a variety of devices are employed to achieve nuclear transfer—e.g., employing Sendai virus to effect fusion of the nuclear donor cell with the enucleated egg. A technique originally successful in mice and now in pigs relies on mechanical impregnation by the microinjection of a karyoplast. Instead of stimulating cleavage with multiple, gentle electric shocks effectual in sheep, mouse, and pig eggs are stimulated with one strong electric impulse. And various treatments may be used in various combinations, such as piezo-actuated microinjection in mice[27] and pigs[28] and double-nuclear transfer technique wherein the donor nucleus, transplanted to an enucleated mature oocyte (a temporary reprogramming vehicle), is allowed to swell before transfer to an enucleated previously fertilized egg already prepared for cleavage.[29] Finally, species have peculiar species specific needs, such as the requirement of pig fetuses for no fewer than three additional fetuses in a shared uterus.

Synchronizing Cytoplasm and Nucleus

Part of Campbell's and the Roslin crew's research was devoted to testing their theory that successful development of nuclear/cytoplasmic chimeras depended upon synchronizing the egg's cytoplasm and the transferred nucleus at the commencement of cleavage.[30] The problem is that the cell cycle in oocytes is unlike that in somatic cells. Unlike somatic cells that routinely go through cycles of DNA synthesis followed by division, or enter quiescence following division in the G_1 or G_0 stages, egg development proceeds through a long period of arrest following DNA synthesis and prior to division.

In almost all mammals, all oocytes have completed virtually all their premeiotic DNA synthesis prior to birth, but oocytes will only resume meiosis and ovulate upon reaching maturity—about the time of menarche in human beings.[31] The period between the virtual completion of DNA synthesis and the completion of meiosis is known as the first "meiotic arrest" and lasts, in human beings, anywhere from eleven to fifty years.

In mature mammals, a primary oocyte reaching its own maturity is at the end of its first meiotic arrest, known as the germinal vesicle stage. Immediately prior to ovulation, the chromosomes resume meiosis, separating from each other (the diakinesis stage), and the nucleus, or germinal vesicle, breaks down—GVB or GVBD. The primary oocyte then completes the first meiotic division, giving rise to a secondary oocyte and an abortive polar body.

At ovulation, the secondary oocyte enters a second meiotic arrest (or MII phase), with dense chromosomes exposed to cytoplasm having a high concentration of mitosis (maturation or M-phase) promoting factor (MPF). Fertilization then produces a zygote and triggers activation and the precleavage cascade: A flush of calcium ions results in the MPF concentration plunging; meiosis goes to completion producing a mature egg, or fertilized ootid, and a second polar body. The male pronucleus, containing DNA from the spermatozoon, and the female pronucleus, containing DNA from the egg, form and move centrally, approaching each other but not fusing; DNA is replicated in both the male and female pronuclei, which is to say, the cell enters the S phase of the mitotic cycle. Finally, paternal and maternal chromosomes mingle (on the metaphase plate) and the zygote undergoes cleavage, dividing to form the first two blastomeres.[32]

In theory, as Campbell first suggested, cloning is most likely to be successful when the cytoplasm of the egg and the transferred nucleus are geared to enter the precleavage S phase simultaneously. In practice, the Roslin crew showed that a donor nucleus in virtually any phase of the cell cycle falls into synchrony with the egg cytoplasm by the end of the precleavage cascade (normally several hours after fertilization), but subsequent development is arrested unless the transferred nucleus is from a cell in the G_1 or G_0 stage— prior to the S phase—and not in G_2—following the S phase.

"Shooting in the dark" research is always going to produce mixed results. Initially, the procedure used to produce enucleated eggs (subsequently patented by Campbell and Wilmut), at best, resulted in the development of a lamb that died soon after birth.[33] Ultimately, the same procedure produced the oocyte used to make Dolly.

Likewise, the chance of normal development is supposed to be enhanced when nuclei are transferred to enucleated oocytes prior to the commencement of the precleavage cascade—although one of the first two cloned sheep, Morag, was created with an oocyte enucleated at the end of the cascade.[34] Subsequently, the Roslin team showed that cleavage, blastocyst formation, and subsequent development into a healthy clone are more likely when a nucleus is given a chance to make all its mistakes (synchronize and reprogram) in one oocyte before transfer to a second oocyte where everything counts.

Reprogramming the Nucleus

Successful cloning depends on reprogramming the donor nucleus so that its nuclear progeny can express all the genes required for totipotency—making an embryo with cells differentiated into germ and all somatic lines and cell type.[35] The sheer enormity of reprogramming billions of nucleotides in the genome, and the requirements of different differentiated cells to activate and inactivate different genes would seem to make reprogramming an impossible task.[36] However, Dolly,

> the first animal of any kind ever to be created from cultured, differentiated [ovine mammary epithelial {OME}] cells taken from an *adult* . . . confutes once and for all the notion that has virtually been dogma for 100 years, which says that once cells are committed to the tasks of adulthood then they cannot again be totipotent.[37]

Wilmut and Campbell argue that the new nucleus can be reprogrammed by the cytoplast and support successful cloning. For a number of reasons,

Campbell, and subsequently other members of the Roslin group, believe that the quiescent state of the cell cycle (G_0) is "a special state in which chromosomes are particularly amenable to reprogramming . . . [and that] *all* cells pass through a G_0 state *en route* to differentiation."[38] Campbell first made this point in a secret memo to Wilmut:

> The fact that the G_0 state is associated with cell differentiation suggests that this may provide a nuclear/chromatin structure which is more amenable to remodeling/reprogramming.[39]

In order to produce donor cells in the quiescent state of the cell cycle (G_0), cells were cultured in media with reduced (10 percent to 0.5 percent) amounts of fetal calf serum, and hence reduced amounts of growth factors, for a week prior to nuclear transplantation. This was the procedure (also patented by Campbell and Wilmut) that produced the nuclei used in cloning the first cloned ewes, Megan and Morag.

Cloners at Roslin, as well as elsewhere, attempted to ascertain the reprogrammability of nuclei from cells of increasingly older embryos. Donor cells of three types were tested: the inner cell mass (ICM) of early blastocysts, the embryo disks [ED] of later blastocysts, and ED cells raised in tissue culture. The development of clones was supported by nuclei from all these cells, including ED cells subcultured three times (fourth passage cells) which were accordingly christened TNT_4 cells (totipotent for nuclear transfer$_4$).[40]

Based on techniques for culturing mouse ES cells,[41] ED cells of advanced blastocysts were cultured on a feeder layer of mouse fibroblasts in a medium containing newborn serum—which "makes the cells of the sheep embryo discs feel comfortable"[42]—fetal calf serum—which provides the growth factors that promote cellular proliferation—and recombinant human leukemia inhibition factor (LIF)—which discourages differentiation.[41] Unlike mouse ICM cells, which retain their undifferentiated, rounded, embryonic profile during subsequent passages through tissue culture, sheep cells flatten in culture and become fibroblast-like, producing marker proteins of differentiation (cytokeratin and nuclear lamin A/C), and occasionally becoming aneuploid (having abnormal numbers of chromosomes).[43] The cultured sheep-embryo cells resemble somatic cells and not murine ES cells.

Likewise, adult cells from which donor nuclei would be retrieved were raised in tissue culture under conditions of protein starvation intended to render cells quiescent. Cells presumed to be in the G_0 phase of the cell cycle were then utilized as nuclear donors.

When the technique was successful, the reintegrated egg and nucleus underwent cleavage followed by divisions of the blastomeres. The nuclear/

cytoplasmic chimera, still within its egg membrane (zona pellucida), was coated with agar.[44] Thirty to forty agar-coated cocoons were placed within an oviduct of a temporary recipient ewe. Six days later, following the formation of a blastocyst, the agar cocoons were recovered, hatched from the agar, and developing blastocysts were transferred to permanent recipients, the prenatal foster mothers or surrogates, where the blastocysts resumed development.

The procedure is known as "embryo transfer," although no embryo is as yet present in the blastocyst. Further development occurs following implantation and gives rise to extra-embryonic membranes and the sheep's style of contact-cotyledonous placenta. An embryo finally commences development, followed, in turn, by a fetus.

Five months later (actually 147–156 days, depending on the breed), a lamb is, or should be born, although, in the case of cloning, it is generally delivered by cesarean section ("neonate" is thus a misnomer). Surgery is typically required because cloned livestock are often abnormally large for unknown reasons. Nevertheless, when a sexually reproducing adult develops, the assumption is that everything that took place after embryo transfer was perfectly normal.

No one can fail to be impressed by cloning even at a 2 percent success rate, but the assumption that the clone takes the same route to development as any normal organism seems a bit naive. The clone has inevitably dealt with challenges unheard of in normal development and may very well have responded with devices well beyond anything normal.

The embryologist and early cloner, Hans Spemann, never ceased to be impressed by the inventiveness shown by embryos attempting to solve the experimental challenges he threw at them. Spemann suggested that embryos were equipped with "double insurance," backup that promoted regulation by allowing embryos to find a healthy mean between opposing, deleterious influences.[45] The cost of "double insurance" would be small change considering its value for meeting challenges thrown at embryos. One should not be surprised if nuclear/cytoplasmic chimeras reveal an investment in multiple insurance, and successful clones employ abnormal ways of solving development's problems.

TAKING ANOTHER LOOK AT STEM CELLS

What are the possibilities that stem cells can serve as an eternal source of self-renewing cells capable of giving rise to each and every type of cell in the organism? This would seem a tall order for cells that were originally identified in *in vitro* research on lymphocyte and blood formation.

Stanley Shostak

Defining Stem Cells

The definition of stem cells has changed over the years and is especially ambiguous at the moment.[46] The simplest definition, which works for plants (meristems) but not for animals, is that stem cells are self-renewing through cell division as well as capable of generating every type of differentiated cells. This definition ignores stem cells's central role in multicellular animals, namely, their capacity to arrive at a site "in an undifferentiated state and . . . generate one or more differentiated cell types."[47] A more complex definition that works better for animals is

> [cells] able to reproduce themselves throughout the life-span of the animal, and . . . give rise to differentiated cells . . . [or] visibly undifferentiated . . . [cells] often thought to undergo obligatory asymmetric division to yield one stem cell daughter and one daughter destined to differentiate.[48]

Still other definitions emphasize the cell's multiple potentialities for differentiation, its determination via a history or lineage, its sensitivity to circulating growth factors, and its ability to respond to local stem cell niches or cues in its microenvironment.

The idea of stem-cell motility is reminiscent of cancer-cell metastasis—a power function of circulating cells with limited affinities and stochastic opportunities. After circulating stem cells enter an organ, they must then respond to the surrounding microenvironment in a healthful and not malignant way.

All organs take precautions against penetration by wandering cells, but some organs are more resistant than others. Resistance seems especially keen in indigenous organs (see Chapter 3), such as the masses of striated muscle present in the skeletal system. These organs are ordinarily stable but may be restored following trauma by replacement, or satellite, cells. Hopefully, such replacement mechanisms will allow stem cells entrée. Layered, or melting-pot organs, such as the integument and gut, are constructed and maintained by indigenous cells with the addition of foreigners. The surface, epithelial layers of these organs contain internal, proliferative populations which may accommodate stem cells much the same way they accommodate other foreigners in their midst. Colonized organs, such as bone marrow, seem to depend on specific stem cells for physiological renewal and may be relatively accessible to generalized stem cells.

Possibly more than one type of cell is required to meet all the demands and expectations placed on stem cells. Epithelial cells, in particular, seem to have peculiar requirements for stem cells.[49] For example, proliferative epithelial cells are "transit cells," neither stem cells nor terminally differentiated cells. Differentiation in stratified integumentary epithelium (epidermis), pseudostratified respiratory epithelium, and simple enteric epithelium seem to be more a function of local conditions than the previous history of the cell, cell lineage, and circulating growth factors. Nevertheless, epithelia respond to trauma and to grafts by rallying their cells ordinarily residing outside the proliferative community. Differentiating epithelial cells may represent a cryptic reserve stem cell population or cells capable of dedifferentiating and mobilizing in response to local conditions.

On the other hand, the traditionally recognized difference between reserve stem cells and active stem cells may not betoken two different types of stem cells. Epitomized by satellite cells of skeletal muscle, reserve stem cells are dormant (quiescent G_0–G_1) until aroused by traumatic injury. Active stem cells, such as hematopoietic stem cells, maintain tissues in the steady-state by balancing mitotic activity (cycling between G_1– S–G_2–M) and differentiation. Reserve and active stem cells may be distinguished in experimental practice but may not be fundamentally different as far as the organism is concerned. For example, in the nervous system, cells seem staid in their ways from early development onward, but reserve stem cells participate in relatively slow turnover as well as differentiation following traumatic loss.[50] If reserve and active stem cells are representatives of the same sort of cell under different conditions, then generalized stem cells might also "act principally in tissue renewal, thus ensuring an organism's long-term survival."[51]

The success of stem-cell therapy will ultimately depend on "stem-cell omniscience"—the cell's ability to detect every organ's requirements for stem cells, to reach any location where stem cells are needed, and to meet the requirements for differentiation encountered upon arrival in an organ. Indigenous, melting-pot, and colonized organs will presumably send out different signals given differences in their accessibility to foreign cells; stable and proliferating cell populations will make different demands reflecting their ability to mobilize reserves; and stem cells will have to respond to different sorts of global and local cues if they are to fall into the different lineages and historic trajectories required to fulfill their pluripotential promise. Furthermore, some stem cells may be mobilized on an as *needed basis,* while others may be recruited regularly on a physiological or *renewal basis.*

Great progress in stem-cell therapy can be anticipated in the near future as a result of learning more about stem-cell antigens—representing the expression of certain genes, such as *PAX6.*[52] Knowing a cell's molecular identity allows researchers to study cell properties without having to observe those properties, and stem cells are increasingly equated to cells expressing some genetic marker and displaying some token of activity without regard to what the cells are or do in organisms. One can measure proliferation, for example, without observing cell division. Retroviruses, which infect only dividing cells and move to progeny *ad infinitum,* allow one to trace cell lineages as long as retrovirus expression is not down-regulated.[53] Labeled bromodeoxyuridine (BrdU) and labeled thymidine allow one to identifying all the cells dividing at one time, even if these labels are diluted by successive cell divisions and eventually become undetectable.[54] Defining stem cells molecularly may seem to place a premium on convenience at the expense of reliability, but it is the wave of the future and the way of progress.

NAMING STEM CELLS

Stem cells are named primarily in two ways: (1) by the age of the originating organism, hence, embryonal stem (ES) and adult stem cells; and (2) by the chief type of cell produced by the stem cell, such as germ stem (or germ-line stem [GS]) cells which give rise to sex cells of the germ line, and hematopoietic stem cells (HSCs) which give rise to all adult blood cell lineages (red blood, myeloid, and lymphoid cell lineages).[55] Hematopoietic cells with the potential of differentiating into a narrower range of cell types than HSCs are generally called blast forming units (BFUs) or colony forming units (CFUs). Other stem cells are not named so much as associated with the very tissue the stem cells are supposed to form (satellite cells associated with skeletal muscle), with part of this tissue (the proliferative or germinative cells of the epidermis), or even the differentiated cells of the tissue (liver hepatocytes).

The objective of scientific nomenclature is to specify precisely, but regrettably, stem cell nomenclature has not been coined systematically, and thus the most commonly used terms allude to vague properties of cells.[56] For example, because ES cells are supposed to differentiate in the adult into any tissue whatsoever, pluripotentiality in ES cells is confused with and sometimes thought to be identical to transdifferentiating or the change of cells from one sort of determination to another. Hematopoietic BFUs and CFUs, for example, demonstrate increasingly narrow potentials for differentiation, but, in adults, hematopoietic stem cells may differentiate into a variety of cell types[57] and vice versa,[58] although *bone fide* HSCs elude, if not defy, detection.

Embryonal Stem (ES) Cells
Current definitions of so-called embryonal stem cells (also embryo, or embryonic stem cells) or ES cells are unfortunately vague. ES cells are sometimes defined as cells derived from the blastocyst's (preembryo's) inner cell mass (ICM) or cells from early epiblast, especially if these cells retain their rounded dimensions and proliferate freely under special tissue culture conditions (i.e., provided

with "feeder cells"). The problem with this definition is that it does not identify the other peculiar capacities of stem cells. ES cells have also been defined as "simply stem cells that come from embryos."[59] The problem with this definition is that it does not exclude cells, such as germ stem (GS) cells, and especially malignant carcinoma cells which perform many of the same tricks played by ES cells, especially after treatment in tissue culture (exposure to human leukemia inhibition factor [LIF] and b-fibroblast growth factor [bFGF]). For purposes of replacement therapy, the most important definition of ES cells would seem an operational one: After injection into blastocysts, ES cells take part in forming all parts of embryos and extra-embryonic membranes (with the exception of chorionic epithelia and syncytia) and subsequently differentiate into any cell of the organism.

ES-like Cells

Ambiguity surrounding ES cells is rooted in history. The story of ES cells does not begin with their discovery and characterization in 1981,[60] but two decades earlier with Leroy Carlton Stevens's (b. 1920) study of teratomas.[61]

Non-malignant teratomas, typically found in gonads, are thought to be derived from primitive germ cells. These tumors are found in a variety of mammals but are best known in inbred strains of mice. They consist of disorganized but usually well differentiated tissues with a limited capacity for growth, and they retain these characteristics when grown ectopically (outside normal sites). Malignant teratomas, called teratocarcinomas, on the other hand, are known only in mice, although a few strains (C57BL/6 and AKR) are resistant to producing teratocarcinomas. They contain undifferentiated cells with unlimited proliferative capacity and a tendency to metastasize. Both nonmalignant and malignant teratomas occur spontaneously in mice, but both can also be produced experimentally by transplanting embryos or their parts to extra-uterine sites—known as ectopic sites.[62]

Stevens began by transplanting mouse embryos into testes. He found embryo-derived teratocarcinomas, called embryomas or embryoma cell foci, and a wide variety of differentiated somatic tissues: epithelia, neural, and connective, sometimes in organized and highly differentiated aggregates. When minced and introduced into fresh mouse hosts, the malignant stem cells grew, and, when re-transplanted at intervals of two to four weeks, the more malignant, faster growing stem cells became predominant, while the more differentiated somatic tissues disappeared. Steven also injected embryomas into the peritoneal cavity of mice. There, the foci grew in an ascites form, as single cell suspensions, as aggregates of small and solid embryoid bodies (EB), or as larger more complex masses with a central cavity and hematopoietic differentiation.

Both primary embryo-derived teratocarcinomas and re-transplanted tumors gave rise to permanent tumor-cell lines in tissue culture. Some lines, grown on a feeder-layer of growth-inhibited fibroblasts, became "feeder-layer dependent," but others, established in the absence of a feeder layer, were especially tolerant to alterations of their tissue culture environment. These lines, which were either developmentally pluripotent (multipotent) or nullipotent (impotent) embryonal carcinoma (EC) cells, became the stocks from which EC cell (ECC) lines were subsequently established.

Many pluripotent ECC lines are so prone to differentiate that unless maintained in an exponential growth phase (with a generation time of only fourteen to sixteen hours, i.e., requiring subcloning every forty-eight hours or less), they differentiate spontaneously and irreversibly, suspending proliferation and losing tumorgenicity in the process. However, particular ECC lines differ in their predisposition to differentiation, and some differentiate only in response to specific inductive stimuli.

In vivo, ECC lines (e.g., PCC4) differentiate as solid, nonmetastatic tumors. *In vitro,* they can be induced to differentiate by a variety of conditions: from mere high density to removal of feeder layers; by drug-induction from retinoids (especially all-*trans* retinoic acid [RA]) to bipolar compounds, such as dimethyl sulphoxide (DMSO) and hexamethylene bis-acetamide (HMBA); by immersion in serum-free medium, and plating on fibronectin-coated plastic surfaces.[63] Some ECC lines (e.g., F9) typically are "nullipotent," failing to differentiate and producing tumors of pure teratocarcinoma cells upon reintroduction to host animals, although in the presence of retinoic acid the same cells may differentiate into endoderm-like cells.

Malignancy and embryogenesis thus crossed paths at EBs, ECs, and ECC lines. Indeed, when ES cells were first discovered, their chief importance was thought to be for research on the nexus of differentiation and cancer.

> ES cell lines, which are established from peri-implantation mouse blastocysts (Evans and Kaufman, 1981; Martin, 1981) have many properties in common with embryonal carcinoma (EC) lines established from the malignant stem cells of teratocarcinomas, including the ability to colonize the somatic tissues of chimaeric mice following injection into host blastocysts.[64]

Or, in the words of Gail Martin, one of the discoverers of ES cells:

> The most compelling evidence for the close relationship between the tumor stem cells and normal embryonic cells is the fact that stem cells taken either from teratocarcinomas or from embryonal carcinoma cell cultures can participate in the development of completely normal adult mice when combined with embryonic cells by the technique of blastocyst injection. . . .[65]

Interest in ES cells only switched from cancer and differentiation to renewal and stem-cell replacement therapy when limited therapeutic success with determined stem cells (bone marrow transplants) suggested that more abundant, and easily available, pluripotential stem cells might improve therapeutic efficacy.[66]

Will the Real ES Cell Stand Up!

When ES cells (originally called EK cells or embryo-derived pluripotential cells) were finally described in 1981, they were characterized correctly but not simply. ES cells were cells derived from the mouse inner cell mass (ICM),[67] capable of proliferating while retaining a completely normal karyotype (40XX or 40XY chromosomes) when cultured on a feeder layer of fibroblasts.[68] ES cells also remained rounded *in vitro* instead of flattening and becoming fibroblast-like and retained the antigenic complexion of embryonic cells.[69]

Like some ECC lines, ES cells were capable of being tweaked into differentiating *in vitro*.[70] Thus, bone morphogenic protein 4 (BMP4) induced ES cells and teratocarcinoma cells to differentiate into mesenchymal-like cells (presumably a mesodermal derivative); retinoic acid induced ES cells to differentiate into neurons (a neuro-ectodermal derivative); and exposure to pancreatic bud tissue pushed ES cells in the direction of pancreatic-cell precursors (an endodermal derivative).

Furthermore, growing cultures of ES cells proceeded to form lumps of EBs which, in suspension, became tiny cysts, capable of differentiating complex tissues if allowed to reattach and spread out in petri dishes. Most importantly, when reintroduced into blastocysts, the ES cells differentiated into cells of all tissue within the developing mouse, including cells of the germ line.[71]

Here then was the first major difference between ES cells and cells from ECC lines: "Work using ES cells evolved from earlier experiments using embryonal carcinoma (EC) cells, which have very similar properties except in their germline-colonizing potential."[72] This feature of ES cells was capitalized upon even while ES cells were still considered "embryo-derived teratocarcinoma cell lines." Genetically manipulated *in vitro,* by targeted and nontargeted mutagenesis, mutated ES cells were left to sort themselves out upon injection into blastocysts. These cells wound up in all sorts of tissues in the "chimeric" mice, but when they arrived in the germ line, mice with the desired mutation could be reproduced sexually. These patented, so-called "knock-out" mice, proved a boon to medical researchers and the ledgers of patent holders.

ES cells and teratocarcinoma cells continued to be confused, since the same strain of mice, 129 SvE, which produced ES cells had also produced several ECC lines, but differences were gradually specified. In contrast to ES cells, ECC lines grew as tumors, specifically teratocarcinomas, when introduced into adult male mice, and ECC lines generally failed to colonize normal tissue (exhibited a restricted pattern) and often failed to differentiate normally when reintroduced into blastocysts, forming tumors instead, both pre- and postnatally. Unlike ES cells, moreover, ECC lines had abnormal karyotypes (chromosome number and appearance) and never contained a Y chromosome.

Notwithstanding these clarifications, ES cells remained in a conceptual limbo. Strictly speaking, ES cells had "been produced *only* in mice; in fact they ha[d] been produced only from one or a very few particular strains of mice."[73] Wilmut et al, while testifying at length to their unsuccessful attempts to extract ES cells from sheep embryos, argued convincingly for the absence of ES cells in livestock.[74] In other animals, ES cells are identified by comparison with mouse ES cells: morphology (rounded rather than flattened in tissue culture), a normal karyotype (quantity and quality of chromosomes), an ability to proliferate endlessly (depending on conditions), the expression of specific antigenic markers, and differentiation into cells of specific types under particular conditions of tissue culture. The crucial test of pluripotentiality following injection into blastocysts is not met in the case of human ES cells[75] and human primordial germ cells,[76] since one cannot resort to blastocyst injection as long as current ethical tastes prevail.

The relationship of ES cells to other stem cells is also uncertain. The possibility of ES cells serving as universal stem cells, capable of changing into any other kind of stem cell, is attractive but undemonstrated. The late appearance of adult stem cells opens the possibility that they have local origins independent of ES cells. Adult stem cells may even arise by dedifferentiation and hence not be ES-like cells at all.

Finally, some lines of mouse ES cells continue to behave suspiciously like teratocarcinoma cells. They differentiate spontaneously into masses of disorganized neurons, cartilage, and muscle, or, occasionally, into teratomas with well developed organs (an eye, hair, or tooth).

Stem-cell Replacement Therapy

Prospects for stem cells in replacement therapy stagger the imagination

> With the proper combinations of growth and differentiation factors, mouse ES . . . and EG [embryo germ cell] . . . cultures can generate cells of the hematopoietic lineage and cardiomyocytes . . . In addition, mouse ES cells have been used to generate *in vitro* cultures of neurons . . . skeletal muscle . . . and vascular endothelial cells . . .[77]

Incredibly, transplanting mouse neural-ES cells into rats with nine-day old spinal contusions and treated with cyclosporine (to suppress graft rejection) resulted in modest but significant improvement in locomotory function compared to control rats. Grafted cells, migrating as far as 8 mm from the site of transplantation, survived for up to five weeks as differentiated astrocytes, oligodendrocytes and neurons![78] One can also be encouraged by the efforts of the University of Pittsburgh neurosurgeon Douglas Kondziolka,[79] who transplanted neural stem cells into the brains of twelve stroke patients, and Anders Björklund and Olle Lindvall, of Lund University in Sweden, who grafted immature neurons from aborted fetuses into the brain of patients with Parkinson's disease where, in one instance, the grafted cells were making dopamine ten years after surgery.[80]

Most of the situations for which stem-cell replacement therapy has been prescribed involve some acute need, but stem-cell replacement can also work where need is chronic, such as the replacement of effete or worn-out blood cells. Chronic replacement may also be important for slowly turning over tissues such as parts of the central nervous system. For example, subventricular zone astrocytes (specifically, slowly proliferating type B cells) from the adult mammalian forebrain are multipotent neural stem cells normally and in regenerating brains *in vivo*. These cells also have the ability to grow into multipotent neurospheres in the presence of ectodermal growth factor (EGF) *in vitro*.[81]

Probably the biggest surprise for stem-cell researchers has been "alternate stem-cell differentiation" or transdifferentiation, the ability of stem cells to change their bias, or determination, and differentiate in new directions. Not all types of stem cells may be capable of any trick whatsoever, but "the inherent developmental potential of stem cells isolated from diverse tissues or organs may be more similar than previously anticipated."[82]

The kinds of restorations produced experimentally seem truly miraculous:

> It has recently been shown that genetically marked bone marrow can contribute to the regeneration of skeletal muscle . . . and of liver [ductular cells and hepatocytes] . . . in the host animal. In one study, the graft was composed of purified hematopoietic stem cells. . . . [83]

And

> Locally delivered primitive bone marrow cells promoted successful treatment of large myocardial infarcts after the completion of ischaemic cell death. This therapeutic intervention reduced the infarcted area and improved cardiac haemodynamics.[84]

And

> Most striking is the report that genetically marked mouse cells de-
> rived from the embryonic or adult brain and expanded in vitro as
> spheres [floating aggregates as opposed to cellular monolayers] were
> transplanted to an irradiated host mouse and gave rise to blood cells
> and other more primitive hematopoietic cells....[85]

This is not to say that all efforts at replacement therapy have been successful. Indeed, many years of frustrating results in nerve-precursor transplants to Parkinson's disease sufferers are sometimes explained by low
concentrations of stem cells in primary grafts (tissues from donors), effects
of the transplantation process itself (low survivorship of grafts following
transplantation), or the failure of stem cells to regenerate *in vivo* after proliferation *in vitro*.

The efficacy of enriching the concentration of stem cells in transplants
was demonstrated in 1996 when Margaret Goodell of the Whitehead Institute
for Biomedical Research, Massachusetts Institute of Technology, used a
fluorescent vital dye (Hoechst 33342, that binds to DNA in live cells without
killing them) to concentrate a "side population" (SP) of slowly proliferating
(cells in G_0– G_1 of the cell cycle) and proliferative cells (in the S–G_2–M
subpopulation) representing only 1–3 percent of the adult mouse bone marrow. The enriched transplant was capable of restoring normal blood cell
lineages to lethally irradiated mice.[86]

The organism seems perfectly capable of getting stem cells where they
are needed and when they are needed. Stem-cell homing and repopulation
depend on a "key and lock" mechanism involving keys of soluble chemo-
attractants, chemokines or ligands, issued by tissues at a stem-cell destina-
tion, and locks of chemokine receptors in the surface of stem cells.[87]
Chemokines are a class of cytokines, similar to growth factors, which are
known to selectively attract particular leukocytes to sites of inflammation.
Chemokine binding to receptors on cell surfaces "spark[s] off intracellular
signaling cascades that prompt migration towards the chemokine source."[88]
Not surprisingly, cancers seem to work the same way, and metastasis to
remote sites may be a function of the over expression of chemokine receptors
in tumor cells.[89] Stem cells and cancer cells follow the trail of chemokines,
adhere tightly to the (endothelial) cells lining blood vessels, and migrate
toward the source of the chemokine. Once at the site, the cells respond to
local conditions, known as the "niche," and move into their renewal and
differentiation phase.

The organism also seems perfectly capable of regulating the size of a
stem cell population, and even mouse blastocysts (preembryos) that are either

enlarged or reduced by the addition or deletion of cells give rise to neonates of normal size.[90] Even teratocarcinoma cells injected in small numbers into blastocysts are likely to be incorporated as normal cells in normal tissues rather than give rise to tumors.[91] It would seem that a great deal about normal tissues and organs is regulated by circulating growth factors, such as ectodermal growth factor, and organisms are not likely to be overwhelmed by stem cells.

Cloning also opens an avenue for creating therapeutic doses of stem cells. According to Wilmut et al, "therapeutic cloning" was the impetus for starting the research at Roslin in the first place.[92] Some day, cloning will allow "the patient's own cells to make healthy replacements for dysfunctional tissues—pertinent to patients with conditions as common and diverse as Alzheimer's disease or diabetes".[93]

MAKING IMMORTALS

Immortalization requires three major adjustments in human beings: (1) They must be *permanently juvenilized* in order to remain in a developmental mode and prevent net-negative changes from gaining an edge; (2) they must be equipped with *exotic stem (es) cells*; (3) they must be provided with an indwelling *generator,* a new organ, introduced into embryos and capable of generating es stem cells in perpetuity. Miraculously, these requirements may work synergistically.

Juvenilizing alone promotes longevity. For example, killing the germ line causes a 60 percent increase in longevity in *C. elegans* and extends the lifetime of short-lived *Drosophila.*[94] But this effect of juvenilization is not the primary reason for germ-line elimination. The objective is to replace GS cells with es cells and supersede gonads with a permanent generator of es cells. Immortality would then result from the interplay of signals regarding requirements for es cells arising in the human organism and the generator's ability to mobilize these cells to meet the demands for tissue renewal.

A cloned blastocyst would seem an ideal candidate for a generator of es cells, and installing it as early as possible in the host would seem the ideal situation for fostering its devolution as a new organ. The blastocyst/generator would produce its own es cells and could serve as a reservoir for additional stem cells or genetically modified (GM) stem cells. The blastocyst's penchant for implantation and placenta-formation would be put to use establishing circulatory channels between the generator and the host. The same vessels supplying the generator with sources of circulating nutrients and oxygen and sinks for waste products would also serve as the exit ports for es cells produced in the generator.

The blastocyst *qua* generator would aid in permanent juvenilization. Hormones, such as estrogen and progesterone, and circulating factors, such as ectodermal growth factor and somatostatin, produced by the blastocyst as it implants would interact with the host's endocrine system, suppressing gonadal development much as early pregnancy suppresses maturation.

The blastocyst/generator should be a clone of the individual being immortalized, not only to minimize the possibility of immunological rejection (see below), but to maximize the likelihood that es cells will recognize and read the host's own messages correctly. Given the vast individual differences found among human beings, it would seem a sure bet that, compared to foreign cells, the host's own es cells are more likely to appreciate the host's needs for stem cells, mobilize themselves in adequate numbers, respond to chemokines, identify stem-cell niches, and respond to their own cues with appropriate differentiation.

MAKING GENERATORS

The use of cloned blastocysts for generators may also solve most of the problems of synchronizing and reprogramming the host and generator. Clones raised to the point of blastocysts are natural generators of ES cells. Indeed, blastocysts do not even have to be coaxed to make ES cells, since this is precisely the task nature has assigned to them for making embryos, and it is a rare egg that has no embryo (a "wind egg" in birds, a barren germinal vesicle in mammals). The blastocyst cultured *in vitro* prior to implantation in the host also offers the option of supplementing the blastocyst's ES cells with "designer" es cells made by genetic modification to meet specific needs, such as correcting hereditary defects in the developing immortal.

Internalizing the generator in the individual host may not be too difficult either. Certainly, acquired-immune tolerance and the successful creation of "knock-out" mice shows just how available blastocysts are for taking up and accommodating foreign cells. Problems of rejection and genetic incompatibility should not arise as long as generators are installed early, and the earlier the better.[95]

CLONED GENERATORS

The first clones of vertebrates—artificial identical twins—were produced by isolating blastomeres.[96] The same process, reproduced in livestock, led to the production of identical lamb twins[97] and herds of identical cows which, had they panned out commercially, might have utterly changed agribusiness.[98]

Today, this early work is mainly of interest for its theoretical implications for the doctrine of nuclear equivalence, namely, that all of the cells and organisms produced from a single cell are genetically identical. The importance of their identity is that, like the parts of identical twins, the parts of cloned mammals can be grafted to each other without incurring the wrath of the immune system, so notorious when grafts are made between genetically non-identical mammals. As a consequence of having identical genomes, cloned organisms have virtually interchangeable parts.

The simplest way to create a cloned generator would seem to be to employ microtechnology to separate human blastomeres in much the same way Hans Spemann used loops of hair to separate salamander blastomeres. The technique is already known to be efficacious in live stock.[99]

Both blastomeres would then be raised in culture to the early (free) blastocyst stage (Stage 3, 0.1–0.2 mm diameter),[100] four days post ovulation (dpo). At this time, the blastocysts are inspected for normalcy and one of the two blastocysts is transferred to the uterus of the mother or a surrogate mother—a prenatal foster mother—where the blastocyst implants and begins producing extraembryonic membranes and soon thereafter an embryo. The other blastocyst is frozen at this time, or, alternatively, the blastocyst is ligated again to make two blastocysts, and both are frozen.

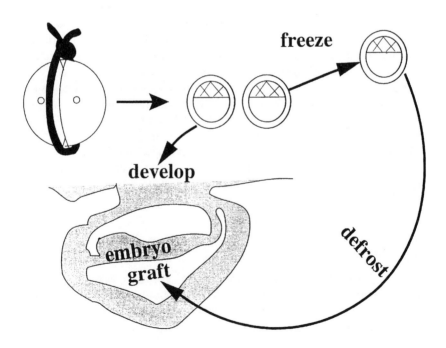

At about 16 dpo the embryo reaches the notochordal process stage (Stage 7, 0.4 mm diameter). Primordial germ cells appear (in the vicinity of the allanto-enteric primordium) but do not yet begin their travel through the embryo. Within two days, the embryo has reached the neural groove stage (Stage 8, 1.0–1.5 mm length), and the intra-embryonic mesoderm has split, giving rise to the rudimentary intra-embryonic body cavity (coelom). At that time, the frozen blastocyst would be defrosted.

About two weeks after embryo transfer (18 dpo), the defrosted blastocyst or blastocysts would be inserted into the host's developing coelomic cavity and, with the help of fiber-optics-assisted microsurgery, grafted to the embryo's mesonephric ridges in the vicinity of the future gonadal ridges. This maneuver would be performed while the uterine rudiments, specifically the apical portion of paramesonephric ducts, are present in both sexes and before primordial germ cells have monopolized the rudimentary gonads. The blastocyst/generator would then have several days to "implant" in the developing mesonephric ridges before primordial germ cells arrived (Stage 13, 28 dpo, 4–6 mm length).[101]

The host embryo would then continue developing into a fetus, while the blastocyst(s) devolves into the generator. Having colonized the rudimentary gonadal ridges, the generator's es cells would preempt the niches ordinarily occupied by primordial germ cells. The generator itself would then be incorporated and integrated into the fetus in place of its gonads. About eight months later, the sterile, but immortalized, individual would be born, or more likely delivered surgically, just to play safe.

FORCING BLASTOCYSTS TO DEVOLVE INTO GENERATORS

Turning a blastocyst into a stable organ will not be a trivial task. Presently, blastocysts transplanted outside the uterus prove disastrous to the host. In ectopic, or tubal, pregnancies, blastocysts burrow through host tissue, creating hemorrhage and death in the absence of timely surgical intervention. Moreover, in mice, a blastocyst at the six to seven day stage, containing a so-called egg cylinder prior to neurulation, or just its parts without extra-embryonic membranes and ectoplacental cone, are likely to turn into a tumor when transplanted beneath the kidney capsule of syngeneic, or semi-syngeneic, histocompatible recipients. Tumors may be harvested as early as four to five weeks after grafting, but, at six to seven weeks, the tumors are unmistakable teratomas. They lack undifferentiated teratocarcinoma cells and appear cystic (containing holes), with large, fibrous areas.[102] Within the tumors, in the vicinity of cavities, ECCs sometimes form EBs resembling post-implantation embryos, consisting of an inner mass of ECCs surrounded by a layer resembling endoderm.[103]

How then can grafted blastocysts be kept from acting like tumors and producing tumor cells? Two approaches hold some promise for solving these problems. The organism's own defenses may kick in to prevent runaway implantation, and antibodies to surface receptors may be applied to blastocysts in order to direct host/generator affinities.

The organism's own defenses center in the uterus which offers normal resistance to implantation and stops the invasion of a blastocyst before it reaches the deep muscular layers. The embryo receiving the blastocyst graft will not have a uterus, but the graft would be placed in the vicinity where gonadal ridges will arise, and those ridges in both male and female embryos will contain the rudiments of a uterus.[104] Ordinarily, the zona basalis of the uterus knows the secret for stopping the invasion of the implanting blastocyst. Possibly, some of that secret knowledge is already available in the rudimentary uterus running down the gonadal ridge, and, just possibly, a rudimentary ability to contain blastocyst implantation will be sufficient to control implantation by the blastocyst generator. If not, a second approach would remain an option, namely, to treat the blastocyst with antibodies to receptors prior to introducing it into the perspective host.

In either event, the constrained blastocyst installed in the vicinity of the embryonic mesonephros should be serviced by abundant blood vessels, presumably joined by lymphatic vessels and nerves. The ES cells produced by the ectopic blastocyst might then prove to be es cells and not their pathogenic siblings (EC cells and ECC lines).

Keeping Generators within Limits

The generator ensconced in the immortal's body must devolve into a resident organ and not develop into a Siamese twin! The problem of preserving normality in the generator's cells while turning it into a new organ might seem monumental, but the anecdotal records collected by sonographers performing routine ultrasonic diagnoses of human pregnancy suggest that the solution may be at hand. Twinning, it would seem, is much more common during early pregnancy than at late pregnancy and at birth. The disappearance of twins during the course of pregnancy, while usually attributed to resorption by the uterus, may also be explained by absorption into the surviving twin. Were this the case, a lot of human beings would be "chimeras," having both their own original cells and those of an absorbed twin. Placing a twin under wraps, therefore, may not be as difficult as one might initially imagine, especially when the twin is a clone.

An alternative solution to the problem of preventing the generator's development is suggested by the success of J. M. Slack in creating headless tadpoles.[105] Some features of embryos would seem to come under quite local control which can thence be altered without affecting the rest of the embryo. If Slack can manage to make headless tadpoles through genetic manipulation, it should be possible to make arrested blastocysts through genetic manipulation, or, better still, by mimicking the effect of genes chemically or physically. For example, loading the generator with progesterone or providing it with implants containing the hormone may prevent unwanted development the same way progesterone slows larval development in salamanders.[106]

Regulating a Generator

Having overcome the problems of installing and containing a generator, getting it to operate properly should be relatively easy. Ideally, the devolved generator will remain embryonic despite the presence of circulating hormones and growth factors which would otherwise push it in the direction of differentiation. By keeping the immortal in a preadolescent holding pattern, no progression of cues for critical and sensitive periods would throw the generator off track. Where trauma might create conflicting information, problems can be averted by timely intervention.

Some problems might not materialize. One problem might even provide a useful solution to another without either becoming problematic. For example, the generator's effect on the host may actually work toward juvenilization and hence immortalization. Specifically, normal embryos release factors that modulate maternal responses, such as the maintenance of the corpus luteum. One would guess that the arrested generator would produce hormones whose overriding effects would be juvenilizing. The generator might then regulate the host as the host regulates the generator. As for problems discovered after immortals are created, immortality will allow enough time to find their solutions.

GENERATOR-HOST COMPATIBILITY

The generator, providing an eternal source of stem cells, would literally be a "fountain of youth," in the sense of providing fresh cells that keep the organism in a permanently youthful condition. Virtually all the breakdowns and deficits associated with aging from cardiovascular accidents, cerebral thrombosis (stroke), and pneumonia, would be prevented or rectified by continuous, cellular replacement. As a devolved, and fully-integrated organ, the generator would hardly increase oxidative stress or place any other burden on the organism.

Buried deep in the abdomen, the generator would be out of harm's way with regard to UV-induced DNA damage, genomic methylation, and the silencing of tumor-suppressor genes. Even cancer would be conquered, since the "mutator phenotype"—the age-dependent increase in cancer stem cells due to mutations in genes governing genome stability—would not kick in. Given a normal rate of spontaneous mutation in the generator (approximately

2×10^{-7} per gene per cell division), the rate of mutations would be "well below the predicted value of between four and ten rate-limiting, stochastic events for tumour initiation and progression."[107] Furthermore, with constant renewal, the immune surveillance system would be continuously up and running. Instead of curing cancer in order to promote longevity, generators will cure mortality, thereby preventing cancer.

Compatibility between generator and host is a Pandora's box yet to be opened fully, but where its edges have been pried, its contents are not particularly alarming.[108] Mammals, especially the early mammal and its mother, are a lot more porous than ordinarily thought, as witness the presence of proteins and even cells from both mother and fetus in each other's circulation. Thus, "the boundary around the individual is being pushed out to include others in the process of its self-definition."[109] The presence of a generator in an immortalized individual simply pushes the envelope further.

A cloned blastocyst developing into a generator within a host organism should meet all the conditions for immunological compatibility between generator and host. Were a non-cloned generator grafted to an immunologically competent adult, the adult host's immuno-surveillance system would detect the generator and the stem cells it produces and consider them nonself (foreign), triggering the host's host versus graft reaction.[110] In the absence of immuno-suppressive drugs, such a reaction would result in the rejection of the generator. Alternatively, and more disastrously, immuno-competent cells produced by the generator would recognize the host as nonself, and reject it in the bizarre graft versus host reaction leading to the host's death.

The problems of immuno-surveillance might be avoided by inducing so-called "acquired-immune tolerance" in the host. First theorized by (Frank) Macfarlane Burnet (1899–1985) in 1949[111] and demonstrated by Peter Medawar (1915–1987) in the early '50s,[112] acquired-immune tolerance is induced when donor tissues are present in the developing host.[113] The host organism is thereafter able to accept grafts from the same donor as "self," not only accepting grafts of the original tissue, but grafts from virtually anywhere in the donor's body.

Actually, Medawar stumbled upon what was to become an important clue to acquired-immune tolerance. While studying the ability of identical twins to accept grafts from each other, Medawar discovered a high frequency of polymorphism of blood groups in nonidentical, or fraternal, twins and, subsequently, a high frequency of acquired-immune tolerance among these twins. Both the polymorphism and acquired-immune tolerance were attributed to the direct transfusion of blood over anastomoses between the twins's circulatory systems *in utero*. The ability of host organisms to support cells transferred to them *in utero* throughout a lifetime clearly raises prospects for an immortalized host tolerating both a generator introduced early in its lifetime and the es cells produced by the generator.

Medawar also brought to light the cause of congenitally defective calves known as freemartins. These are female calves that shared the mother's uterus with a male twin. Genetic incompatibility between the female calf and the very cells that rendered her immuno-tolerant to her brother produced the birth defects. Fortunately for immortalization, this type of incompatibility can be circumvented if the blastocyst/generator is a virtual identical twin created by cloning. Instead of transfused stem cells provoking pathological development, stem cells arising from a clone of the host would be not only compatible with the host, but genetically identical with the host. The beauty of using a cloned blastocyst as the rudimentary source of the generator and installing it early in the host's development is that the host would benefit from the double insurance of acquired-immune tolerance and genetic compatibility.

Epilogue: Reprise & Prediction

But the phrase "God is dead" . . . synthesizes the idea of God with time, becoming history and man. It says at one and the same time: God existed *and* he is dead *and* he will rise from the dead, God has become Man *and* Man has become God.

—Gilles Deleuze, *Nietzsche and Philosophy*

Everything, then, must happen as if an independent memory gathered images as they successively occur along the course of time; and as if our body, together with its surroundings, was never more than one among these images, the last is that which we obtain at any moment by making an instantaneous section in the general stream of becoming.

—Henri Bergson, *Matter and Memory*

What largely defines our experience of ourselves and the world is that we are subjects. In our society, growing up often means putting up with being treated as objects and enduring our lack of freedom by promising ourselves that someday we, like grownups, will do only what *we* want to. Dependence and passivity are viewed as infantile characteristics, inappropriate for the model adult (at least the adult male).

—Susan Oyama, *The Ontogeny of Information*

Becoming Immortal began by examining the biological premises that challenge prospects for making immortal human beings and ended by laying out the technical possibilities for doing just that. In this epilogue, I examine what immortals would be and what life would be like in a world shared with immortals.

The immortal human being would resemble extant mortal preadolescent human beings of about eleven years of age, with an individual appearance (phenotype) acquired through the interaction of hereditary material (genotype) with a physico-psycho-social structure known as the "environment." Indeed, the only physical difference between mortal preadolescents and immortals would be that the immortals would be of different chronological ages. Because the immortals's tissues, organs, and systems would be maintained and repaired eternally through the differentiation of self-renewing, pluripotential exotic stem (es) cells released by an internal generator, immortals would not mature or age.

The principles for making *Homo sapiens* forma *immortalis* are well established in canonical biology (see Chapter 1). Biology prescribes that an individual organism, such as any one of us, consists of two parts: the germplasm, or nuclear genes, made of heredity units, and the somatoplasm made of cytoplasm, including organelles. Germplasm flows immortally from generation to generation through germ lines of eggs and spermatozoa, while somatoplasm branches off the germ line at nodes of fertilization or points of recombination, forming somatic lines, or cell lineages that comprise mortal individuals. From the point of view of biologists, achieving immortality depends simply on reversing these roles, creating an endless flow in the somatic line at the expense of the germ line.

The problem for making immortal human beings is that nothing in our Darwinian evolution (see Chapter 2) or normal course of development (see Chapter 3) offers the remotest possibility of performing the sea change of somatic and germ lines. Biological change is not limited to evolution and development, however, and a window of opportunity would seem open in preadolescence for stabilizing individuals around the positive process of life. At that stage of development, degenerative changes would not yet have taken the upper hand in the balance with growth, differentiation, and sculpturing.

Ways of affecting the desired sea change are suggested by the exceptional changes thought to have occurred in early life forms (see Chapter 4). Early life on Earth may have produced cells with nuclei (eukaryotes), sex, death, and multicellular organisms through devolution, the fusion and/or fission of life forms. A new organ, the generator, might be engineered by mimicking these devolutionary processes.

The generator would begin as a cloned blastocyst and turn into a perpetual source of immunologically and genetically compatible es cells dwelling within the organism. The generator would wholly replace gonads, and es cells would permanently supplant germ lines, and hence juvenilize the human being forever (see Chapter 5).

Only two questions remain: What are the realistic prospects for immortalization? What adjustments will be required for life among and with immortals?

PROSPECTS FOR IMMORTALIZATION

NOT ON THE AGENDA, BUT ...

The realistic prospects for immortality are hard to judge simply because immortality research is not presently on the agenda of any national agency, nonprofit enterprise, or even biotech startup company. Rather, "human-machine synthesis is seen as the next stage of human evolution"[1] and the avant-garde of research devotes itself to work on cyborgified longevity. I expect that the cyborgification of human beings will continue, since it is profitable and efficacious in many circumstances. My guess is that cyborgian replacement therapy will become the mode for mortal human beings, and the human-machine synthesis will only be enhanced if mortals ever attempt to compete in longevity with truly immortal beings.

The human-machine lobby will probably attempt to dampen enthusiasm for immortality, but the growth of an immortality lobby will ultimately overwhelm resistance. I imagine that such a lobby will emerge rapidly once the first immortal mammals are produced. These mammals, probably sheep to begin with, will undoubtedly be generated for all the same reasons that clones are presently being generated—to perpetuate organisms with unique and valuable qualities. If, for example, one would like to have a clone of sheep producing human clotting factor IX,[2] one would like to have such sheep producing the factor in perpetuity. Inevitably, it will be cheaper to produce one or another factor from immortal animals than suffer the uncertainty and expense of producing mortal animals. I predict that the same commercial forces presently encouraging research on cloning will shortly be promoting research on immortality.

Frankly, I cannot imagine that the successful immortalization of other mammals will not be followed swiftly by pleas for the immortalization of human beings. The frustrations precipitated by the inevitability of death presently confronting mortals will not go away and will only be exacerbated by the immortality of other mammals—our cousins.

COMMERCE AND REGULATION

Managing reproduction has always been a lucrative business. If the experience of infertility services, such *in vitro* fertilization (IVF) clinics, is any indication, immortalization will "take off" once it is an available option for human beings.

> Infertility services have been transformed from a small medical specialty to a $2-billion-a-year industry. Couples seeking IVF are spending $44,000 to $200,000 to achieve a single pregnancy. Infertility specialists are now the highest-paid doctors, with experienced ones making an average of $625,000 per year.[3]

Moreover,

> When egg donation began in 1984, Richard Seed paid donors just $250. By 1994 the going rate was $1,500. In 1998 St. Barnabas

Hospital in Livingston, New Jersey, boosted its rate from $2,500 to $5,000 during an egg donation bidding war. But the largest fee— $35,000—is being offered by an anonymous couple who specifically want an attractive, intelligent, *Princeton* woman's egg.[4]

At these prices, immortality will rapidly become a major growth industry. Immortalization will certainly be too expensive to be performed on the offspring of average citizens, but this is not to say that it will not be done by those who can afford it, or, at great sacrifice, by those who cannot.

Presumably, governments will take a hand in regulating immortality under pressure from one or another class, but regulation need not be arbitrary. If only because so much of the biotechnology of immortalization will have been developed commercially, and "bottom-line economics rules," regulations governing immortality and the choice of having immortal children will probably follow the same rules adopted for IVF and surrogacy, namely, regulating "as little as possible" and hoping the private sector acts responsibly. In any case, current trends in globalization may create a free market atmosphere for immortalization, rendering meaningless any local efforts at regulation.

Alternatively, less salubrious scenarios pit governments against individuals. As immortals become common, governments, led by mortals, might feel threatened, and may attempt to place limits on the number of immortals women are allowed to produce. Indeed, governments might mandate the authority to decide who shall be born immortal. In an age of unprecedented wealth and massive poverty, of local recession and global capitalism, governments might coerce parents to choose immortalizing an embryo or face forced abortion and sterilization.[5] Reproductive freedom of individuals might even be sacrificed to eugenic abstractions such the "purity of race" or some such Nazi aberration.[6]

On the other hand, recognizing the threat of the population explosion, governments may foster immortalization as a device for curbing human reproduction.[7] An enlightened government might make immortalization available through its national health service or its equivalent in insurance. Access to immortalization might even be recognized as a universal right and made available to the offspring of all women on Earth. The cost of immortalization might then be borne by international agencies and the procedure performed without charge to winners of a worldwide lottery administered by UNESCO. The hidden agenda of such a program would be to prevent rich nations from dominating the future immortal world with their nationals, but care would also have to be taken to prevent the segregation of immortals and discrimination either for or against them. These problems, to whatever degree they materialize, might moderate as the number of immortals increases in proportion to the number of mortals in populations around the world.

THE DIFFICULT MATTER OF CHOICE

The immortality that I have described would not be available to anyone alive today. On the contrary, the "gift" of immortality would be a legacy bestowed on children by a conscious decision of their mortal parents, or governments, as the case may be. Those most affected by the decision would have no choice regarding their immortality (barring suicide, which is always an option). How should parents make such a choice?

What does a mortal parent say to an immortal child when asked, "Why did you make me immortal?" Unless I am mistaken, generational conflict could enter a new, high-energy orbit unless suitable answers are available. I can just imagine the "wrongful immortality" suits (and "wrongful mortality" suits for that matter) brought by children against their parents, but I cannot imagine the judicial outcomes.

Why, after all, would anyone want to make their children immortal? One possibility is that parental choices are rather bleak to begin with, so why not. Alternatively, would-be parents might want to offer a child the best possible future available through bio/medical technology, or they might want to guarantee the perpetuity of their line without having to worry about future fecundity, including the fecundity of descendants. Furthermore, when something becomes technologically feasible, it frequently becomes subliminally desirable, and parents may immortalize their children for no more complicated reason than "keeping up with the Joneses." The current craze for ultrasonic diagnosis of pregnancy has, more often than not, no other rationale than fashion.

Another, more philosophical reason to immortalize one's children is that as long as death looms, every other issue of human existence takes a back seat. As the pressing issue of mortality is left behind, immortal human beings could go on to solve the remaining problems of life and bring about the true Millennium. Thus, by helping to build a world of immortals, one also bestows upon it a legacy of peace and well being.

The issue of choice may not be problematic for many parents. Parents (or at least would-be mothers) have exercised choice over having offspring ever since reproduction became separable from sex, that is, ever since birth control, contraceptives, and abortion became practical and widely available. But choice has frequently been elevated to prospective parents through attractive advertisements, if not education and guidance. Indeed,

> [l]ate-twentieth-century humans—some privileged ones—are faced with staggering decisions: which transforming technologies to use, when, on whom and with whose permission, for whose benefit?[8]

My guess is that immortality will be sold in much the same way that the bio/medical industry sells all the paraphernalia and procedures of the other new reproductive technologies (NRT). Marketing moguls seem to have been weaned on alphabet soup and find appeal in acronyms rather than rhymes or reasons. All sorts of technofetal and cyborgbaby testing and diagnosis are available: alpha-feto-protein testing (AFT), amniocentesis, blastomere analysis before implantation (BABI), chorionic villus sampling (CVS), computer assisted semen analysis (CASA), electronic fetal monitoring (EFM), fetal karyotyping, prenatal screening, scalp monitors, and ultrasound imaging. Likewise, choice is available in technologically assisted reproduction (TAR) or assisted reproductive technology (ART): technoconception or artificial insemination (AI), cryopreservation, donor egg insemination (DI), embryo transfer (ET), gestational surrogacy, infertility therapies, intrauterine growth retardation (IUGR), intrauterine transfusion, in-vitro fertilization (IVF) with or without ovum donation, gamete intra-fallopian transfer (GIFT), microsurgical epidydymal sperm aspiration (MESA), pellucida zone drilling (PZD), semen banks, surrogacy, superovulatory drugs, and zygote intra-fallopian transfer (ZIFT). To which should now be added stem cell preservation from placental blood.

I, for one, cannot oppose this technology while at the same time taking advantage of it, whether directly or indirectly, although I am concerned with issues of ownership (who is profiting?) and power (who is choosing). Taking my cue from Donna Haraway, I would rather wrest control over technology than oppose it.

Then again, do potential parents have the right to choose immortality for their offspring? The issue falls into the category of ethical dilemmas currently concentrated in debates over parental rights for choosing the sex of offspring. Presently, a fetus of the "right" sex is chosen by aborting fetuses of the "wrong" sex, and "choice" is inextricably clouded by problems surrounding abortion. Were such choices freely available to everyone, one can imagine that half the population of the world will disappear in one generation. But what is life worth for unwanted "human detritus" suffering through a mortal lifetime with wounded self-esteem?

A similar issue arises when aborting fetuses with chromosome 21 trisomy detected by prenatal screening. Most individuals born with this trisomy are capable of enjoying life given an opportunity, and no comparison is warranted to fetuses with other karyotypic aberrations, who are not likely to survive long after birth. Similarly, neonates with genes for "late-onset genetic disorders" (such as Huntington's disease) might have good and productive lives prior to the onset of any disability. At that point, the issue of "life with dignity" merges with "death with dignity" and the option of assisted suicide emerges—not the option of abortion.

Possibly the best argument for leaving the choice of immortality to parents is the principle of "procreative autonomy . . . embedded in any genuinely democratic culture."[9] Coined by Ronald Dworkin,

[t]he right of procreative autonomy has an important place . . . in Western political culture . . . The most important feature of that culture is a belief in individual human dignity: that people have the moral right—and the moral responsibility—to confront the most fundamental questions about the meaning and value of their own lives for themselves, answering to their own consciences and convictions . . .[10]

John Harris, Sir David Alliance Professor of Bioethics at the University of Manchester and director of the Centre for Social Ethics and Policy, would probably extend the rights granted under reproductive autonomy to parents willing to have immortal children (created by the internalization of a generator as described here).

If you are interested in the ethics of creating people then, so long as existence is in the created individual's own best interests, and the individual will have the capacity for autonomy, then the motives for which the individual was created are either morally irrelevant or subordinate to other moral consideration.[11]

Ruth Deech, chairman of the Human Embryology and Fertilisation Authority, believes, however, that

reproductive autonomy cannot mean the freedom to breed as one likes. Many societies, including our own, have rules about, for example, incest, underage sex, bestiality, adultery, and abortion for good, principled reasons.[12]

While her discussion focuses on cloning, her objections would probably extend to producing immortal children.

Issues surrounding the creation of immortals will flow across every border. "Africans who view people as both uniquely individual and as intimately connected by relationships to others in the present, past, and future"[13] may see immortality quite differently from Europeans. The issues will not go away by themselves, and informed debate would seem preferable to sliding silently into the unknown.

TECHNOLOGY AND HUMAN DIGNITY

The flip side of technological progress is frequently the erosion of human dignity. Immortality is not likely to be any different, and debates over human dignity surrounding immortality are not likely to be resolved to everyone's satisfaction.

Controversy over artificial means of controlling human life generally settles on two problems (which may be one and the same): objections to human experimentation and to treating human beings as means to ends (objectification).[14] I can offer no solution to the problem posed by human experimentation without indulging in self-contradiction, since achieving immortality will inevitably require human experimentation. I would imagine that, contrary to the experience with other forms of cyborgian birthing, such as *in vitro* fertilization and embryo transfer, experiments with other animals will precede human experimentation.[15] Current law would seem to preclude the possibility of using human beings in experimentation on immortality until research on other animals has demonstrated the efficacy and safety of the procedure.

My guess is that the first efforts at internalizing a generator of es cells will be for treating a human embryo or fetus having a genetic disease such as progeria (rapid, abnormal aging). Experimentation has always been tolerated more readily for treating a life-threatening condition than purely for learning something new.

The problem of objectification, however, remains open. The most exacting version of the problem is drawn around the Kantian principle that a human being should never be thought of as a means toward an end but always granted the dignity and status of an end in itself. This principle is invoked when ethicists proscribe the use of human beings for experimentation without informed consent. Thus, if embryos and fetuses are considered human beings incapable of granting informed consent, they could not be used in experiments to immortalize and could hardly serve as sources of clones and stem cells.

More than one individual would be involved in the process of immortalization, and the problem of informed consent hinges on a larger issue, namely, the status of individuals involved in pregnancy. Certainly a woman is generally capable of giving informed consent and, if it is her individuality and dignity that is to be respected, the Kantian objection may be surmountable. Her donation of an egg for the purpose of creating a cloned generator would be as legitimate as any adult donating an organ. Indeed, the state warrants organ donation, providing the donor-card is attached by individuals to their driving license. How large a leap is it then to the legitimacy of the same woman giving informed consent to have the generator she spawned inserted in the blastocyst implanted in her womb? The only issue remaining would be that the process is initially "experimental," but even were the process to fail, one might rationalize it if "some good came out of the loss," that is, if something were learned from the experiment.

ADJUSTMENTS REQUIRED BY IMMORTALIZATION

No mortal can presently have any idea what life will be like for the immortals, the kind of social life the immortals will establish or the society mortals and immortals will create. One can be sure, however, that initially the immortals' problems will seem endless.

Some problems can be anticipated and should be met with adequate prophylaxis. The genome of immortals would initially encompass a small part of the human genetic pool, a fraction of the biodiversity represented by human beings. Such a pool should be expanded as quickly as possible to offset the possibility of new diseases spreading rapidly among immortals. In the absence of adequate counter measures, new diseases might wipe out the first immortals in a single pandemic.

Other problems are unforeseeable. Will the immortals bond together, identify with each other as a group, seek their own protection and mutual advantage in clans? Would the immortals perform the same sorts of antisocial behavior performed by mortals? Would the death penalty have to be invoked to deter murder by immortals? How would immortals deal with the death of mortal loved ones? Denied the comfort of going to paradise themselves, where loved ones are reunited, what comfort could be offered to immortals doomed to live forever bereft of parents, mortal siblings, and friends—even other immortals killed by accident?

Moreover, how will ordinary mortals react to immortals? Will mortals grant them "minority status" and attempt to suppress them. Will mortals objectify immortals and tend to place them in the category of artifact, "something manufactured" rather than a "natural human being" entitled to all the protections granted by law and permitted by fair play?

CONTEMPLATING IMMORTAL LIFE

I may be worrying needlessly. Chances are, the immortals' problems will not be that different from ours. For example, pressure on traditional families and kinship structures will certainly continue following immortalization. Technology, however, will be as much the parent of immortals as mortal parents. But we too have been replacing the family with some more nebulous institution ever since *in vitro* fertilization and surrogacy were invented. As Lori Andrews, the dean of lawyers specializing in the birth industry, points out, "In the Clone Age, it would be possible for a child to have five parents: a sperm donor, egg donor, surrogate mother, and the couple who intended to raise the child."[16]

In the case of surrogacy, parental assignment is usually awarded to those who pay for the procedure.[17] If the same policy applies to immortalized people, parenthood may be decided by the highest bidder. The State, which will inevitably pick up a share of the tab, might also demand a role in parenting or, at least, in assigning parenthood. Paying this piper, however, may utterly destroy anything presently resembling family.

No doubt other answers will be offered, but immortal children will out-live their parents and the problems of immortality will move on to the kinds of adjustments immortals will have to make to each other. Will this world of the immortals be recognizable to extant mortals? I have only a faint idea of just how different it will be and can only offer conjectures about what mortals, like ourselves, will learn from this new world—about ourselves and about immortals.

Probably, in much the same way that children have adjusted to talking toys and reasoning computers, immortal human beings will adjust to their situation and find new and novel ways to cope with their reality. These ways may, however, be incomprehensible to mortals, at least at first. As Sherry Turkle has reported about "postmodern" children,

> Faced with ever-more-complex computational objects, children are now in the position of theoretical *bricoleurs,* or tinkerers, "making do" with whatever materials are at hand, "making do" with whatever theory can fit a prevailing circumstance. They cycle through evolution and psychology and resurface ideas about motion in terms of communication of bits.[18]

In contrast

> When today's adults "cycle through" different theories, they are uncomfortable. Such movement does not correspond to the unitary visions they were brought up to expect. But children have learned a different lesson from their cyborg objects.[19]

Borrowing from Donna Haraway, Turkle concludes

> In this sense, today's cyborg [substitute immortal] children, growing up into irony, are becoming adept at holding incompatible things together. They are cycling through the cy-dough-plasm into fluid and emergent conceptions of self and life.[20]

My guess is that the immortals will make an adjustment to immortal life, while mortals will find it too cyborgian for comfort.

THE WORLD OF IMMORTALS

I should say something about what I think the world may look like to immortals. I approach this task with trepidation, not only because I appreciate how utterly speculative my opinion must be, but because I feel uncomfortable in the immortal's world as I see it.

I imagine that the most glaring difference in the world of immortals in contrast to my world will be the experience of time in the sense of past, present, and future. Everything about life as I know it, having lived my life in a modern, developed, and still developing, Western culture, is predicated on this sense of time, and it is precisely this sense that will be radically different for people who live forever. Instead of "living by the clock," time will be immaterial for the immortals. It will be infinitely accessible, neither running down nor running out. The difference will not be how an infinity of time affects the immortal's values—whether the immortals will be lazy by today's standards (I imagine they will acquire a work ethic through nurture and will be as interested in completing tasks as we are)—but how an infinity of time will affect everything about perception and the experience of life.

In Western culture, time is ubiquitous. It permeates everything. Even language, our chief means of communicating, requires conjugation, and one can hardly conceive of a sentence in any European language (certainly English) that does not have time already built into it. For the immortals, however, time will be replaced by infinite duration, the present expanded to eternity. Even familiar terms, such as *lifetime*, will cease to have their familiar meaning. Rather than a finite duration, or a period before death, a lifetime will stretch outward forever from the beginning of consciousness.

Time is always more than time. It is money, power, and inevitably, a source of conflict. Writers of inspired literature long ago struggled with time. Divining a connection between timelessness and power, these writers attributed immortality to God (and gods). Unrestrained by natural laws, God's incoherence was pawned off as a consequence of omnipresence. Philosophers, too, remind us of the fragility of time. The present, deprived of duration, is destroyed the instant it appears.

Ordinarily, one lives in the present because the transition of future and past passes without any bump. This passage will make no sense for the immortals. For the immortals, an infinite present will rupture the transition of future and past, or, put another way, the present will spread infinitely into the past and future.

And what about time's creations, mortal life and experience? Of course, the sun will rise on immortals just as it does on mortals, and immortals and mortals will feel its warmth. They will share the same admiration for a beautiful, bright day and experience the same joy at the coming of a verdant springtime. But the immortal's sun will not be the same as the mortal's sun, nor will anything else perceived by the immortals be the same as that perceived by mortals. What is crucial to the difference in perception is that the senses will not define the present for the immortals. The senses will identify moments, and life for the immortals will be a cornucopia of sensory perceptions, but moments will not be recalled in seriatim, akin to the passage of time. When the present is no longer pierced by the arrow of time, by the coming future and the receding past, then perception will implode and time will disintegrate.

An analogy may help clarify what I imagine by the present experienced by mortals and the implosion of time to be experienced by immortals. The so-called "persistence of vision" is often invoked to account for the blurring of an object moving quickly before our eyes (for example, the wings of insects or small birds in flight) and for our ability to see continuous movement when viewing cinema rather than rapidly changing frames on the big screen. Thus, persistence of vision explains in physiological terms the continuity which, in cognitive terms, is called movement.[21]

The question is, what will the persistence of vision translate into for immortals? Here is where the world of the mortals will differ most sharply from the world of the immortals, because what a mortal perceives as movement, an immortal will perceive as time, and what an immortal perceives as movement, a mortal will perceive as time. Ironically, the same physiology of persistence shared by immortals and mortals will present a barrier to communication and understanding—one that will be overcome only with utmost difficulty.

What about the other senses? In much the same way that the persistence of vision creates the sense of movement on a screen, the persistence of other senses (smell, taste, touch, hearing) creates the continuity called aroma, flavor, feeling, language, music, etc. In other words, the persistence of senses is precisely the physiological explanation for all the cognitive experiences of life, for the very connection between past and future, indeed for the very existence of the present.

Of course, the immortals will have cognitive experiences, but there the similarity with the mortals ends. Instead of time moving inexorably onward, creating continuity between fleeting experiences, continuity takes flight for the immortals and does not come back to Earth again in a lifetime.

The persistence of senses may illuminate another difference between the world of mortals and immortals. For me, as for many others over 60 years of age, time has sped up acutely as it moves toward its one and only end. Memory thus changes, and, occasionally, a persistent remnant of an early experience comes thundering out of the past and back to life. It may even strike with its original force. In the words of Henri Bergson:

> But the truth is that our present should not be defined as that which
> is more intense: it is that which acts on us and which makes us act;
> it is sensory and it is motor—our present is, above all, the state of

our body. Our past, on the contrary, is that which acts no longer but which might act, and will act by inserting itself into a present sensation from which it borrows the vitality.[22]

The immortals will, no doubt, also have memory, but it will not speed up or slow down while life and time stand still. For the immortals, none of the faults and pains of memory that come with age will materialize. Immortality has its compensations.

AT WHAT COST?

It has never been my intention to pretend that immortality could be achieved without sacrifice. Beyond all the problems of communication, the simple pleasures offered by birth, if not death, will be increasingly rare as more and more people enter the population as sterile immortals. Moreover, the preference some of us have for human diversity may not be rewarded as richly as it is today, since some human traits will, no doubt, not be represented among the immortals.

How the immortal humans will look and behave is a matter of conjecture, but some consequences of the indwelling generator would seem inevitable, most conspicuously the morphological and physiological juvenilization of the immortals. Unquestionably, the immortals will be in unbelievably good physiological shape. They will be ballet dancers, gymnasts, karate experts with great stamina and grace. Immortals will not resemble the Eloi envisaged by H. G. Wells in *The Time Machine*,—fragile, easily fatigued, of slight stature, "a hairless visage, and the same girlish rotundity of limb."[23] They will appear neither masculine nor feminine and remain sexually immature forever, but these side effects would not be handicaps in a society where everyone lives forever. There,

> [u]nder the new conditions of perfect comfort and security, that restless energy, that with us is strength, would become weakness . . . For such a life, what we should call the weak are as well equipped as the strong, and indeed no longer weak.[24]

Forever prepubescent, the immortals will not suffer from the inevitable, deleterious effects of aging that follow sexual maturity, but unlike the rather dull witted, "five year olds" discovered by the Time Traveler in *Time Machine*, the preadolescent immortals will be in a perpetual learning mode. They will be capable of acquiring languages flawlessly and without effort. They will never exhaust their mental potential and will always be at their peak of poetic and mathematical creativity. In other words, a world of immortals will be filled with intellectual excitement and dedicated to creative enterprise. Even chronologically older immortals would not lose their intellectual edge, and society might very well return to esteeming the "ancients" without the biting edge of *ressentiment.*

> Those spiritual and intellectual values which remain untouched by the process of aging, together with the values of the next stage of life ... [will no longer have to] compensate for what has been lost. Only if this happens can we cheerfully relive the values of our past in memory, without envy for the young to whom they are still accessible.[25]

Furthermore, although immortals will not exhibit secondary sexual dimorphism, they will be polymorphous and will enjoy uninhibited pre-adolescent sexuality without the complications of pregnancy. In all likelihood, immortals will quickly evolve socially and spawn a culture without sexism, without homophobia, without stigma attached to sterility, and without the threat of a population explosion resulting from unrestrained sexual reproduction.

On balance, the cost of immortality would seem acceptable, and *Homo sapiens* forma *immortalis* should "live happily ever after." One might expect a society much as Wells first (if mistakenly) described for the Eloi:

> Social triumphs, too, had been effected. I saw mankind housed in splendid shelters, gloriously clothed, and as yet I had found them engaged in no toil. There were no signs of struggle, neither social nor economical struggle. The shop, the advertisement, traffic, all that commerce which constitutes the body of our world, was gone. It was natural on that golden evening that I should jump at the idea of a social paradise.[26]

The biggest challenge would be convincing the remaining, adult *Homo sapiens* forma *mortalis* to permit, by and large, the disappearance of that part of their culture built on sexuality and commerce. If, *Homo sapiens* f. *mortalis* cannot be convinced to yield gracefully, I foresee a disastrous schism developing in the species. I imagine *Homo sapiens* f. *immortalis* suffering the same fate that awaited Wells's Eloi attacked by the voracious Morlocks. They will meet the enemy only to discover that "the enemy is us."

Notes

NOTES TO PREFACE

1. Anderson, 2001
2. Shostak, 1998.
3. Shostak, 1999.
4. Wilmut et al., 1997.

NOTES TO CHAPTER 1

1. Nesse and Williams, 1996.
2. Bova, 1998.
3. Sherrington, pg. 221, 1964.
4. Courtillot (pp. 140–142, 1999) lays the odds or score at 7 to 1 in favor of "death from the mantle."
5. Courtillot (pg. 144, 1999) also tells us: "Humans are injecting the same potentially toxic gases into the atmosphere, at rates . . . comparable to those that may have been produced by an impact or the laying down of a giant lava flood."
6. Tipler, pg. 18, 1994.
7. Cell is from the Latin for containing cavities; diminutive of cell or small room. Clone is from the Greek akin to *klan* for throng; also *klad* for twig or branch.
8. Hall, 2000.
9. Ricklefs, 1998.
10. Nuland, pg. 44, 1994.
11. Lewontin, pg. 103, 2000.
12. Hayflick, pg. 268, 2000.
13. See Kirkwood, Chapter 6, 1999; de Grey, 1999.
14. Also see Clark, 1996, 1999; Nesse and Williams, 1996.

15. The larger figure depends on eliminating all the causes of death accompanying aging. Nesse and Williams, 1996; Hayflick, 2000; Olshansky, et al., 2001.

16. See Tipler, 1994, for review of religious and scientific constructions of Heaven.

17. Although a "working draft" of the human genome has been released (International Human Genome Consortium, 2001), the genome is far from 100% sequenced. Ninety percent of the gene-rich euchromatic portion of the genome is sequenced and assembled into a whole with reasonable precision, but only a quarter of the whole genome is "finished" to the exclusion of all gaps.

18. Bova, pg. 98, 1998.

19. Jazwinski, 1996.

20. Sohal and Weindruch, 1996; Campisi, 2000; Finkel and Holbrook, 2000.

21. de Grey, 1999; Melov et al., 2000.

22. Rose, M., 1998. Also see Nesse and Williams, 1996; Kirkwood, 1999.

23. Kirkwood and Austad, pg. 233, 2000.

24. Jazwinski, 1996.

25. Properly abbreviated *D. melanogaster* but usually identified simply as *Drosophila*.

26. The names of genes and mutants are conventionally written in italics.

27. See de Grey, 1999 and Toussaint et al., 2000; Wolkow et al., 2000.

28. Imai et al., 2000; Lin et al., 2000.

29. *sir-2* has "31% identity to yeast Sir2 in the conserved core domain." Tissenbaum and Guarente, pg. 228, 2001.

30. Reviewed by Guarente and Kenyon, 2000.

31. Shay and Wright, pg. 840, 2001.

32. Clark, 1996, 1999.

33. Yu et al., 1996.

34. See review by Oshima, 2000.

35. Martin and Oshima, 2000.

36. Martin and Oshima, pg. 263, 2000.

37. Stem cells are not totipotential, as sometimes advertised, lacking the ability, like the fertilized egg, to develop into an entire organism.

38. See Wilmut et al., 2000 for a history of large mammal cloning beginning in E. J. Chris Polge's laboratory at the Cambridge's Unit of Reproductive Physiology and Biochemistry (better known as the Animal Research Station).

The Danish veterinarian Steen Willadsen is credited with "twinning" early sheep embryos (beginning with two-cell but going to eight-cell) and developing methods, later used in cloning sheep—electrofusion to combine the enucleated oocyte with the nuclear donor cell; reinserting embryonic cells (blastomeres) in membranes (zona pellucida); coating with agar; incubating within ligated sheep oviducts, where blastocysts developed; transferring to prenatal foster mothers. Willadsen is also credited with making a chimeric "geep" by mixing goat and sheep cells in blastocysts, and, most importantly, with carrying out nuclear transfer and cloning sheep with nuclei from eight- and sixteen-cell embryos, and calves by transferring a nucleus from cultured ICM cells.

Wilmut et al. also discussed the successes and problems (such as the large fetus syndrome) of twinning and cloned cattle. Cloning with nuclei from eight- and sixteen-cell embryos was begun by Neal First at the University of Wisconsin, especially in elite cattle by the biotechnology firms, W. R. Grace and Company, Granada, and Genmark. James McGrath and Davor Solter, at the Wistar Institute of Anatomy and Biology in Philadelphia, are credited with producing mouse blastocysts following the fusion of one zygote or blastomer from 2-cell embryos to a mechanically enucleated zygote with the aid of Sendai virus.

Early work by Wilmut himself led to the birth of Frostie, the first calf developed from a frozen embryo. Lawrence Smith is credited with introducing to Roslin, in the late 1980s, cloning by nuclear transfer in mice and sheep. In collaboration with Wilmut, Smith produced three cloned lambs with nuclei transferred from blastomeres of sixteen-cell embryos, and one with a nucleus transferred from an ICM.

39. Wilmut et al., 1997.

40. "Donor" and "to donate" are euphemisms employed by scientists for livestock, their cells, and nuclei, and for the process of taking their living materials.

41. Ashworth et al., 1998; Signer et al., 1998; Solter, 1998.

42. See Wilmut et al., 2000.

43. Wilmut et al., pg. 4, 2000. Several commercial biotech companies reside on the Roslin campus "one of which (known as PPL [Pharmaceutical Proteins Ltd.]) was heavily involved in the creation of Dolly and Polly" *(ibid.)*. PPL has since merged with TransPharm Inc. of Blacksburg, Virginia, to become PPL Inc. Roslin Institute began its own biotech startup—Roslin Bio-Med—which, in May 1999, was bought by California-based Geron.

44. "Cultured" refers to tissue culture (also known as *in vitro*), a standard method for maintaining cells outside an organism in plastic dishes. When grown in nutrient medium, the cells are usually capable of cell division and hence must be transferred occasionally to fresh dishes. Each transfer is called a passage.

45. According to Wilmut et al., pg. 4, 2000,

46. Polly's genome includes the transgene construct, known as pMIX1, containing the human *FIX* gene and the ovine beta-lactoglobulin promoter.

47. Schnieke et al., 1997. Although Wilmut suggests (in Wilmut et al., 2000) that producing genetically transformed sheep was the primary objective of cloning research, flocks of sheep have already been created by germ-line transgenesis, or the genetic transformation of zygotes by DNA injection into a pronucleus. Beginning in 1990 with the birth of the transgenic sheep, Tracy, human proteins have been "pharmed" (harvesting products of genetically transformed cells). Sheep are currently producing large

amounts of the enzyme, alpha-I-antitrypsin (AAT, from a construct with the beta-lacto-globulin promoter) potentially useful in the treatment of lung disorders, chiefly emphy-sema and cystic fibrosis. Furthermore, transformed mice, known as "knock-out," and less commonly, "knock-in" mice are created by directed mutagenesis of embryo stem cells in culture, followed by injection into blastocysts *in vitro,* transfer to prenatal foster mothers, and subsequent breeding of animals bearing the desired genetic traits. The point of making Polly, as Schnieke et al., 1997 acknowledge, was that "no recipients are wasted generating non-transgenic lambs." (also Wilmut et al., pg. 262, 2000.)

48. Although clearly differentiated (as demonstrated by the presence of antigens, such as the mesodermal marker vimentin), fetal fibroblasts established in primary cell cultures are probably the nearest thing available in most mammals to embryo stem (ES) cells produced by primary cultures of mouse inner cell mass (ICM) cells and have been employed successfully in cloning livestock. Moreover, and perhaps more importantly, fetal fibroblasts have been successfully used as a way to introduce germ-line mutations in sheep (Schnieke et al., 1997; Wilmut et al., 2000) and cattle (Cibelli et al., 1998).

49. Kato et al., 1998. According to Wilmut et al., pg. 253, 2000: "In March 1998 Jean-Paul Renard at INRA, France's national agricultural research agency near Paris, made it known that he and his colleagues had cloned a calf; and they could be absolutely certain that their calf had been produced [with the nucleus] from a fully differentiated cell." Wilmut et al. (pg. 253, 2000) view these results as supporting their claims for "the method . . . developed at Roslin."

50. Wakayama et al., 1998; 2000.

51. nishi et al., 2000.

52. Polejaeva et al., 2000.

53. Baguisi et al., 1999.

54. See Pennisi and Vogel, 2000a, and "News," Pennisi and Vogel, 2000b, and Pennisi and Normile, 2000.

55. According to a "News Focus" article by Vogel (2000), "The patent gives California-based Geron Corp. exclusive rights to "a reconstituted animal embryo pre-pared by transferring the nucleus of a quiescent diploid donor cell into a suitable recipient cell" up to and including the blastocyst stage. That claim includes human embryos, says David Earp, Geron's vice president of intellectual property. Last sum-mer, Geron bought Roslin Bio-med, the commercial arm of the government-funded Roslin Institute outside Edinburgh, Scotland, where Dolly was born in 1996." Also see Wadman, 2000.

56. Wilmut et al., (pg. 269, 2000) suggest five reasons for cloning: "The first is for research—producing even purer laboratory strains; the second is in agriculture and other areas of domestic breeding—replicating elite animals; the third is in animal conservation; the fourth is for multiplying tissues, as opposed to whole individuals, for use in human medicine; and the fifth is human reproductive clinics."

57. Dawkins, pg. 55, 1998.

58. A variety of techniques are used to introduce alien nuclei into cells. In the case of Dolly, an enucleated, mature ewe's oocyte was fused with a single cell, originating from another ewe's udder after freezing for several years and growth in culture.

59. Influences arising from the egg's cytoplasm and other unexplored conditions affecting development are likely to make one's clone different from oneself (notwithstanding its having one's nuclear genes). Wilmut et al. (pg. 17, 2000) are keen to point this out, emphasizing that their four cloned Dorset rams, Cedric, Cecil, Cyril and Tuppence, "are very different in size and temperament, showing emphatically that an animal's genes do *not* 'determine' every detail of its physique and personality."

60. The preimplantation mammalian blastocyst is a "preembryo" in the sense that it does not contain an embryo proper. Lanza et al. (1999) define the human "preembryo" as a preimplantation embryo prior to about 7.5 days post fertilization. I would extend the duration of the preembryo to about 15 days post-fertilization at which time the human primitive streak appears.

61. Actually, of 56 attempts, 6 grew to 4–16 cells and 1 to 16–400 cells which, when plated out *in vitro,* grew with embryonic stem cell-like morphology. Lanza et al., 1999. Also see Dominko, et al., 1999.

62. Pence, 1998.

63. Embryonic stem (ES) cells, in particular, were isolated from mice in 1981 (Evans and Kaufman, 1981; Martin, 1981).

64. In a "News of the Week" summary, Richard Stone (2000) lists 10 types of putative stem cells (neural, heart muscle, insulin-producing, cartilage, blood, liver, skin, bone retinal, skeletal muscle) and 20 diseases or traumas (stroke, Parkinson's disease, Alzheimer's disease, spinal cord injury, multiple sclerosis; heart attacks, congestive heart failure; diabetes; osteoarthritis; cancer, immunodeficiencies, inherited blood diseases, leukemia; hepatitis, cirrhosis; burns, wound healing; osteoporosis; macular degeneration; muscular dystrophy) that would allegedly be ameliorated through stem cell replacement therapy.

65. Thomson et al., 1998; also see Gearhart, 1998.

66. Shamblott et al., 1998.

67. Shamblott et al. (pg. 13729; 1998) report that their PGC-derived cells exhibited "Three distinct mesodermal derivatives . . . antimuscle specific actin-reactive myocytes with prominent eccentric nuclei and cytoplasmic filaments . . . antidesmin-reactive mesenchymal cells . . . and anti-CD34-reactive vascular endothelium. . . . Ectodermal derivatives include cells suggestive of neuroepithelia with nuclear localized anti-S-100-reactive . . . and antineurofilament-reactive cells . . . Endodermal derivatives include anti-a-1-fetoprotein-reactive cells, which appear within the interior of some EBs [embryoid bodies] as well as form the exterior layer . . . Several types of anticytokeratin-reactive epithelia were seen, including nests of relatively undifferentiated cells . . . and simple cuboidal epithelial layers . . ."

68. Dickson, 2001; Vogel, 2001.

69. The journals were not far behind, e.g., Stone, 2000.

70. See, for example, any issue of *Stem Cell Research News eLetter* on-line at info@stemcellresearchnews.com. Also Talbot, 2001.

71. Kolata, pp. 236–7, 1998.

72. Wilmut et al., pg. 75, 2000.

73. For the sake of argument, I define a religion as a club to which members, known as believers or worshippers, pay tithes rather than taxes or dues.

74. Weismann, 1912.

75. Dawkins, 1965, 1976, 1982.

76. Problems of nomenclature abound since the advent of surrogacy, and even the term, "biological parents," referring to the source of egg and spermatozoon, will become problematic in the age of cloning (see Andrews, 1999).

77. Unfortunately, the germ line is the part of the body one does not ordinarily think of as oneself or immortality would present no problem. The somatic lines, which for the most part comprise the body proper and are ordinarily thought of as the self, are stuck in mortality. The problem for achieving immortality is not so much that life defies immortality, but that the wrong part of organisms is immortal. The question is, "How can the body of somatic lines toss off the mortal coil and exchange places with the germ line, thereby making somatoplasm immortal?"

78. Judson, pg. 506, 1979.

79. Abir-Am, pg. 360, 1982.

80. Schrödinger, (1944) 1967.

81. Schrödinger, (1944) 1967: "the strong mutual bond of the atoms which keeps a molecule in shape was a complete conundrum to everybody" (pg. 50).

82. Schrödinger, (1944) 1967: "the enigmatic biological stability is traced back only to an equally enigmatic chemical stability" (pg. 50).

83. Watson, pg. 18, 1969.

84. Watson, pg. 18, 1969.

85. Watson, pg. 28, 1969.

86. Watson, pg. 30, 1969.

87. Judson, pg. 232, 1979.

88. Now known eponymously as "Watson/Crick-pairing," every nitrogenous base in one strand is ordinarily matched by its complementary nitrogenous base in the other strand: for every adenine, there is a thymine; for every cytosine, there is a guanine— A–T, C–G.

89. Watson and Crick, pg. 737, 1953.

90. The double helix of DNA consists of two antiparallel strands of nucleic acids, each a polymer of nucleotides bearing nitrogenous bases turned inward. These strands must be separated before new nitrogenous bases can complement those in the

original strands. The nitrogenous bases are brought to the DNA as triphosphate nucleosides which polymerize under the influence of enzymes into the DNA strands.

91. One can get the story "from the horse's mouth" in Kornberg, 1982.

92. Eukaryotic cells are cells with nuclei (karyons) and organelles as opposed to prokaryotic cells lacking nuclei and organelles.

93. Protoctistans include all unicellular microorganisms exclusive of the animals, fungi, and plants. "There are no single-celled animals or plants" (Margulis et al., pg. xi, 1990).

94. Who received many Nobel Prizes in Physiology or Medicine in subsequent years.

95. Judson, pg. 576, 1979; Monod, pg. xii, 1971.

96. Smith, 1998.

97. This is not to say that biotech and pharmaceutical firms will not attempt to capitalize on "life's secret." Biacore, a high-tech biomolecular research firm, advertises itself as "Unlocking the Inner Secret of Life," in *Science,* 286, 3 December 1999.

98. Kevles, pg. 19, 1992; Gilbert, 1992.

99. Personal communication with permission from unpublished manuscript, 22 January 2000.

100. The most important objection is that no mouse would want its tail cut off, and some form of psychic volition was an important component of Lamarck's principle.

101. Of course the exceptions far exceed the rule, and a variety of processes, such as imprinting and gene rearrangement, make serious inroads in the generality of the central dogma.

102. Kay, pg. 111, 1993.

103. Delbrück, pg. 1315, 1970b.

104. Delbrück, pg. 1312, 1970a.

105. See. e.g., Kauffman, 1993; Capra, 1996.

106. Weismann, 1882.

107. See Gall, 1986.

108. Sgrò and Partridge (pg. 2521, 1999) put the proposition this way: "One theory about the evolution of aging suggests that genes with beneficial effect early in life also have deleterious effects later on."

109. Harrison, 1964.

110. Joza et al., 2001.

111. Alexis Carrel (1873–1944) was awarded the Nobel Prize for Physiology or Medicine in 1912 for developing long-term tissue-culture techniques. See Kirkwood, Chapter 7, 1999, for a brief critique of Carrel's work and an introduction to the subsequent work of Leonard Hayflick.

112. The cells may be exposed, for example, to genes encoding the human papilloma virus E6 and E7 or transformed with the simian virus oncogene encoding the SV40 large T antigen.

113. Moreover, "immortalized" cells frequently produce cancer upon reintroduction into otherwise healthy animals.

114. Smith and Pereira-Smith, pp. 63–64, 1996.

115. See Hayflick, 1994.

116. "In fact, . . . results show that the telomeres lengthened with each generation" (Wakayama et al., pg. 319, 2000). Cloning efficiency dropped in the reiterative process, and no cloned mice were produced in the fifth generation in one cloned line and the only live-born in another cloned line was cannibalized by its foster mother, terminating that line too.

117. For review and citations see Smith and Pereira-Smith, 1996; de Lange, 1998; Shay and Wright, 2001.

118. See Blackburn, 2000.

119. DePinho, pg. 250, 2000.

120. Holliday, 1996.

121. Bodnar et al., 1998.

122. Rudolph et al., 2000.

123. Potten and Loeffler, pg. 1017, 1990.

124. Tang et al., 2001.

125. Mathon et al., 2001.

126. Weinberg, 1998.

127. Human telomerase stops working as cells differentiate. See Hagmann, 2000.

128. Campisi, pg. 2062, 2000; also see Jazwinski, 1996.

129. Artandi et al., 2000.

130. Kiyono et al., 1998.

131. Romanov, et al., 2001.

132. Jazwinski, pg. 54, 1996.

133. Crick, 1958.

134. RNA differs from DNA predominantly in three ways: in being primarily single stranded; having monomers of ribonucleotides instead of deoxyribonucleotides; and substituting the pyrimidine uracil (U) as the complement to adenine (A) in place of thymidine (T).

135. RNA enzymes, ribozymes, are increasingly recognized as playing important roles in nuclear and cytoplasmic physiology.

136. Ultimately, Schrödinger anticipated codons as well. As he explained:

What we wish to illustrate is simply that with the molecular picture of the gene it is no longer inconceivable that the miniature code should precisely correspond with a highly complicated and specified plan of development and should somehow contain the means to put it into operation (Schrödinger, pg. 66; 1967).

137. Haeckel, pg. 5, 1992.

138. Haeckel, pg. 4, 1992.

139. For an interesting gloss on Haeckel's contribution to the twentieth century, see Gasman, 1998.

140. Potten and Loeffler, 1990.

141. Margulis, 1996.

142. Lovelock, 1990, 1996; Margulis, 1996, 1998.

143. Dawkins, 1965, 1976, 1982.

144. See Haraway, 1997.

145. Schiffmann, Y., pg. 153, 1997,

146. Monod, 1971, pg. 81.

NOTES TO CHAPTER 2

1. Rose, M., pp. 110 ff., 1998. Also see Nesse and Williams, 1996.

2. Kirkwood and Austad, 2000.

3. Darwin used "evolved" only once in *Origin*, preferring "development" or "transmutation of species" to "evolution," and he does not claim the idea for his own. In the "An Historical Sketch" prior to Chapter I, Darwin cites "Some few naturalists . . . [who] have believed that species undergo modification and that existing forms of life are the descendants by true generation of pre-existing forms" (Darwin, pg. 53, [1859] 1968). The phrase "descent with modification" also appears in the summary of topics in Chapter VI entitled "Difficulties of the Theory" (Darwin, pg. 158, [1859] 1968). Darwin continued to use this language throughout the six editions of *Origin* (Darwin, pg. 17, [1872] 1958; Darwin, pg. 205, [1872] 1958).

4. Seilacher et al., 1998.

5. Darwin, [1859] 1968.

6. Ruse, pg. 80, 1999.

7. Ruse, pg. 54, 1999.

8. Ruse, pg. 55, 1999.

9. Ruse, pg. 163, 1999.

10. Darwin, (1892) 1989.

11. Ruse, pg. 83, 1999.

12. Desmond and Moore, 1994; Ruse, 1999.

13. Darwin, pg. 450, [1872] 1958. The quotation is from the sixth edition. The phrase, "by the Creator" did not appear in the first edition (1859).

14. See Numbers and Stenhouse, 1999.

15. Thomas R. Malthus published his well known *Essay on the Principle of Population* in 1798. It reached six editions by 1826 and was translated into several languages. Malthus was indebted to David Hume and others, including Robert Wallace, who had calculated that human beings did not actually propagate according to the maximum rate available or even at a constant rate, but their increase was prevented by various causes. See footnote, Thompson, page. 143, 1992.

16. Ruse, pg. 171, 1996.

17. Ruse, pg. 142, 1996.

18. Ruse, pg. 140, 1996.

19. Ruse, pg. 143, 1996. Ruse adds (pg. 209, 1996), "The full causes of evolution may still be shrouded in mystery, but the fact is beyond doubt and the paths are becoming much clearer."

20. Ruse, pg. 237, 1996.

21. Desmond, 1994, 1997.

22. Ruse, pg. 278, 1996.

23. See Rose, M., 1998, for speculation on "what might have been."

24. Eclipsing this success, H. B. D. Kettlewell, one of Weldon's associates, later demonstrated experimentally the usefulness of selection in explaining melanism among moths (although the adequacy of that explanation is now in doubt). Majerus, 1998.

25. Ruse, pg. 235, 1996.

26. Ruse, pg. 241, 1996.

27. See Rose, M., 1998.

28. Provine, pg. 25, 1971.

29. Segregation is most easily understood as a consequence of hereditary units separating (segregating) during the manufacture of sex cells and recombining in the production of offspring.

30. Bateson coined the word *genetics* (but not *gene*) for the study of particulate heredity.

31. Johannsen's target was not Gregor Mendel, whose law of independent assortment militated against the chromosomal theory, but August Weismann, whose hypothetical nuclear particles had been widely identified with Mendelian factors. Weismann's scheme for how hereditary factors entered metabolism and influenced development was especially loathsome to Johannsen, and his coinage of gene and other neologisms was intended to drive a wedge between notions of inheritance and development.

32. Bateson would ultimately capitulate in humiliation to Morgan, and Morgan would receive the Nobel Prize in Physiology or Medicine in 1933.

33. Mutations occupied the same place in De Vries's theory of evolution as "sports," à la William Bateson, and later, "hopeful monsters," à la Richard Goldschmidt.

34. Provine, pg. 55, 1980.

35. Darlington, pg. 78, 1980.

36. Lewontin (pp. 48–49, 2000) tells us, "The environment of an organism is the penumbra of external conditions that are relevant to it because it has effective interactions with those aspects of the outer world."

37. Genotype and phenotype were also coined by Johannsen in order to encapsulate and solidifying the difference between heredity and development.

38. Lewontin, pg. 23, 2000.

39. Lewontin, pg. 36, 2000.

40. Dobzhansky, 1980; Adams, et al., 1980.

41. I might also mention N. W. Timoféeff-Reffovsky, who is celebrated for "talking to physicists," and figures prominently in Schrödinger's *What is Life?*

42. The term, *modern synthesis* seems to have been coined much later, by Julian Huxley (1887–1975), as the subtitle for his book, *Evolution: The Modern Synthesis.* London: Allen and Unwin; 1942.

43. The new synthesis sometimes glows with even more luster. Along with the integration of Mendelian genetics and natural selection, the "modern synthesis" is credited with the integration of "systematics, paleontology, and ecology . . ." Stenseth, pg. 1490, 1999.

44. Ruse, pp. 316–7, 1996.

45. Ruse, pg. 318, 1996.

46. "Fitness" continues to be used to describe the "fit" between morphology and environmental constraints as well as the probability of leaving offspring, and some authors suggest that the two definitions may not be far apart in practice. Richard Lewontin (pg. 44, 2000), for example, tells us:

> . . . the use of the term *fitness* for the numerical force of natural selection generally reinforces the image of the properties of the organism being molded to the specific requirements of the environment.

47. Ayala and Fitch, pg. 7692, 1997.

48. Ruse, pg. 410, 1996.

49. Ayala and Fitch, 1997.

50. Gould and Vrba, 1982. Greene (pg. 2, 1986) succinctly defines a preadaptation as "a feature that promotes increased performance of a task that was not associated with the origin of that feature."

51. Mayr, 1988.

52. Van Valen, 1973.

53. See Mayr, 1994.

54. Eldredge and Gould, 1972.

55. The term, "adaptive radiation" can be traced to Henry Fairfield Osborn (1857–1935), who gave it its distinctly non-selectionist, saltatory flavor, portraying it as an evolutionary explosion, the abrupt appearance of radiating lines of progression from an ancestral form. Edward Drinker Cope (1840–1897) also found many "trends" among radiating lines.

56. Initially, the paleontological record seemed incompatible with gradualism, but punctuated equilibrium was ultimately modified to accommodate gradualism, albeit of a rapid variety. See Eldredge, 1985.

57. Alvarez et al., 1980.

58. Courtillot, pg. 92, 1999.

59. "Niche" is as difficult to define as "fitness." Richard Lewontin (pg. 44, 2000) argues that both are merely useful metaphors otherwise lacking precision:

[I]n ecology, *ecological niche* is a technical term universally used to denote the complex of relationships between a particular species and the outside world. But the use of the metaphor of a niche implies a kind of ecological space with holes in it that are filled by organisms, organisms whose properties give them the right "shape" to fit into the holes.

60. Hutchinson, 1959.

61. Wilson, 1975. Wilson did not coin the term *sociobiology*. It was popular in Europe around the turn of the century with Haeckelian enthusiasts.

62. Ruse, pg. 473, 1996.

63. Dawkins, 1965, 1976, 1995, 1997.

64. Dawkins, pg. 84, 1995.

65. Lewontin and Hubby, 1966.

66. Lewontin, pg. 87, 2000.

67. Ohta, 1996.

68. Nei, 1987; Nei and Hughes, 1991.

69. Sogin, pg. 182, 1994.

70. Philippe et al., 1994.

71. The influenza A virus evolves at a rate of 5.7×10^{-3} substitutions per site per year. The HA1 domain of the hemagglutinin gene of human influenza A viruses, for example, is evolving about a million times faster than cellular genes. See Fitch et al., 1997.

72. Atkins, 1993.

73. Eukaryotes comprise all members of the Domain Eucarya having cells with nuclei which form chromosomes that participate in mitosis.

74. Ponting and Blake, pg. 200, 1999.

75. Made from an mRNA template, the cDNA lacks a promoter (a control region of DNA capable of initiating transcription) and frequently the "duplicate" gene is a "pseudogene," unavailable for transcription in the absence of a suitable promoter. When the gene is inserted into a chromosome downstream to a promoter, however, the gene may be transcribed when the promoter is activated.

76. Hillis, pg. 351, 1994.

77. Hillis, pg. 360, 1994.

78. Actually, the concepts of orthologous and paralogous homology are not entirely new. Without knowing it, Richard Owen, in the first half of the nineteenth century, named an organismic equivalent of paralogy, namely, serial homology, which implies homology among structures within an organism. Owen also named a taxonomic equivalent of orthology, namely, taxic homology, although it is usually just called homology. Taxic homology implies homology among structures in different species.

79. Morgan's "beads on a string."

80. International Human Genome Consortium, 2001.

81. Chakravarti, pg. 823, 2001.

82. Baltimore, pg. 814, 2001.

83. Rubin, 2001.

84. Wolfsberg et al., pg. 824, 2001.

85. Bock et al., 2001.

86. Pollard, pg. 842, 2001.

87. Pollard, pg. 843, 2001.

88. Murray and Marks, pg. 844, 2001.

89. Futeal et al., pg. 850, 2001.

90. Evolution as such is also something human beings have not observed directly, since we lack sufficient years.

91. Hayflick, pg. 268, 2000.

92. Hayflick, pg. 268, 2000.

93. Shostak, 1993c.

94. Druffel et al., 1995.

95. Data from *Encyclopedia Brittanica,* 1998.

96. See Williams, 1997.

97. "Cope's Rule," that evolving groups tend to increase in size, may be incorrectly attributed to Cope. According to Paul Polly (1998), quoting Charles Depéret, the source was B. Rensch.

98. Courtillot, pg. 9, 1999.

99. See Chapter 4 for discussion of endless life in viruses and prokaryotes.

100. Men generally remain fertile into senility, although their sperm count decreases with age. Men's life expectancy is generally less than women's but parallels that of women in different societies more or less closely.

101. See Nesse and Williams, 1996; Kirkwood and Austad, 2000; Shanley and Kirkwood, 2001.

102. Sgrò and Partridge, 1999.

103. See Rose, M., 1998.

104. Kirkwood, pg. 195, 1999.

105. Ronald Fisher, for example, was a notorious misogynist who married solely to raise the level of the human gene pool with his own genes. Haldane, Kol'tsov, and Philipchenko were also dedicated eugenicists although not vulgar misogynists. Others, notably Lancelot T. Hogben, whose "work ranged from cytogenetics to the inheritance of intelligence . . . [was] uncompromisingly opposed [to the mainline eugenics movement] . . ., identifying it with 'ancestor worship, anti-Semitism, colour prejudice, anti-feminism, snobbery, and obstruction to educational progress.' " Kevles, pg. 123, 1985.

106. Rose, M. pg. 100, 1998.

107. Numbers and Stenhouse, 1999.

108. Rose, M., pg. 145, 1998.

109. Bookstein, pg. 209, 1994.

110. Bookstein, pg. 215, 1994.

111. Bookstein, pg. 223, 1994.

112. Lewontin, pg. 97, 2000.

113. Goodwin, pg. 239, 1994.

114. Rose, S., 1998. The 31,780 genes conceded by the public human genome rough draft and 39,114 genes conceded by the private Celera sequence making up the human genome constitute about one percent of human DNA (Bork and Copley, 2001). See International Human Genome Sequencing Consortium, 2001.

115. See Jablonka and Lamb, 1995; Latham, 1999.

116. Viruses are rarely considered living, and viral species are only ambiguously defined. Therefore, even pathways of mutations revealed by sequencing analysis of viral genes and the emergence of new viral strains are not considered evidence capable of testing the evolution of viral "species." See Maizels and Weiner, 1993.

117. Thompson, pg. 123, (1942) 1992.

118. Cnidarians with cells entirely exposed to internal or external surfaces can have cell turnover indefinitely, or so it would seem. Shostak, 1974.

119. "Onco-," from the Greek for mass, identifies a tumor but usually refers to cancer. The normal genes encoding products controlling the cell cycle are maligned as "oncogenes" for no reason other than the convention of naming genes after mutants.

120. E1A permits the transcription of the first (early) adenovirus proteins, and it binds to Rb protein, inactivating its regulatory effects. Likewise, E1B binds to p53.

Apoptosis is one of the consequences of interaction among transcriptional regulators E1A and E1B binding to tumor suppressor proteins. p53 seems to select cells for apoptosis that have irretrievably damaged DNA and those cells near the center of tumors suffering from hypoxia (see Kinzler and Vogelstein, 1996).

121. See Haffner and Oren, 1995.

122. Convention dictates that genes are printed in italics, while their encoded proteins appear in normal roman.

123. See Wyllie, 1995.

124. See Lane, 1994. For synopsis see Macdonald and Ford, 1997. Briefly, Rb forms a complex with transcription factors (TFs), otherwise required for the production of adenoviral proteins and the activation of genes encoding proteins that cause quiescent (G_0) cells to commence DNA synthesis (enter the S phase). p53 is a transcription factor which activates genes encoding proteins that inhibit G_1 (e.g., the cyclin-dependent kinase inhibitor p21). Normally, both proteins cause the arrest of cells in the G1 phase of the cell cycle. The release of transcription factors by the transforming proteins of oncoviruses or their interaction with p53 frees cells from arrest (transforms and immortalizes them) and permits the replication of viruses.

125. The repeated use of such words as "domain" must suggest to the uninitiated reader that biologists are singularly unimaginative in coining terms. I remind the reader that words are currency and, when a word has already acquired legitimacy, it is likely to be used repeatedly by those striving to legitimize their own work.

126. Hesketh, pg. 320, 1997.

127. Donoghue, 1989; Coddington, 1988; Greene, 1986; Wanntorp, 1983.

128. Bova, pg. 230, 1998.

129. E.g., see Sgrò and Partridge, 1999.

130. Diamond, 2000; Holdaway and Jacomb, 2000. About a dozen species of moas—huge, long-lived and slow-breeding, flightless birds—became extinct as a result of hunting by Maoris who probably arrived in New Zealand in the thirteenth century. Assuming that moas only began to breed at five years and did not reach their reproductive peak until twelve years, at which time they might have reared one chick per year, and further assuming that the first Maori colonists (consisting originally of 100 individuals) killed only one female adult a week per twenty persons, the entire population of moas (originally 160,000) would have become extinct in just 160 years.

131. Diamond, 2000.

NOTES TO CHAPTER 3

1. Sherrington, pg. 107, 1964.

2. von Baer's birth is given as 1792 in *Larousse,* 1994.

3. The temptation to attribute development to a drive toward completion sometimes proves irresistible, and contemporary developmental biologists frequently imply

that an embryo develops "in order to" reach successive plateaus rather than "because of" the operation of causal mechanisms. Conceptually, invoking a goal to explain development is akin to saying "the end justifies the means" in order to excuse great and horrendous acts. Rather than a conventional formula that promotes efficient communication, teleological expressions turn causality or culpability upside-down and derail communication.

4. von Baer, (1837) 1967.

5. As a consequence, von Baer was opposed to Darwin's materialist explanation for evolution.

6. Schiffmann, Y., pg. 155, 1997.

7. von Baer, pg. 57, (1837) 1967.

8. Groves and Bronner-Fraser, 1999.

9. See Shostak, 1991, for details and citations.

10. For example, brain cells have turned into blood. Bjornson et al., 1999.

11. van der Kooy and Weiss, pg. 1439, 2000.

12. Goodell et al., 1996.

13. See Slack, 2000; Potten and Loeffler, 1990.

14. Peterson et al., 1997.

15. van der Kooy and Weiss, pg. 1439, 2000.

16. Hörstadius, 1950; Le Douarin, 1982; Groves and Bronner-Fraser, 1999; Mayor et al., 1999.

17. Marrow takes its name from the fatty yellow medulla of long bones in adults. The adventitial cells forming yellow marrow are of uncertain origin but are not derived from connective tissue adipocytes. The hematopoietic tissue is red marrow, typically found in membranous bones.

18. One might add that the spleen and hemal nodes in livestock would have no red blood cells without a circulatory system, but red blood cells do not proliferate in these organs.

19. The late post-structuralist philosopher, Gilles Deleuze explains (pg. 275, 1989):

A series is a sequence of images which tend in themselves in the direction of a limit, which orients and inspires the first sequence (the before), and gives way to another sequence organized as series which tends in turn towards another limit (the after). The before and the after are then no longer successive determinations of the course of time, but the two sides of the power, or the passage of the power to a higher power.

20. Oocytes at earlier stages are able to fuse with spermatozoa but do not develop successfully into embryos.

21. Nonreproducing worker bees and genes for delayed fecundity may seem to contradict the notion of life culminating in sexual reproduction, but numerous rationales bring these phenomena under the aegis of neo-Darwinism. Basically, Darwinian

fitness may yet peak in nonreproductive organisms engaged in the maintenance of siblings or even in organisms delaying their own fecundity (see Chapter 2).

22. For the present purposes, a clone is all the products of vegetative (asexual) reproduction of an organism.

23. Alternatively, individuals will perform a parthenogenesis-like process of automixis with the same result.

24. Interestingly, when longevity is extended from about 17–25 days to 60 days or longer in *C. elegans,* by the imposition of crowded conditions, caloric restriction, or mutation (i.e., *daf-2*), the worm remains a so-called dauer larva. See Kirkwood and Austad, 2000; Wolkow et al., 2000.

25. Oyama, pp. 219–220, n1; 2000.

26. See, for example, Schiffmann, D. A., 1997.

27. Steelman and Kocher, pg. 168, 2000.

28. For a discussion of asexual reproduction in comparison to sexual reproduction see Shostak, 1991. Also see Walther, 2000.

29. The P19 mouse cell line, for example, can be tweaked into differentiating into combinations of nerve, fat, cartilage, smooth, cardiac, and skeletal muscle.

30. See Nanny, 1985; Sapp, 1985; Gall, 1986.

31. See Latham, 1999.

32. Leblond and Walker, 1956. Also see Slack, 2000.

33. Potten and Loeffler, 1990.

34. Miller et al., 1999; Gussoni et al., 1999.

35. Altman, 1962; Doetsch et al. 1999. Also see Gage, 2000.

36. Bjornson et al., 1999; Mezey et al., 2000; Rietze et al., 2001.

37. Goodell, et al., 1996.

38. See Shostak, 1991 for specifics and citations.

39. Spemann, 1938.

40. See Kolm and Sive, 1997.

41. Gerhart and Kirschner, 1997.

42. Joza et al., pg. 551, 2001.

43. Morgan was awarded the Nobel Prize in Physiology or Medicine in 1933 for his work on the chromosomal theory of inheritance and its confirmation of Mendel's principles.

44. Morgan, pg. 8, 1927.

45. Morgan, pg. 8, 1927.

46. Abbé's death is given as 1908 in Gardner, 1960, and Hughes, 1989.

47. For a chronology of events see Baker, 1988; Hughes, 1989; de Grey Harris, 1999.

48. Quoted from Libby, pg. 267, 1922. The phrase, *"Omnis cellula e cellula,"* frequently attributed to Virchow, was first used, according to Henry Harris (pg. 33; 1999), as an epigraph by François Raspail (1794–1878).

49. Today, cell division is viewed as virtually neutral by way of influencing genes. Cleavage is relieved of any mechanistic role in distributing nuclear determinants.

50. Johnson, 1985.

51. Mahowald, 1977.

52. Kalthoff, 1979; Nüsslein-Volhard, 1979; Gehring, 1987.

53. See Davidson, 1986.

54. Sulston and White, 1980.

55. Foucault, 1973.

56. Schiffmann, Y., 1994, 1997.

57. Wolpert, pg. 8, 1969.

58. Nijhout, pg. 221, 1999.

59. Child, 1941.

60. Turing, 1952; Meinhart, 1982; MacWilliams, 1983; Schiffmann, Y., 1991, 1997;

61. Rose, pg. 186, 1999.

62. Rose, pg. 201, 1999.

63. Haeckel's true multicellular animals, or Eumetazoa, are generally called Metazoa. His category of simpler multicellular sponges, or Parazoa, are generally called Porifera.

64. In 1900, Haeckel put it this way: *"Ontogenesis is a brief and rapid recapitulation of phylogenesis,* determined by the physiological function of heredity (generation) and adaptation (maintenance)." Haeckel, pg. 81, 1992.

65. Haeckel is more likely to have called such structures "palingenic," or old structures resembling those present in ancestors and "preserved by a constant heredity," as opposed to "coenogenic," or new structures evolved *"disturbing development . . .* [and] varying adaptation" to embryonic or larval life (Haeckel, pg. 143, 1992).

66. Clayton, 1953.

67. Latham, pp. 3–4, 1999.

68. McClay and Wessel, 1984.

69. Brown, 1971.

70. Roth, 1991; Rieppel, 1994. Also see Raff, 1994, 1996.

71. Roth, 1991; Rieppel, 1994. Also see Raff, 1994, 1996.

72. de Rosa et al., 1999.

73. Aquinaldo et al., 1997.

74. Conway Morris, 1989, 1994a, b, 1998; Gould, 1989.

75. Schiffmann, D. A, 1997.

76. Wu and Anderson, 1997.

77. See Dennett, 1995.

78. Maturana and Varela, pg. 96, 1998.

79. Aristotle, 1991. For more on the history of embryology and developmental biology see Shostak, 1998.

80. More recently, the bacteriologist, Jacques Monod was widely quoted as having said, "What is true in *E. coli* [a bacterium] is true in elephants."

81. von Baer also published the first recognizable description of the mammalian egg ([1827] 1966) and is generally credited with the discovery of germ layers in vertebrates, although he credits germ layers to his friend Christian Pander (1794–1865), to whom he dedicated his book.

82. Oppenheimer, pg. 163, (1940) 1967.

83. Roux's journal went through several transformations over the years:

Development Genes and Evolution: Berlin: Springer-Verlag, c1996–

Former title: *Roux Archives of Developmental Biology*

Former title: *Wilhelm Roux's Archives of Developmental Biology:* Berlin, New York, Springer-Verlag; title changed to *Roux's Archives of Developmental Biology*

Roux's Archives of Developmental Biology: The Official Organ of the EDBO; Berlin; New York: Springer-Verlag, 1986–1996.

84. Child, 1941.

85. Turing, 1952.

86. Schiffmann, Y. (1997) shows that many of Child's results are explained if adenosine triphosphate (ATP) works as a Turing inhibitor with a Turing wavelength. Furthermore, Child's conception of succeeding metabolic patterns corresponds to a single Turing gradient of cyclic adenosine monophosphate (cAMP) and ATP.

87. Willadson, 1979; also see Wilmut et al., 2000.

88. Harvey, 1766

89. By the end of the seventeenth century, Marcello Malpighi (1988–1992) would make the controversial claim that rudimentary chicks were present in hen eggs even prior to incubation.

90. Grobstein, 1965.

91. See Renfree, 1982.

92. Harris, pg. 3, 1999.

93. von Baer, (1827) 1966.

94. Oppenheimer, (1940) 1967.

95. Jablonka and Lamb, 1995; Steele et al., 1998.

96. Mainenschein, 1985.

97. See, e.g., Latham, 1999.

98. Martin, 1998.

99. See Quammen, 1996.

100. Bonnet (1762) 1985

101. Today, such a plan would have to include the possibilities for confronting contingency and capitalizing on chaos, although these are only remotely alluded to by those contemplating plans attributed to DNA.

102. Weismann's priority to nuclear determinants is disputed. Writing on founding parents of genetics and their reductive concept of hereditary material, Ruth Hubbard (pp. 70–72, 1990) explains:

> They hypothesized that these [hereditary] characteristics were mediated by a hereditary substance inside cells, which different ones of them denoted by different names. Galton called it "stirp," Karl Nägeli "idioplasm," and August Weismann "germ plasm." Some of them assumed that the genetic substance that is transmitted to successive generations is made up of particles, which Darwin called "gemmules," Weismann "ids," Hugo De Vries "pangenes," and finally W. Johannsen "genes"—the name that stuck. The concepts or things represented by these various terms were not the same. But the fact that all of them were invented to denote hypothetical hereditary particles suggests that there was a strong ideological need to assume the existence of material substances, often particles, located within individuals, that transmit traits from one generation to the next.

103. Sapp, pg. 45, 1994, traces the ideas elaborated by Weismann back to the gemmules of Darwin, which de Vries called pangenes. In 1882, Weismann published an early version of his concept of germ plasm which he developed more completely in 1886 (translated to English in 1893 and 1912).

104. Roux, (1888) 1964.

105. For a recent example see Vickery and McClintock, 1998.

106. Kageura and Yamana, 1983; Hamburger, 1988.

107. Oppenheimer, pg. 161, (1940) 1967.

108. Thomas Hunt Morgan (1866–1945) at Columbia University was incensed by Weismann's ideas on germ plasm's role in development and physiology.

109. Slack et al., 1993; Garcia-Fernàndez and Holland, 1994; Holland et al., 1994; Agosti et al., 1996; Holland and Garcia-Fernàndez 1996; Zhang and Nei, 1996; Averof and Patel, 1997.

110. Nagy and Grbic, pg. 280, 1999.

111. Nagy and Grbic, pg. 278, 1999.

112. Garcia-Bellido, 1975; Crick and Lawrence, 1975.

113. See Nijhout, 1999 for discussion of the plethora of responses of tissues to the same ecdysteroid message in insects.

114. See Child, 1941.

115. Turing, 1952.

116. See Sapp, 1990.

NOTES TO CHAPTER 4

1. See Dennett, 1995, for discussion of adaptationism.

2. See specifics and citations in Shostak, 1999.

3. Introns are ordinarily stretches of RNA that interrupt transcripts, but "early introns" would have been stretches of RNA on either side of coding sequences and capable of annealing or ligating themselves together into larger genetic units as well as removing themselves autocatalytically.

4. Walter Gilbert may have retreated from his "introns early theory of genes"—also known as the "exon theory of genes"—but RNA may still have played a variety of roles in the RNA world and linear life would still have had its excitement. Gilbert et al., 1997.

5. E-mail message: spliced leader sequences in cnidarians.

Date: Fri., 17 Dec. 1999 09:31:54 -0800
From: Rob Steele <resteele@UCI.EDU>
To: cnidaria@UCI.EDU

6. Wellauer et al., 1976; Scheer and Dabauvalle, 1985.

7. Stability of viruses and genes is an illusion due to intrusions from the four-dimensional world of cells that correct errors in replication.

8. Crawford and Milkman write (pp. 80–82, 1991):

The well-known enteric bacterial *trp* [*tryptophan*] operon (all genes contiguous, two pairs fused, regulated by both repression and attenuation) is seen with or without the (G)D fusion in all enteric bacteria, together with their close relative *Vibrio.* This arrangement is seen nowhere else except, remarkably, in *Brevibacterium lactofermentum,* a high GC Gram-positive organism. This leads to the strong inference of later gene transfer at some time after the loss of the pathway.

9. Lawrence and Ochman, 1997, 1998.

10. Lawrence and Ochman, 1997, 1998.

11. Doolittle, pg. 2127, 1999.

12. Tourasse and Gouy, pg. 167, 1999.

13. Gogarten et al., 1989.

14. Woese, 1998.

15. For example, Altschul and Koonin, 1998.

16. "Lateral gene transfer" is frequently used to identify both the movement of genes within a cell—from organelle to nucleus—and between cells of different species. Horizontal gene transfer is more often used for the transfer of genes between members of different species. Where I am not compelled by a quotation to use lateral gene transfer in both contexts, I have endeavored to use the expression for gene transfer from organelle to nucleus and horizontal gene transfer for all other forms of gene movement. Vertical gene transfer always refers to gene transfer through cell division—a genetic lineage within a cell or generational line.

17. Nelson et al., 1999.

18. Logsdon and Faguy, pg. 749, 1999.

19. Doolittle and Logsdon, 1998.

20. If prokaryotes mastered these features, they seem to have been out-competed by eukaryotes, since extant prokaryotes do not exhibit sexual reproduction, aging, and death by senescence.

21. I ignore here, for the sake of brevity, plasmodial organisms in which a single cytoplasm contains vast numbers of nuclei, and oligonuclear organisms in which a single cytoplasm contains a small number of nuclei. Oligocellular organisms consisting of a small number of cells are included in multicellular organisms.

22. Gene rearrangement in cells of the immune system creates a conspicuous exception.

23. Yang, et al., 1985; Lang, et al., 1997; Andersson et al., 1998.

24. Lamour et al., 1994; Tateno et al., 1995.

25. Charlesworth and Langley, 1991; Houck et al., 1991; Cummings, 1994; Syvanen, 1994.

26. Cavalier Smith, 1987, 1992, 1999; Douglas et al., 2001.

27. Doolittle, pg. 2127, 1999.

28. Shostak, 1974, 1977,

29. Shostak, 1993a, b, Shostak and Kolluri, 1995.

30. Shostak, 1981, 1993b, c, Shostak and Tammariello, 1969.

31. Shostak, 1998, 1999, *in press*.

32. Sapp, 1987, 1994.

33. Margulis, 1991a, c, 1998, especially 1991b. Also see Wilson et al., 1985.

34. Cavalier-Smith, 1999.

35. Goff and Coleman, 1995; Goff et al., 1997; Williams and Polaszek, 1996. Also Shostak, *in press.*

36. Shostak, pg. 151, 1999.

37. Shostak, pg. 203, 1999.

38. Shostak, pg. 237, 1999.

39. International Human Genome Consortium, 2001; Venter, Adams, Myers et al., 2001.

40. Traditional Darwinists would suggest that similar traits in organisms are due to the trait's presence in a common ancestor and its inheritance by descendants, with the help of stabilizing selection. Differences in traits, on the other hand, are due to mutation and disruptive or directional selection (see Chapter 2). See Rubin, 2001. Bork and Copley, 2001, urge caution around ideas of missing genes.

41. The movement of viruses would seem yet another problem, and cross-species transmission is the perennial concern in xenotransplantation. See Paradis et al., 1999.

42. Maynard Smith and Szathmáry, pg. 105, 1999.

43. See Maynard Smith and Szathmáry, 1999.

44. Ploidy refers to the number of chromosomal sets present in the nucleus. Haploid cells have one set, diploid cells two, and polyploid more than two. Euploidy refers to any multiple of correct sets and aneuplody to an incorrect set.

45. The maximum found in eukaryotes is about 200 picograms DNA. In dinoflagellates, 50–60 percent of the nuclear DNA consists of non-encoding repeats.

46. These sites are called fission membranes.

47. Margulis, 1991a, b, c, 1998, Margulis and Cohen, 1994, Margulis et al., 1996.

48. Andersson et al., 1998.

49. *Rickettsia prowazekii* is the agent of louse-borne typhus in human beings.

50. Lang et al., 1997. *Ri. prowazekii* also has physically more DNA than *Re. americana* (1,111,523 base pairs [bp] in *Ri. prowazekii,* compared to 69,034 bp in *Re americana* mtDNA), almost a quarter of which excess is attributed to non-coding DNA.

51. Smith et al., 1992; Kidwell, 1993; Gillham, 1994.

52. Adams et al., 2000.

53. Oliveira et al., 1999.

54. Clark and Roger, 1995; Rosenthal et al., 1997; Roger et al., 1998; Upcroft and Upcroft, 1998.

55. Guarente and Kenyon, pg. 261, 2000.

56. The term *plasmatischen Gene* was first introduced by Hans Winkler in 1924 to designate "self-reproducing submicroscopic entities" (Sapp, pg. 72, 1987) making

up the cytoplasm, in contrast to *Genom,* which denoted the collection of genes in nuclear chromosomes. Soon thereafter (1926), Fritz von Wettstein, coined *Plasmon* for genetic elements in the cytoplasm and, between 1924 and 1935, Otto Renner produced an "impressive body of data [and] concluded that plastids were genetically different as autonomous self-duplicating bodies, which might show changes comparable to gene mutations." (Sapp, pg. 76, 1987). Otto Renner coined *Plastidom* for the genetically-autonomous self-duplicating entities of plastids, although the remainder of the *Plasmon* remained discrete from the genome of the nucleus, leaving the question of its relationship to nuclear genes wide open.

57. Sapp, 1987.

58. Sapp, pg. 169, 1994

59. Lwoff was awarded the Nobel Prize for Physiology or Medicine jointly with Jacob and Monod in 1965 for discoveries in the genetic control of enzymes and viral synthesis.

60. Lederberg was awarded the Nobel Prize for Physiology or Medicine jointly with Tatum and Beadle in 1958.

61. See Sapp, 1994.

62. Sapp, pg. 121, 1987.

63. Cavalier-Smith, pg. 299, 1991.

64. Tartar, 1961; Nanny, 1985.

65. Margulis, pp. 320–321, 1991a.

66. Sonnonborn, 1967.

67. Mittwoch, 1978; Bell, 1982.

68. Just, 1939; Yanagimachi, 1988.

69. Jaffe and Gould, 1985; Bleil and Wassarman, 1980; Wassarman, 1987.

70. Sea urchins provide the conspicuous exception.

71. Longo, 1987.

72. Hanson, pg. 265, 1977.

73. Cachon et al., 1990.

74. Actually, RNA primer synthesis by primase is required rather than new DNA synthesis on the unwound template strand. Michael et al., 2000.

75. Raff, pg. 38, 1996.

76. Lamarck, (1809) 1984.

77. See Coleman, 1964.

78. Cnidarian colonized organs consist of specialized areas in tentacles where battery cells collect and aim large numbers of cnidocytes.

79. Grell & Ruthmann, 1991. *Tricoplax,* or "hairy plate," is 2–3 mm in diameter, with dorsoventral polarity but no anterior/posterior axis or right and left sides. It

consists of a double layer of ciliated epithelium resting on a basement membrane, and it lives by scavenging—sliding over a food item and digesting it via activities of ventral epithelial cells. *Tricoplaxa* also expands into a ball. A thin mesenchyme occupies the space between the epithelia, but no internal organs are present, and *Tricoplax* has no nervous system.

80. Schlegel et al., 1996; Sogin, 1994.

81. Finnerty and Martindale, 1998.

82. Shostak, pg. 181, 1998. Also see Shostak, 1993a, b, Shostak and Kolluri, 1995.

83. See Hickman, 1999.

84. Lom, 1990; Perkins, 1991.

85. The 18S rDNA was collected from five species of myxozoans (Myxosporea, *Henneguya* sp. 1 & 2; *Myxobolus* sp. 1 & 2; *Myxidium* sp. 1) and two sequences from *Myxidium lieberkuehni*. Smothers et al., 1994; Schlegel et al., 1996. Also see Vossbrinck et al., 1987.

86. The 18S rDNA came from representatives of the same three genera of myxozoans analyzed by Smothers et al., 1994 and Schlegel et al., 1996. Siddal et al., pg. 966, 1995.

87. Goff and Coleman, 1995; Goff et al., 1997.

88. Williams and Polaszek, 1996.

89. Kobayashi et al., pg., 762, 1999.

90. Knoll and Carroll, 1999; Martindale and Kourakis, 1999.

91. Kobayashi et al., pg. 762, 1999.

92. Marcum and Campbell, 1978, Campbell, 1979; Martin and Thomas, 1981, 1983.

93. Hall and Wake, 1999.

94. Hörstadius, 1950; Le Douarin, 1982; Groves and Bronner-Fraser, 1999; Mayor et al., 1999.

95. Werner, 1988.

96. Swalla and Jeffery, 1996.

97. Hall and Wake, pg. 15, 1999. Also see Davidson et al., 1995.

98. Hanken, pg. 66, 1999.

99. See monographs by de Beer, 1951; Gould, 1977.

100. Williamson, 1992.

101. Williamson, 1991.

102. Williamson, 1988.

103. Williamson, 1996, Williamson & Rice, 1998.

104. Williamson, 2001.

105. Zeh and Zeh (2000) suggest that the barriers mounted by viviparous species may be higher than those mounted by oviparous species.

106. Arnold, 1997.

107. Since the energy of any isolated system is constant, as stipulated by the first law of thermodynamics, once work has been performed or energy expended by a body, it cannot be returned to its original state despite the expense of energy from the surrounding parts of the system, as stipulated by the second law of thermodynamics.

108. Hence Maxwell's "demon" wrestles with Nietzsche's "eternal return." For a contrary discussion of physical and philosophical issues of eternal return see Tipler, 1994.

109. Among others, Goodwin, 1984, 1994; Kauffman, 1993; Prigogine and Stengers, 1984; Schiffmann, Y., 1994, 1997; Smith, 1998.

110. Kauffman, 1993.

111. Turing, 1952; Schiffmann, Y., 1994, 1997.

112. E.g., Shostak, 1991.

113. Vellai and Vida, pg. 1574, 1999.

114. Remark attributed to Wolpert by J. M. W. Slack, pg. 3, 1983.

115. For a sobering gloss on Haeckel's influence see Gasman, 1998.

116. Hall and Wake, pg. 12, 1999.

117. Hickman, pg. 23, 1999. Also see Webb, 1999.

118. "Genetic" used by Haeckel, as in "genetic relationship" (pg. 70, [1901] 1992), is short for genealogical.

119. LaBarbera, pp. 3–4; (1951) 1985.

120. Garstang, (1951) 1985.

121. Maturana and Varela, pp. 46–47, 1998.

122. A physical system is defined by a particular amount of matter with specifiable properties—chemical composition, mass and volume in addition to pressure and temperature. Such a physical system resides in a stable condition at equilibrium which has been reached spontaneously while exchanging energy and material with its environment.

123. Smith and Pereira-Smith, 1996.

124. Miller, pg. 72, 1996.

NOTES TO CHAPTER 5

1. Wilmut et al., 2000 cite two general reasons for cloning human beings: "to-recreate some dead loved one" (pg. 307) and "to replicate very special individuals" (pg. 308). Neither reason is considered acceptable, especially because they fail to take into account the welfare of the child, including its psychological welfare.

2. Anne McLaren (pg. 1775; 2000) believes "That wide usage of the term [clone] since the 1980s has helped change its meaning even in biological circles. . . ." The use of "clone" for asexually reproduced organisms or even organisms grown from isolated cells such as carrots and tobacco are expressly excluded.

3. See DiBerardino, 1997. Nuclear transfer in mammals was later performed in mice and other species, especially rabbits by Derek Bromhall.

4. McLaren, pg. 1775, 2000.

5. Wilmut et al., pg. 74, 2000.

6. See Andrews (1999) for a fascinating discussion of the legal complexities surrounding these questions.

7. The philosopher, Jean-François Lyotard (pg. 112, 1989) strikes a similar cord: "What is pertinent for distinguishing the sexes is the relation to death: a body that can die, whatever its sexual anatomy, is masculine; a body that does not know that it must disappear is feminine. Men teach women of death, the impossible, the presence of absence."

8. Driesch, (1892) 1964. Also see Mocek, 1974.

9. Driesch's result was repeated and extended with more gentle methods for separating blastomeres by others, including Thomas Morgan in his role as embryologist.

10. Weismann, 1912.

11. Roux, (1888) 1964.

12. See Shostak (1991) for details and citations. Also see Vickery and McClintock (1998) for what may be the "final word" on the subject.

13. For summary of his experiments, see Spemann, 1938.

14. See DiBerardino, 1997.

15. Wilmut et al., 1997.

16. Vertebrates do not actually form a single zygotic nucleus. The pronuclei interdigitate but do not fuse. Rather, chromosomes mingle on the metaphase plate of the first cleavage division, and nuclei containing paternal and maternal chromosomes only form in the first two blastomeres (see Longo, 1987).

17. Even in cases where nuclei undergo changes in chromosomes during early development (known as chromosomal diminution) or similar processes involving the breakup of chromosomes, the "essential" parts of chromosomes are thought to be carried forward through development without change. See Davidson, 1986.

18. Willadsen, 1979.

19. See history of mammalian cloning in Wilmut et al., 2000.

20. See DiBerardino, 1997, for details and citations.

21. Solter, 1998; Ashworth et al., 1998; Signer et al., 1998.

22. Wakayama et al., 1998.

23. Wilmut et al., 2000.

24. Gurdon et al., 1976.

25. Solter, 1998; Ashworth et al., 1998.

26. Enucleation is performed by micromanipulation: the egg, secured at the tip of a holding pipette, is penetrated by a micropipette in the vicinity of the first polar body and chromosomes in the second meiotic metaphase are sucked up along with some surrounding egg cytoplasm. A fluorescent dye, which binds to DNA, is employed and the presence of chromosomes within the micropipette confirms the enucleation.

27. Wakayama et al., 1998.

28. Onishi et al., 2000.

29. Also see News Focus by Pennisi and Normile, 2000.

30. See Wilmut et al., 2000, especially Chapter 8, "Keith and the cell cycle."

31. The tiny fraction of DNA synthesis continuing is presumably involved in DNA recombination and repair.

32. The reader might like to consult my embryology textbook (Shostak, 1991) or any other embryology textbook for a general description of the cellular controls of meiosis and mitosis during cleavage.

33. The procedure is known as MAGIC, an acronym coined by Keith Campbell, meaning "Metaphase-Arrested G_1/G_0 Accepting Cytoplast." The alternate procedure, GOAT, is the acronym, also coined by Keith Campbell, for "G_0 Activation and Transfer."

34. "Morag was made with a low-MPF, universal recipient cytoplast." Wilmut et al., pg. 227, 2000.

35. The zygote is ordinarily the only totipotent cell, since it alone has the ability to create an entire embryo and, subsequently, an adult.

36. All cells express only a small portion of their entire genome. The exception is primary oocytes in the lampbrush phase (e.g., in amphibian eggs) where "run-through" gene expression literally runs through the entire genome.

37. Wilmut et al., pg. 232, 2000. Wilmut et al. (pg. 248, 2000) admit that the actual cell donating the nucleus was of an unknown phenotype, although "[n]inety per cent of the cells that were cultured to make Dolly were indeed mammary epithelial cells (OME) but there were also "other differentiated cell types, including myoepithelial cells and fibroblasts" . . . [and] a small proportion of relatively undifferentiated stem cells able to support regeneration of the mammary gland during pregnancy." Ultimately, Wilmut et al. (pg. 254, 2000) trim their claim, asserting "that unequivocally specialized cells *can* give rise to whole clones."

38. Wilmut et al., pg. 222, 2000.

39. Wilmut et al., pg. 224, 2000.

40. The procedure for making clones from TNT_4 cells was subsequently patented by James McWhir and Keith Campbell.

41. Evans and Kaufman, 1981.

42. Wilmut et al., pg. 214, 2000.

43. The Poll-Dorset fetal fibroblasts, code-named PDFF, used in the cloning of Cedric, Cecil, Cyril and Tuppence were from seven different fetuses, one of which was male.

44. In this sense, the chimera does not form different parts but is formed by different parts (a nucleus and cytoplasm from different animals).

45. See Spemann, 1938.

46. Lajtha, 1979.

47. Benfey, pg. R171, 1999.

48. Slack, pg. 1431, 2000.

49. Slack (2000), on the other hand, sees epithelia as quintessential stem cell tissues.

50. Doetsch et al., 1999; McDonald et al., 1999; Gage, 2000.

51. van der Kooy and Weiss, pg. 1439, 2000.

52. For example, sophisticated monoclonal antibodies for specific surface gly-colipid- and glycoproteins. A "cocktail of antibodies" identify the HSC cell lineage in mice: antigens (B220, Gr-1, Mac-1, CD4, CD5, and CD8) and alkaline phosphatase (Goodell et al., 1996).

53. Walsh and Cepko, 1988.

54. Altman, 1962.

55. Embryo stem (ES or EK) cells are also known as embryonic, embryonal, and embryo-derived stem cells.

56. Potten and Loeffler (1990) discuss several additional problems of nomenclature.

57. Mezey et al., 2000.

58. Bjornson et al., 1999.

59. Wilmut et al., pg. 162, 2000.

60. Evans and Kaufman, 1981; Martin, 1981. Indeed, at the time they were largely equated with teratocarcinoma cell lines. But see Edwards (2001).

61. Stevens, 1960.

62. Stevens, 1975. Also see Damjanov et al., 1987.

63. Rudnicki and McBurney, 1987.

64. Hooper, pg. 3, 1992.

65. Martin, pg. 5634, 1981.

66. Rudnicki and McBurney, 1987.

67. Evans and Kaufman (1981) actually derived their ICMs from blastocysts whose implantation was delayed by ovariectomy. ICMs were recovered as large egg

cylinder-like structures consisting of small, rounded cells surrounded by endodermal-like cells attached to the culture dish.

68. The feeder layer of nonproliferative cells was intended to provide the ICM cells with requisite (but unknown) factors for maintaining proliferation while retaining cell stability.

69. Antigens typically present on mouse embryo cells include M1-22-25, the Forssman antigen, and I Ma (lacto-N-iso-octaosyl ceramide). In addition, proteins separated from ES cells in two-dimensional gels resemble those of EC cells isolated from teratocarcinomas.

70. See News Focus by Vogel, 1999.

71. Bradley et al., 1984. See Papaioannou, 1982.

72. Hooper, pg. xi, 1992.

73. Wilmut et al., pg. 55, 2000.

74. Wilmut et al, 2000.

75. Thomson et al., 1998.

76. Shamblott et al., 1998.

77. Shamblott et al., pg. 13726, 1998.

78. McDonald et al., 1999.

79. See News, Marshall, 2000.

80. Piccini, et al., 1999. See News, Barinaga, 2000.

81. Doetsch et al., 1999; van der Kooy and Weiss, 2000; Rietze et al., 2001.

82. Gussoni et al., pg. 390, 1999.

83. Slack, pg. 1433, 2000. Ferrari et al., 1998; Petersen et al., 1999; Gussoni et al., 1999.

84. Orlic et al., pg. 704, 2001.

85. Gage, pg. 1435, 2000. Cites Bjornson et al., 1999. The blood cell types produced included myeloid and lymphoid cells as well as early hematopoietic cells.

86. Goodell et al., 1996.

87. Peled et al., 1999.

88. Liotta, pg. 25, 2001.

89. Müller et al., 2001.

90. Tarkowski, 1959.

91. Mintz and Illmensee, 1975.

92. My search of the literature indicates that the term, *therapeutic cloning* was used for the first time in the title of an article published by Michael West's group (Lanza et al., 1999).

93. Wilmut et al., pg. 328, 2000.

94. See review by Guarente and Kenyon, 2000. Also see Rogina et al., 2000.

95. Internalizing the generator could be accomplished in older hosts as well.

96. See DiBerardino, 1997.

97. Willadsen, 1979.

98. See Wilmut et al., 2000.

99. Willadson, 1979.

100. The "Stages" referred to here are Carnegie Stages. See England, 1994, for a recent review of human stages of development.

101. Cloned blastocysts derived from blastomeres, from split blastocysts (preembryos), or nuclear/cytoplasmic chimeras could also be implanted into a late fetus or neonate or possibly individuals at even later stages of development. However, implantation in the early embryo (before gonads are occupied by primordial germ cells) would seem to provide the best opportunity for the devolution of the blastocyst into a new organ (i.e., the generator).

102. Teratocarcinomas, in contrast, are larger and contain cellular foci of embryonal carcinoma, clusters of small, malignant stem cells, with little cytoplasm surrounding a well-developed nucleus, easily distinguished from surrounding, spindle-shaped connective tissue-like cells.

103. Damjanov et al., 1987.

104. The uterus is formed from the fused ends of the paramesonephric ducts which appear in embryos of both sexes (i.e., the early embryo is androgynous).

105. See Slack, 1999.

106. See Rose, 1999.

107. DePinho, pg. 248, 2000.

108. See Poinar and Poinar (1999) for a description of the immunological problems encountered by parasitoid insects.

109. Martin, pg. 138, 1998.

110. Grafts between identical twins are an exception.

111. See Burnet, 1969.

112. Medawar, 1986.

113. Burnet and Medawar shared the Noble Prize in Physiology or Medicine in 1960 for this work.

NOTES TO EPILOGUE

1. Croissant, pg. 285, 1998.

2. McGreath et al., 2000.

3. Andrews, pg. 48, 1999.

4. Andrews, pg. 95, 1999.

5. Lewontin, 1997.

6. See Clover, 1998.

7. Lewontin, 1997.

8. Mentor, pg. 69, 1998.

9. "Procreative autonomy" was coined by Ronald Dworkin to bring marriage laws and the rights of childbearing into the mainstream of ethical issues within the context of modern democracies.

10. Dworkin, pp. 167–8, 1993. Quoted from Harris, pg. 90, 1998.

11. Harris, pg. 68, 1998.

12. Deech, pg. 97, 1998.

13. Benatar, pg. 171, 1998.

14. Dumit and Davis-Floyd, 1998.

15. According to Lori B. Andrews (1999) the Cambridge embryologist, Robert Edwards, and his obstetrician collaborator, Patrick Steptoe, had performed no animal experimentation prior to the *in vitro* fertilization and embryo transfer that led to the birth of Louise Brown on July 25, 1978, "the world's first in vitro fertilization baby" (pg. 15). Andrews explains later, "In vitro was done on women in 1978, but not on baboons until 1979 and chimps until 1983" (pg. 33).

16. Andrews, pg. 18, 1999.

17. See Cussins, 1998.

18. Turkle, pg. 325, 1998.

19. Turkle, pg. 328, 1998.

20. Turkle, pg. 328, 1998.

21. Undoubtedly, we would have a concept of movement even without the "persistence of vision," since movement is attributed to displacements which we do not generally perceive (from the movement of the sun and stars across the heavens to the movement of atoms above absolute zero Kelvin).

22. Bergson, pg. 240, (1904) 1991.

23. Wells, pg. 74, (1895) 1996.

24. Wells, pg. 80, (1895) 1996.

25. Scheler, pp. 62–63, 1961.

26. Wells, pg. 79, (1895) 1996.

Glossary

---

adaptive landscape: range of evolutionary possibilities viewed as adaptive hills and ill-adapted valleys; organisms optimally adapted to one set of ecological circumstances are unlikely to adapt to another.

adaptive radiation: apparently related fossils appearing in the same strata as if evolving rapidly from the same ancestral population.

AI: artificial insemination; suspension of spermatozoa introduced manually into female genital tract.

allele: gene, especially one of a group found alternately at the same locus on a chromosome.

allopatric speciation: origin of species from geographically isolated subpopulations.

amino acids: organic compounds having an amine group (-NH$_2$), the organic acid group (-COOH), and residual groups bound to carbon; one of twenty such organic components of polypeptides or proteins.

amniocentesis: aspiration of fluid and cells from amniotic cavity; procedure to obtain fetal cells for the diagnosis of hereditary disease.

amnion: extraembryonic membrane; closest to embryo in amniotic vertebrates covers embryo and yolk sac.

androgens: male steroid sex hormones associated with increased muscle mass.

aneuploid: an abnormal number of chromosomes.

antibodies: circulating immunoglobular proteins with a high affinity for substances known as antigens; similar immunoglobulins attached to lymphocytes.

antigen: (1) substances capable of evoking an immunological reaction such as the production of antibodies; (2) substance combining with a specific antibody.

APC: antigen-presenting cell; a macrophage or dendritic cell which has taken up and processed an antigen for later interaction with a competent immunoreactive lymphocytes.

apoptosis: cytological and nuclear events accompanying programmed cell death especially condensation and fragmentation of dying cell's nucleus.

Archaea (also **Archaebacteria**): Domain of life; type of prokaryote.

area pellucida: portion of avian egg and cellular blastoderm that gives rise to embryo proper and extraembryonic membranes.

asexual reproduction: reproduction entirely by the body's own (somatic) cells without the participation of sex cells.

ATP: adenosine triphosphate; molecule utilized in energy- and phosphate-transferring reactions within cells.

B cells: type of lymphocyte especially capable of reacting with other cells of the immune system by producing specific antibodies.

Bacteria (also **Eubacteria**): Domain of life; type of prokaryote including *Escherichia coli* and blue green bacteria (cyanobacteria).

base pairing: Watson/Crick pairing; couplets of complementary nitrogenous bases (A–T or U; C–G) linking stands of nucleic acids together.

Bauplan (pl.: *Baupläne*): theoretical construction plan for related organisms.

Bilateria: animals (metazoans) with three germ layers in gastrula and bilateral (rarely radial) symmetry in adults.

biosphere: portion of Earth's surface and surrounding atmosphere containing all organisms living on Earth.

blastocoel: cavity within an early embryo; cavity within a blastula.

blastocyst: preembryonic stage of mammalian development in which a layer of outer cells (trophectoderm or trophoblast) encloses an eccentric group of cells (inner cell mass) and a fluid-filled cavity (blastocyst cavity).

blastoderm: layer of embryonic cells.

blastomere: embryonic cell, especially cell produced by cleavage.

blastula: stage of embryonic development following cleavage and preceding gastrulation.

bone marrow (strictly **red bone marrow**): blood- and lymphocyte-forming tissue in cavity of bones.

Caenorhabditis elegans (also ***C. elegans***): a free-living round-worm found in soil and frequently used in developmental and genetic research.

Cambrian: geological Period at beginning of Paleozoic (Phanerozoic) Era.

cDNA: complementary (copy) DNA; DNA made by reverse transcriptase complementary to an RNA template.

cell cycle: succeeding periods of cell division, or mitosis, and interphase.

cellular turnover: physiological replacement of cells in stable organs and systems.

cellularization: formation of the cellular blastoderm in the embryos of some insects at end of cleavage.

central dogma: doctrine that DNA determines everything about proteins and, therefore, the way an organism interacts with its environment, but the organism's environment determines nothing about DNA and, therefore, has no influence on heredity.

chloroplast: cell organelle found in plants and algae capable of conducting photosynthesis; organelle derived from cyanobacteria.

chorion: membrane over watery cavity; outermost extraembryonic membrane.

chromosome: (1) rod-shaped, colored body appearing in eukaryotic cell prior to cell division and separating into two identical bodies during division; (2) nucleic acid bearing hereditary information.

cladistics: method for weighing similarities and differences among sets of organismic characteristics, especially molecular sequence-data, used to propose patterns of branching evolution.

cleavage: cell division in fertilized egg and blastomeres.

CNS: central nervous system; portion of nervous system consisting of brain and spinal cord in vertebrates.

codon: triplet of nitrogenous bases in messenger RNA directing the incorporation of a specific amino acid into a polypeptide or protein.

conjugation: sexual-like coupling in algae and protozoans; formation of cytoplasmic bridge and movement of chromosomal segment between bacteria.

cortical inheritance: heredity attributed to the outer portion (cortex) of cells as opposed to the nucleus.

cpDNA: DNA present in chloroplasts.

CR: caloric restriction.

cryopreservation: method of rapid freezing used in preserving eggs, spermatozoa, or blastocysts; preservation of cells, tissues, embryos, or organisms by freezing.

cyclic-AMP: cyclic-adenosine monophosphate; secondary cellular messenger thought to act as morphogen.

cytogenetics: use of cytological methods in study of heredity, especially the number and appearance of chromosomes.

cytokinesis: division of cytoplasm following division of nucleus.

cytoplasmic determinants: elements of cytoplasm including organelles which influence developmental patterns, morphogenesis, and cell differentiation.

cytoplasmic DNA: DNA present in plasmids of prokaryotes, episomes or organelles of eukaryotes.

cytoplasmic inheritance: inheritance attributed to cytoplasm, especially to cell cortex and organelles.

Darwinism: doctrine of evolutionary change brought about gradually through accumulation of inherited qualities via natural selection.

determinism: mosaicism; doctrine that development is caused by invariant agents (determinants) as opposed to varying (regulative) conditions.

differentiation: processes leading to acquisition of cellular-, tissue-, and organ-specific characteristics.

diploblastic (didermic animal): having two cellular layers in gastrala members of the Radiata.

direct development: development of embryo to juvenile or adult without intervening larval stage and metamorphosis.

directed mutagenesis: altering gene through the uptake of sequences containing complementary DNA.

DNA: deoxyribonucleic acid; generally double-stranded nucleic acid containing adenine, cytosine, guanine, and thymine, the deoxribose sugar, and phosphate.

domain: (1): portion of DNA encoding a specific part of a protein; (2) largest taxonomic division of living things.

dpo: days post ovulation; indication of days following fertilization and of development.

Drosophila: genus of fruit flies; frequently short for *Drosophila melanogaster.*

EB: embryoid body; endodermal-like cells surrounding core of embryo-carcinoma cells grown *in vivo* or appearing as lumps *in vitro*; cysts of embryonic carcinoma cells capable of some differentiation.

EC: embryonal carcinoma (also **ECC**: embryonic carcinoma cell): malignant cells derived from stem cells of teratocarcinomas.

ECM: extracellular material (or matrix).

ED: embryo disk; portion of late blastocyst giving rise to embryo; used as source of nuclear donors in cloning; source of embryonal stem cells.

EF: elongation factor; proteins operating in the elongation of polypeptide chains during translation.

endosymbiont: algae, bacteria, and sometimes viruses living permanently within an animal's cells.

enhancer: transcription factor which increases the rate of transcription for a specific gene.

enucleated oocyte: egg prepared for nuclear transfer by removal of its nucleus; cytoplast.

epiblast: layer of cells formed by inner cell mass of blastocyst or avian blastoderm.

epigenesis: concept of development and differentiation from unformed and undifferentiated material.

episome: (non-organellar) cytoplasmic DNA; may move to chrosome.

ES cells: embryonal (also embryonic and embryo) stem cells; proliferative and pluripotential cells derived from the inner cell mass capable of differentiating into every type of cell following transfer to a blastocyst.

es cells: exotic stem cells; foreign stem cells derived from a clone and capable of performing the same roles as ES cells or stem cells normally present in organisms.

Escherichia coli (also ***E. coli***): a bacterium normally found in the colon or large intestine of mammals and frequently used in genetic studies of prokaryotes.

ESS: evolutionary stable strategy; behavior that admits no competitor.

EST: expressed sequence tags; segments of cDNA used for sequencing, aligning sequences during genetic mapping, and finding genes in chromosomal DNA.

ET: embryo transfer; transfer of blastocyst to the uterus or uterine duct of surrogate mother.

Eucarya: Domain of life containing all varieties of organisms whose cells have at least one nucleus, a cytoskeleton, frequently membranous organelles, and unique, large ribosomes; eukaryotes.

female pronucleus: haploid nucleus formed in the egg following its second meiotic division.

fertilization: fusion of mature egg with spermatozoon; formation of zygote or fertilized egg.

fibroblasts: spindle (fusiform) or star-shaped (stellate) cell found in connective tissue; a spindle or star-shaped cell in tissue-culture.

food chain (also **food web**): system of nutrient transfer from producers (typically plants, algae, and bacteria) to consumers (typically animals and protozoans).

founder population: colonizers; part of large population, representing a limited portion of a gene pool, at beginning of an evolutionary lineage.

G_0: quiescent stage of cellular interphase; indefinitely prolonged G_1 phase; typically stage of differentiation; frequently stage of nuclear-donor's cells used for cloning mammals.

G_1: "gap" in cell cycle (interphase) between mitotic division or M stage and DNA synthesis or S phase.

G_2: "gap" in cell cycle (interphase) between DNA synthesis or S phase and mitotic division or M stage.

GAGs: glycosaminoglycans (formerly mucopolysaccharides); important carbohydrate components of connective-tissue matrix.

gametes: germ cells capable of fusing (copulating or fertilizing), including sex cells (eggs and spermatozoa).

gap junctions: areas of intercellular communication formed by connexons containing pores permitting movement of ions and small molecules between cells.

gastrula: embryonic stage characterized by initiation of cell movement and transcription of specific varieties of messenger RNA and by formation of embryonic germ layers.

gene cloning: manufacture of a specific gene or sequence of DNA through recombinant gene-technology and cell culture.

gene expression: strictly, transcription of a gene but, generally, the combination of transcription and translation of a gene's product.

gene pool: all the genes present in a population or species.

gene rearrangement: reassortment of different segments of chromosomal DNA in cells resulting in the production of unique RNA transcripts and specific proteins.

gene targeting: manipulating a gene by using its sequence of nucleotides to select it and introduce or remove segments with the aid of complementary sequences.

gene therapy: possibility of eliminating deleterious genes or introducing healthy ones through directed mutagenesis, recombination, and gene targeting.

genes: units of hereditary information affecting the development of specific traits in organisms, cells, mitochondria, chloroplasts, and viruses; control elements and transcribed portions of double-stranded DNA in prokaryotes, eukaryotes and viruses; similar portions of DNA and RNA associated with reverse transcription in retroviruses.

genetic code: triplet sequence of nitrogenous bases in codons prescribing precisely what amino acid is to be included at a particular location in a polypeptide chain.

genetic drift: changes in a population's gene pool resulting from small sample size or random error.

genic assimilation: integration of genes or portions of genes in a genome following lateral (or horizontal) gene transfer or hybridization.

genome: all the genes in a representative member of a species; the genes comprising a species's gene pool.

genotype: the genes in an individual; frequently, the specific gene or genes (alleles) present at a locus.

germ layers: coherent layers of cells in gastrulas; typically ectoderm, mesoderm, and endoderm.

germ line: theoretical lineage of germ cells (eggs, spermatozoa, or gametes) connecting generations.

germinal vesicle: (1) post-blastocyst stage of development; (2) extraembryonic membrane containing mammalian embryo; (3) nucleus of early oocyte.

germplasm: nuclear genes; hereditary information transmitted through germ line and capable of influencing development of individual.

GM: genetically modified; typically transgenic crops bearing insecticide-resistant or ripening-retarding genes (e.g., soy and tomatoes).

gonadal ridges: embryonic rudiments of ovary or testis.

gonads: ovary or testis in female or male animals, respectively, or ovotestis in simultaneous hermaphrodites.

group selection: controversial concept of evolution in which the environment selects for a group's characteristics.

GS cells: germ stem cells; precursors of germ cells obtained from gonadal ridge of embryos or fetuses.

hard-wired: embryonic characteristics thought to be prescribed directly by DNA.

Hardy Weinberg Law (equilibrium): the frequency of genes does not change in a large population breeding randomly and undergoing no emigration, immigration, mutation, and natural selection.

Hayflick limit (number): the maximum number of times cells divide in tissue culture following their removal from an organism.

heterozygote: a cell or organism with different genes (alleles) at the same locus on homologous chromosomes.

histones: basic proteins bound to DNA in eukaryotic chromosomes.

homologues: biological structures and molecular sequences resembling one another.

homology: similarity attributed to common ancestry and a failure to change beyond recognition in the course of evolution (biological inertia).

homozygote: a cell or organism with the same gene (allele) at the same locus on homologous chromosomes.

horizontal gene transfer (also **lateral gene transfer or LGT**): transfer of genes between unrelated organisms.

horizontal inheritance: inheritance through cytoplasm; the extranuclear transfer of hereditary material; the uptake of symbionts by offspring from a parent's detritus.

hormone: variety of substances including lipids (steroids), amino acids, small peptides and proteins, released by a variety of cells into the circulatory system and affecting the activities of target cells residing at a distance.

Hox-genes (also *HOX*-**genes**): class of genes whose products influence morphogenesis especially along the anterior-posterior axis of metazoans; class of control or regulatory genes containing a so-called homeobox.

HSC: hematopoietic stem cells; precursor cells of blood-forming lineages.

hybridization: generally, mating between male and female (or hermaphrodite) members of different species; historically, matings between members of different inbred or "pure" lines, especially of plants.

ICM: inner cell mass; portion of blastocyst (preembryo) that gives rise to the embryo proper and extraembryonic membranes other than trophoblast or chorion, source of embryonal stem cells.

imaginal disc (or **disk**): rudiments of adult organs present in the larvae (imagoes) of endopterygote (holometabolic) insects such as the fruit fly.

immortalized cells: cells in tissue culture which divide endlessly and fail to differentiate.

immuno-tolerance: acceptance of an antigen without adverse effects; the failure of an organism to respond to an antigen aggressively through an immune response.

implantation: the process through which an embryo establishes placental contact with maternal tissue.

imprinting (of DNA): a form of non-Mendelian inheritance frequently attributed to the enzymatic methylation of DNA.

inbred strains: laboratory animals produced by brother/sister or mother/son mating.

inclusive fitness: Darwinian fitness; the likelihood (probability) of an organism passing on its genes to a future generation.

indirect development: development of a larval stage (instar, nymph, tadpole, etc.) between embryo and juvenile or adult; generally accompanied by metamorphosis.

induction: intercellular communication resulting in the morphogenesis or differentiation of affected cells.

interphase: (1) period in cell cycle consisting of "gaps" (G_1 and G_2) and DNA synthesis (S); (2) period of cell differentiation (G_0) frequently when cell division is suspended.

IVF: *in vitro* fertilization; fertilization in tissue culture.

K/T border: Cretaceous/Tertiary border; end of the Mesozoic Era and beginning of the Cenozoic Era; break in geological record dated about 65 million years ago.

karyokinesis: mitosis; nuclear division; separation of identical sets of chromosomes.

knock-out (knock-in) mice: transformed mice lacking (or bearing) specific genes created by gene targeting or directed-mutagenesis of embryonic stem cells, followed by screening for desired gene, injecting into blastocysts, transferring to surrogate mother, and selecting gene or mutation in germ-line.

Lamarckism: doctrine of progressive evolution brought about through the inheritance of useful characteristics acquired during a lifetime and the loss of useless characteristics.

leukemia: various cancers of the precursors of white blood cells.

leukocytes: variety of white blood cells.

LGT: lateral gene transfer; transfer of genes between organelles and nucleus in eukaryotes; transfer of genes between members of different species (horizontal gene transfer).

locus: typically, a position on a chromosome occupied by a gene (allele).

lymphocytes: range of small to large T and B cells of the immune system.

lymphoma: various cancers of precursors of lymphocytes and similar cells.

macrophage: cell capable of taking up particulate material.

male pronucleus: nucleus formed by fertilized egg containing the spermatozoon's DNA.

malignant transformation: change from cells observing normal constraints on growth in tissue-culture to cells overgrowing one another in culture and forming malignant tumors when injected into an organism.

marker proteins: specific proteins detected only in specifically differentiated cell-types.

mass extinction: period in geological record marked by the disappearance of large numbers of taxa.

mass cell movement: cells moving in coherent layers; characteristic of germ-layers in vertebrates.

meiosis: the unique type of proliferation found in germ-line cells in which one round of DNA synthesis is accompanied by two divisions resulting in halving the cell's chromosomal number and DNA content.

Mendelism: doctrine of particulate inheritance; underlying premise of modern genetics.

meristem: population of proliferative small cells capping growing shoots and roots.

metabolic gradient: progressive change in the rate of metabolism over an area.

metamorphosis: rapid change between stages in a life cycle, especially a dramatic transition from larva to juvenile or adult frequently involving massive cell death.

metastasis: tissue movement especially the invasive, destructive movement of a cancer.

Metazoa: the division of eukaryotes including radiate and bilateral animals.

methylation: addition of a methyl ($-CH_3$) group to an organic molecule.

MII: second meiotic or metaphase arrest; interruption of the second meiotic division at metaphase in a vertebrate egg.

mitochondria: cell organelles at the center of energy production; main source of adenosine triphosphate (ATP) in eukaryotic cells.

modern synthesis: neo-Darwinism; microevolutionary theory; attempts to harmonize Darwin's concept of gradual changes in traits with changes in the frequency of genes in a population.

monoclonal antibody: a specific antibody produced by cells from a single cell line and reacting with a particular site on an antigen.

monophyly: evolutionary scenario tracing species back to a single origin.

morphogen: substance capable of influencing morphogenesis typically by induction and over a gradient.

morphogenic gradients: continuous or sequential variation in developing structures over an area.

mosaicism: see **determinism.**

mRNA: messenger RNA; transcripts of RNA, modified and processed in eukaryotes, containing an encoding region (open reading frame).

mtDNA: DNA present in mitochondria.

mutant: generally an organism or type of organism representing a variant form of a species; a mutation.

mutation: a variant form of a gene; process leading to a genetic change.

myeloid tissue: cells of bone marrow committed to differentiate as white blood cells.

myoblasts: embryonic, skeletal muscle-forming cells.

myoepithelial cell: (1) cell with properties of both muscle and epithelium derived from neural crest in vertebrates; (2) type of cell forming surface layers in some cnidarians.

myofiber: component of skeletal-muscle in vertebrates consisting of syncytium formed by fusion of myoblasts.

nematodes: round worms; e.g., *Caenorhabditis elegans*.

neo-Darwinism: see **modern synthesis**.

neoepigenesis: a modern concept of regulative development involving differential gene action.

neopreformation: a modern concept of determinant development involving prescribed gene action.

neural crest cells: pluripotential stem cells formed by neural crest in vertebrate embryo.

neuroendocrine cell: neuron-like cell capable of releasing neurotransmitters into circulation.

neuroglial cells: nonconducting, supportive cells of nervous tissue.

neuron: conducting cell of nervous tissue.

neurotransmitters: stimulatory and inhibiting organic molecules (derived from choline, amines, and catecholamines) released by neurons at synapses and motor end-plates.

nitrogenous bases: the ring-shaped molecules (purines and pyrimidines) containing carbon and nitrogen found in nucleotides and nucleic acids; the purines (A = adenine; G= guanine) and pyrimidines (C = cytosine; T = thymine; U = uracil) forming complementary pairs in double stranded portions of nucleic acids (A–T or U; C–G).

nonMendelian heredity: patterns of inheritance that defy analysis by a binomial distribution of genes; hereditary influences exerted by cytoplasm.

nuclear/cytoplasmic chimera: egg with a transferred nucleus in place of its own; the organism developing from such an egg.

nuclear donor: the organism or cell contributing the nucleus to a nuclear/cytoplasmic chimera.

nuclear equivalence: the idea that all cells belonging to a multicellular organism (or any lineage of cells produced by mitotic divisions) have precisely the same genes.

nuclear hegemony: the notion that the nucleus, especially its DNA/genes, determines everything about the life of an organism.

nuclear receptors: transcription factors in the nucleus whose activity depends on binding to specific hormones or other ligands.

nucleotide substitution: the replacement of one nitrogenous base for another in a nucleic acid.

nucleotides: complex biomolecules consisting of a nitrogenous base (purine or pyrimidine), a five-carbon sugar (ribose or deoxyribose) and a phosphate group; component of nucleic acid.

nullipotent: a cell line incapable of differentiating in tissue culture.

oncogenes: normal (cytoplasmic or *c-oncs*), proto-oncogenes, and tumor-suppressor genes encoding proteins playing a variety of roles at cell-division checkpoints; mutant or viral oncogenes (*v-oncs*) conveyed by cell-transforming oncoviruses and associated with cancers.

oocyte: a differentiating female-germ cell whose nucleus is in the first or second meiotic division.

ORF: open reading frame; portion of an mRNA sequence translated by ribosomes into a polypeptide.

organelles: membranous and tubular-filamentous structures in the cytoplasm and cortex of eukaryotic cells.

p53: a protein with tumor-suppressing and apoptosis-initiating activities; absent or altered in many tumors.

Paramecium: a genus of ciliated protozoans used in studies of cortical (cell surface) inheritance.

parasitism: phenomenon of small organisms exploiting large ones while maintaining permanent physical contact.

parasitoids: embryos and larvae living as parasites; larvae provisioned with large organisms by a parent.

parenchyma: the conspicuous or functional cells of an organ.

parthenogenesis: "virgin birth"; development, typically from eggs, without fertilization by spermatozoa.

pattern formation: appearance of embryonic areas such as head, thorax, and abdomen frequently prior to segmentation and other indications of differentiation.

PCD: programmed cell death; notion of genetically determined pathways to apoptosis.

PCR: polymerase chain reaction; a widely used technique for producing virtually identical segments of DNA.

PGC: primordial germ cell; large, circulating or migrating embryonic precursors of germ stem cells.

pharming: branch of biotechnology specializing in obtaining biologically active products from the secretions or bodily fluids of transgenic animals.

phenotype: all the traits characteristic of organisms appearing during their lifetime.

phylogenetic map: an evolutionary scenario sometimes obtained by cladistic analysis.

plasmalemma: cell membrane.

plasmid: cytoplasmic DNA.

plastids: organelles of plants including chloroplasts.

pluripotential cell: cell capable of differentiating into a large variety of cell types.

PNS: peripheral nervous system; portion of the nervous system of vertebrates consisting of nerves and ganglia outside the central nervous system.

polyclone: group or compartment of cells containing different but integrated cell lineages.

polygene: multiple factor; genes regulating the development of quantitative traits.

polymorphism: quantitative or qualitative variation among molecules, genes, or traits.

polypeptide: a protein or subunit of a protein formed by the condensation of amino acids during translation; chain of peptide bonds alternating with carbons bearing the residues of amino acids.

polyploidization: a spontaneous or induced increase in a cells' chromosome number by a whole multiple.

Precambrian: rocks and fossils older than 540 million years and lacking Cambrian-type fossils.

preembryo: blastocyst prior to formation of primitive streak.

preformationism: doctrine that the parts of a developing organism are already present in egg or spermatozoon.

prenatal screening: various ways of testing and diagnosing an embryo or fetus *in utero* generally requiring the extraction of embryonic cells.

primitive streak: depression in the blastoderm or epiblast of amniotic vertebrates which regresses and disappears in the vicinity of the anus or cloaca as the embryo develops anteriorly.

progeria: an inherited aging disorder; the early and abnormal appearance of some features typically associated with aging.

progesterone: the "hormone of pregnancy"; a steroid produced in large amounts by the corpus luteum and placenta and functioning in the maintenance of the placenta during pregnancy.

prokaryotes: Bacteria and Archaea.

promoter: portion of the leading segment of DNA required for transcription of one or more structural or regulatory gene.

punctuated equilibrium: evolutionary theory that periods of rapid evolutionary change intervene with normal periods of relative evolutionary stasis.

Radiata: radially and biradially symmetrical animals (metazoans) with inner and outer cell layers; Cnidaria, Ctenophora, and Placoderma (*Tricoplax*).

rDNA: ribosomal DNA; DNA sequences encoding specific subunits of ribosomal RNA manufactured *in vitro* with the aid of reverse transcriptase and templates of ribosomal RNA.

recapitulation: (1) repetitive morphologic patterns attributed to living things; (2) notion that particular stages in evolutionary history (phylogeny) are repeated in development (ontogeny).

receptor molecules: specific cell-surface, cytoplasmic, and nuclear proteins that bind particular cells, factors, hormones, and ligands triggering unique biological reactions; part of a transduction pathway.

red blood cell: circulating cells of vertebrates containing hemoglobin and normally functioning in the exchange of oxygen and carbon dioxide.

regulative development: indeterminism; doctrine that development is caused by varying (regulative) conditions as opposed to invariant agents (determinants).

replication: the synthesis of strands of DNA as complements to preexisting DNA strands.

replicative senescence: mitotic quiescence arising in cells after a period in culture.

replicators: self-perpetuating entities; germplasm; genes carried forward to new generations in the germ line.

reproductive potential: the greatest number of offspring possibly produced by a female or hermaphroditic member of a species.

reserve stem cell: a quiescent cell which may proliferate and differentiate into cells of a particular type under particular conditions; already determined cells but neither proliferating nor differentiating into a particular type of cell.

residual bodies: portion of spermatids and intercellular bridges shed during the final differentiation of spermatozoa.

reverse transcriptase: enzyme present in retroviruses capable of synthesizing a DNA complement to an RNA template; enzyme used in the manufacture of cDNA.

ribosomal subunit: one of the two parts of a ribosome containing specific RNAs and proteins active in translation in combination with messenger RNA, and transfer RNA.

RNA: ribonucleic acid; nucleic acid containing adenine, cytosine, guanine, and uracil, the ribose sugar, and phosphate.

S phase: stage of cellular interphase, ordinarily between G_1 and G_2 during which DNA synthesis by replication takes place in nucleus.

Saccharomyces cereviseae: brewer's yeast frequently used by geneticists and cell biologists to study gene action and control of cell cycle.

satellite cells: (1) reserve stem-cell populations associated with skeletal muscle; (2) glial cells surrounding neurons in ganglia of peripheral nervous system.

segmentation: formation of similar repetitive units along the length of an animal during its development.

selfish genes: anthropomorphic concept of genes as struggling to enter succeeding generations by exploiting the organisms they create.

sexual isolation: the ability of male and female members of a species to reproduce sexually while failing to reproduce with members of other species.

signal-transduction pathway: intracellular biochemical cascade triggered by an extracellular ligand in combination with a surface receptor, generally ending with an effect on gene expression.

signaling pathway: cascade of reactions involving products of several genes frequently having similar developmental consequences (such as leg development) in widely different animals (from *Drosophila* to vertebrates).

silencer: transcription factor which decreases the rate of transcription for a specific gene.

soma: body, typically excluding germ cells.

somatoplasm: generally equivalent to cytoplasm; the parts of an organism that differentiate under the influence of nuclear genes (germplasm).

SP: side population; a pluripotential, hematopoietic stem-cell population.

spermatocyte: differentiating male-germ cell with nucleus in the first or second meiotic division.

spermatogonia: reserve or active stem cell of the male germ line.

spermatozoon (pl. **spermatozoa**): a differentiated cell of the male germ line of animals able to engage in fertilization.

stem-cell niche: complex of local signals promoting specific stem-cell differentiation.

stroma: the connective tissue portion of organs; the capsule and septa (trabeculae) supporting a parenchyma in organs.

survivorship curve: plot showing number of surviving members of a cohort group (organisms of the same age) as a function of their age.

symbiosis: organisms living in permanent physical contact.

sympatric speciation: the origin of a species within a population of organisms occupying a continuous area.

synapsis (pl. **synapses**): area of close approximation between nerve ending with other nerve or effector cell (e.g., muscle).

syncytium (pl. **syncytia**): type of living organization in which a unified cytoplasm contains several nuclei.

synthetic theory of evolution: New World synthesis; advancement on modern synthesis; welds cytogenetics to dynamics of variations in population.

T cells: various types of lymphocytes; cells capable of reacting with antigen presenting cells (APCs) or other cells of the immune system producing an immune response.

telomerase: enzyme capable of monitoring the length of telomeres and restoring them following their reduction during cell division.

telomeres: repeated sequences at the end of chromosomes in some eukaryotes thought to have a role in determining a cell's proliferative lifetime (its Hayflick limit).

teratocarcinoma: a transplantable, malignant form of mouse tumor (teratoma) derived from embryonic stem cells.

teratoma: nonmalignant and malignant tumors occurring spontaneously in mice or produced experimentally by transplanting embryos or their parts to extra-uterine sites.

Tertiary Period: earliest division of the Cenozoic Era.

TF: transcription factor; *trans*-acting protein capable of interacting with specific segments of DNA and influencing transcription.

tissue culture: various methods for raising and maintaining cells of multicellular organism in glassware or plastic containers; *in vitro* cell culture.

totipotency: the power to develop into a complete organism.

transcription: the synthesis of an RNA transcript complementary to a single strand of DNA.

transduction: (1) delivery of foreign genes to cells by a virus; (2) movement of information into a cell.

transfection: the uptake of foreign genes and their incorporation into a cell's genome.

transformation: hereditary changes due to uptake of foreign DNA (also see **malignant transformation**).

transgenic: sexually reproducing organism bearing foreign genes introduced through biotechnology.

translation: polypeptide (protein) synthesis conducted by a ribosome and based on codons in messenger RNA and their complement in transfer RNA.

transposons: sequences of DNA capable of moving to and inserting themselves into a cell's genomic DNA.

triploblastic (tridermic) animal: having three germ layers in gastrula; members of the Bilateria.

trisomy: the presence of three homologous chromosomes in cells ordinarily having only two.

tRNA: transfer RNA; small RNA molecules which deliver specific amino acids to growing polypeptide chains during translation.

trophoblast (trophectoderm): outer cellular layer of mammalian preembryo or blastocyst.

uterine duct: synonym for oviduct and Fallopian tube.

viral antigens: proteins encoded in a viral genome but produced by cells following infection with the virus.

xenohybridization: fertilization of egg by spermatozoon of an unrelated species.

xenotransplants: transfer of organs or tissues between members of different species.

yolk sac: the extraembryonic membrane associated with yolk in vertebrates with the exception of placental mammals.

zona pellucida: sheath enclosing mammalian egg.

zygote: a fertilized egg.

Bibliography

Abir-Am, P., The discourse of physical power and biological knowledge in the 1930s: A reappraisal of the Rockefeller Foundation's "Policy" in molecular biology. *Social Studies of Science,* 12: 341–82; 1982.

Adams, K. L., D. O. Daley, V-L. Qiu, J. Whelan, and J. D. Palmer, Repeated, recent and diverse transfers of a mitochondrial gene to the nucleus in flowering plants. *Nature,* 408: 354–357; 2000.

Adams, M. B., Sergei Chetverikov, the Kol'tsov Institute and the evolutionary synthesis, pp. 242–278 in E. Mayr and W. B. Provine, *The Evolutionary Synthesis: Perspectives on the Unification of Biology.* Cambridge: Harvard University Press; 1980.

Agosti, D., D. Jacobs, and R. DeSalle, On combining protein sequences and nucleic acid sequences in phylogenetic analysis: The homeobox protein case. *Cladistics,* 12: 65–82; 1996.

Alliez, É., *Capital Times: Tales from the Conquest of Time.* Foreword by Gilles Deleuze. Translated by Georges Van Den Abbeele. *Theory out of Bounds,* Volume 6. Minneapolis: University of Minnesota Press; 1991.

Altman, J., Are new neurons formed in the brains of adult mammals? *Science,* 135: 1127–1128; 1962.

Altschul, S. F. and E. V. Koonin, Iterated profile searches with PSI-LAST—a tool for discovery in protein databases. *Trends in Biochemical Sciences,* "Computer Corner," 23: 444–446; 1998.

Alvarez, L. W., W. Alvarez, F. Asaro, and H. V. Michel, Extraterrestrial cause for the Cretaceous-Tertiary extinction. *Science,* 208: 1093–1108; 1980.

Anderson, B., How to live forever. *Attaché,* March: 48–53; 2001.

Andersson, S. G. E., A. Zomorodipour, J. O. Andersson, T. Sicheritz-Pontén, U. C. M. Alsmark, R. M. Podowski, A. K. Näslund, A-S. Eriksson, H. H. Winkler, and C. G. Kurland, The genome sequence of *Rickettsia prowazekii* and the origin of mitochondria. *Nature,* 396: 133–140; 1998.

Andrews, L. B., *The Clone Age: Adventures in the New World of Reproductive Technology.* New York: Henry Holt; 1999.

Ansell-Pearson, K., *Viroid Life: Perspectives on Nietzsche and the Transhuman Condition.* London; New York: Routledge; 1997.

Aquinaldo, A. M. A., J. M. Turbeville, L. S. Linford, M. C. Rivera, J. R. Garey, R. A. Raff, and J. A. Lake, Evidence for a clade of nematodes, arthropods and other moulting animals. *Nature,* 387: 489–493; 1997.

Aristotle, *The Complete Works of Aristotle:* the revised Oxford translation. Edited by Jonathan Barnes. Princeton: Princeton University Press; 1984 rep. 1991.

Arnold, M. L., *Natural Hybridization and Evolution.* New York: Oxford University Press; 1997.

Artandi, S. E., S. Chang, S-L. Lee, S. Alson, G. J. Gottlieb, L. Chin, and R. A. DePinho, Telomere dysfunction promotes non-reciprocal translocations and epithelial cancers in mice. *Nature,* 406: 641–645; 2000.

Ashworth, D., M. Bishop, K. Campbell, A. Colman, A. Kind, A. Schneike, S. Blott, H. Griffin, C. Haley, J. McWhir, and I. Wilmut. DNA microsatellite analysis of Dolly. *Nature,* 394: 322; 1998.

Atkins, J. F., Contemporary RNA genomes, pp. 535–556 in R. F. Gesteland, and J. F. Atkins, eds., *The RNA World: The Nature of Modern RNA Suggests a Prebiotic RNA World.* Cold Spring Harbor: Cold Spring Harbor Laboratory Press; 1993.

Averof, M. and N. H. Patel, Crustacean appendage evolution associated with changes in Hox gene expression. *Nature,* 388: 682–686; 1997.

Ayala, F. J. and W. M. Fitch, Genetics and the origin of species: An introduction. *Proc. Natl. Acad. Sci. USA,* 94: 7691–7697; 1997.

Baguisi, A., E. Behboodi, D. T. Melican, J. S. Pollock, M. M. Destrempes, C. Cammuso, J. L. Williams, S. D. Nims, C. A. Porter, P. Midura, M. J. Palacios, S. L. Ayres, R. S. Denniston, M. L. Hayes, C. A. Ziomek, H. M. Meade, R. A. Godke, W. G. Gavin, E. W. Overström, and Y. Echelard, Production of goats by somatic cell nuclear transfer. *Nature Biotechnol.,* 17: 456–461; 1999.

Baker, J. R., *The Cell Theory: A Restatement, History, and Critique.* New York: Garland Publishing; 1988.

Baltimore, D., "Our genome unveiled," News and Views (15 February). *Nature,* 409: 814–816; 2001.

Barinaga, M., "Fetal neuron grafts pave the way for stem cell therapies" News (25 February). *Science,* 287: 1421–1422; 2000.

Bell, G., *The Masterpiece of Nature: The Evolution and Genetics of Sexuality.* Berkeley: University of California Press; 1982.

Benatar, S. R., A perspective from Africa on human rights and genetic engineering, pp. 159–189 in J. Burley, ed., *The Genetic Revolution and Human Rights*. The Oxford Amnesty Lectures 1998. Oxford: Oxford University Press; 1998.

Benfey, P. N., Stem cells: A tale of two kingdoms. *Curr. Biol.,* 9: R171–R172; 1999

Benjamin, W., *The Origin of German Tragic Drama*. With an Introduction by George Steiner. Translated by John Osborne. London: Verso paperback edition, 1985.

Bergson, H., *Creative Evolution*. Authorized translation from the French by Arthur Mitchell. New York: Modern Library, Arden Library edition; (1944) 1980.

Bergson, Henri, *Matter and Memory*. Authorized translated by Nancy Margaret Paul and W. Scott Palmer (translation of 5th edition, 1904). Originally published in France as *Matière et Mémoire by Presses Universitaires de France*. New York: Zone Books; 1991.

Bjornson, C. R. R., R. L. Rietze, B. A. Reynolds, M. C. Magli, and A. L. Vescovi, Turning brain into blood: A hematopoietic fate adopted by adult neural stem cells in vivo. *Science,* 283: 534–537; 1999.

Blackburn, E. H., Telomere states and cell fates. *Nature,* 408: 53–56; 2000.

Bleil, J. D. and P. M. Wassarman, Structure and function of the zona pellucida: Identification and characterization of the proteins of the mouse oocyte's zona pellucida. *Develop Biol.,* 76: 185–202; 1980.

Bock, J. B., H. T. Matern, A. A. Peden, and R. H. Scheller, "A genomic perspective on membrane compartment organization," Analysis (15 February). *Nature,* 409: 839–841; 2001.

Bodnar, A. G., M. Ouellette, M. Frolkis, S. E. Holt, C-P. Chiu, G. B. Morin, C. B. Harley, J. W. Shay, S. Lichsteiner, and W. E. Wright, Extension of life-span by introduction of telomerase into normal human cells. *Science,* 279: 349–352; 1998.

Bonnet, C., *Considérations sur les corps organiés,* Texte revu par Francine Markovits et Sophie Bienaymé. Paris: Librairie Arthème Fayard; (1762) 1985.

Bookstein, F. L., Can biometrical shape be a homologous character? pp. 198–229 in Brian K. Hall, ed., *Homology: The Hierarchical Basis of Comparative Biology*. San Diego: Academic Press; 1994.

Bork, P. and R. Copley, "Filling in the gaps," News and Views (15 February). *Nature,* 409: 818–820; 2001.

Bova, Ben, *Immortality: How Science is Extending Your Life Span—And Changing the World*. New York: Avon Books; 1998.

Bradley, A., M. Evans, M. H. Kaufman, and E. Robertson, Formation of germ-line chimaeras from embryo-derived teratocarcinoma cell lines. *Nature,* 309: 255–256; 1984.

Brown, D. B., Antigens of developing *Drosophila melanogaster. Nature* (London), 233: 394–397; 1971.

Burnet, Sir. M., *Self and Not-Self.* Melbourne: Melbourne University Press and London: The Cambridge University Press; 1969.

Cachon, J., M. Cachon, and K. W. Estep, Phylum Actinopoda: Classes Polycystina (= Radiolaria) and Phaeodaria, pp. 334–346 in Margulis, et al., eds., *Handbook of Protoctista.* Boston: Jones and Bartlett Publishers; 1990.

Campbell, R. D. Development of Hydra lacking interstitial and nerve cells ("epithelial Hydra"), pp. 267–293 in S. Subtelny and I. R. Konigsberg, eds., *Determinants of Spatial Organization.* Thirty-seventh Symp. Soc. Dev. Biol. New York: Academic Press; 1979.

Campisi, J., "Aging, chromatin, and food restriction—connecting the dots," Perspective (22 September). *Science,* 289: 2062–2063; 2000.

Capra, F., *The Web of Life: A New Scientific Understanding of Living Systems.* New York: Anchor Books; 1996.

Cavalier-Smith, T., The origin of cells: a symbiosis between genes, catalysts, and membranes. *Cold Spring Harbor Symposia on Quant. Biol.,* LII: 805–824; 1987.

Cavalier-Smith, T. The evolution of cells, pp. 271–304 in S. Osawa and T. Honjo, eds., *Evolution of Life: Fossils, Molecules, and Culture.* Tokyo: Springer-Verlag; 1991.

Cavalier-Smith, T., The number of symbiotic origins of organelles. *BioSystems,* 28: 91–106; 1992.

Cavalier-Smith, T., Principles of protein and lipid targeting in secondary symbiogenesis: Euglenoid, dinoflagellate, and sporozoan plastid origins and the eukaryote family tree. *J. Eukaryot. Microbiol.,* 46: 347–366; 1999.

Chakravarti, A., "Single nucleotide polymorphisms: . . . to a future of genetic medicine," News and Views (15 February). *Nature,* 409:822–823; 2001.

Charlesworth, B. and C. H. Langley, Population genetics of transposable elements in Drosophila, pp. 150–176 in R. K. Selander, A. G. Clark, and T. S. Whittam, eds., *Evolution at the Molecular Level.* Sunderland, Sunderland, MA: Sinauer Associates; 1991.

Child, C. M., *Patterns and Problems of Development.* Chicago: University of Chicago Press; 1941.

Christie, A., *The Murder at the Vicarage.* London: Fontana; 1930 (1981 printing).

Cibelli, J. B., S. L. Stice, P. J. Golueke, J. J. Kane, J. Jerry, C. Blackwell, F. A. Ponce de León, and J. M. Robl, Cloned transgenic calves produced from nonquiescent fetal fibroblasts. *Science,* 280: 1256–1262; 1998.

Clark, C. G. and A. J. Roger, Direct evidence for secondary loss of mitochondria in *Entamoeba histolytica. Proc. Natl. Acad. Sci. USA,* 92: 6518–6521; 1995

Clark, W. R., *Sex and the Origins of Death.* New York: Oxford University Press; 1996.

Clark, W. R., *A Means to an End: The Biological Basis of Aging and Death.* New York: Oxford University Press; 1999.

Clayton, R. M., Distribution of antigens in the developing newt embryo. *J. Embryol. exp. Morphol.,* 1: 25–43; 1953.

Clover, J. Eugenics and human rights, pp. 101–124 in J. Burley, ed., *The Genetic Revolution and Human Rights.* The Oxford Amnesty Lectures 1998. Oxford: Oxford University Press; 1998.

Coddington, J., Cladistic tests of adaptational hypotheses. *Cladistics,* 4: 3–22; 1988.

Coleman, W., *Georges Cuvier Zoologist: A Study in the History of Evolution Theory.* Cambridge: Harvard University Press; 1964.

Conway Morris, S., Burgess Shale faunas and the Cambrian explosion. *Science,* 246: 339–346; 1989.

Conway Morris, S., Why molecular biology needs palaeontology, pp. 1–13 in M. Akam, P. Holland, P. Ingham, and G. Wray, eds., *The Evolution of Developmental Mechanisms.* Development 1994 Supplement. Cambridge: The Company of Biologists; 1994a.

Conway Morris, S., Early metazoan evolution: first steps to an integration of molecular and morphological data, pp. 450–459 in S. Bengtson, ed., *Early Life on Earth,* Nobel Symposium No. 84. New York: Columbia University Press; 1994b.

Conway Morris, S., Eggs and embryos from the Cambrian. *BioEssays,* 20: 676–682; 1998.

Courtillot, V., *Evolutionary Catastrophes: The Science of Mass Extinction.* Translated by Joe McClinton. Cambridge: Cambridge University Press; 1999.

Crawford, I. P. and R. Milkman, Orthologous and paralogous divergence, reticulate evolution, and lateral gene transfer in bacterial trp genes, pp. 77–95 in R. K. Selander, A. G. Clark, and T. S. Whittam, *Evolution at the Molecular Level.* Sunderland: Sinauer Associates; 1991.

Crick, F. H. C., On protein synthesis. *Symposium of the Society for Experimental Biology,* 12: 138–163; 1958.

Crick, F. H. C. and P.A. Lawrence, Compartments and polyclones in insect development. *Science,* 189: 340–347; 1975.

Croissant, J. L., Growing up cyborg: Development stories for postmodern children, pp. 285–300 in R. Davis-Floyd and J. Dumit, eds., *Cyborg Babies: From Techno-Sex to Techno-Tots.* New York: Routledge; 1998.

Cummings, M. P., Transmission patterns of eukaryotic transposable elements: arguments for and against horizontal transfer. *Trends Ecol. Evol.,* 9: 141–145; 1994.

Cussins, C. M., Quit sniveling, cryo-baby. We'll work out which one's your mama! pp. 40–66 in R. Davis-Floyd and J. Dumit, eds., *Cyborg Babies: From Techno-Sex to Techno-Tots.* New York: Routledge; 1998.

Damjanov, I., A. Damjanov, and D. Solter, Production of teratocarcinomas from embryos transplanted to extra-uterine sites, pp. 1–18 in E. J. Robertson, ed., *Teratocarcinomas and Embryonic Stem Cells: A Practical Approach.* Oxford: IRL Press; 1987.

Darlington, C. D., The evolution of genetic systems: Contributions of cytology to evolutionary theory, pp. 70–80 in E. Mayr and W. B. Provine, *The Evolutionary Synthesis: Perspectives on the Unification of Biology.* Cambridge: Harvard University Press; 1980.

Darwin, C. R., *On the origin of Species by means of Natural Selection or the Preservation of Favoured Races in the Struggle for Life,* 6th edition. The Mentor edition, New York: Mentor Book; (1872) 1958.

Darwin, C. R., *On the origin of Species by means of Natural Selection or the Preservation of Favoured Races in the Struggle for Life.* J. W. Burrow, ed. Harmondsworth: Penguin Classics; (1859) 1968.

Darwin, F., Sir, ed., *The Autobiography of Charles Darwin and Selected Letters. London:* Dover; (1892) reprint 1989.

Davidson, E. H., *Gene Activity in Early Development,* 3rd ed. Orlando: Academic Press; 1986.

Davidson E. H., K. J. Peterson, and R. A. Cameron. Origin of bilaterian body plans: Evolution of developmental regulatory mechanisms. *Science,* 270: 1319–1325; 1995.

Dawkins, R., *The Blind Watchmaker.* New York: W. W. Norton; 1965.

Dawkins, R., *The Selfish Gene.* Oxford: Oxford University Press; 1976.

Dawkins, R., *The Extended Phenotype: The Long Reach of the Gene.* Oxford: Oxford University Press; 1982.

Dawkins, R., *River out of Eden: A Darwinian View of Life.* New York: Basic Books; 1995.

Dawkins, R., Human chauvinism. *Evolution,* 51: 1015–1020; 1997.

Dawkins, R., What's wrong with cloning, pp. 54–66 in M. C. Nussbaum and C. R. Sunstein, eds., *Clones and Clones: Facts and Fantasies about Human Cloning.* New York: W. W. Norton; 1998.

de Beer, G. R., *Embryos and Ancestors.* Oxford: Clarendon Press; 1951.

Deech, R., Cloning and public policy, pp. 95–100 in J. Burley, ed., *The Genetic Revolution and Human Rights.* The Oxford Amnesty Lectures 1998. Oxford: Oxford University Press; 1998.

de Grey, A. D. N. J., *The Mitochondrial Free Radical Theory of Aging.* Austin: Laudes; 1999.

de Lange, T., Telomeres and senescence: ending the debate. *Science,* 279: 334–335; 1998.

Delbrück, M., A physicist's renewed look at biology: twenty years later. *Science,* 168: 1312–1314; 1970a.

Delbrück, M., Preliminary write-up on the topic "Riddle of Life." Berlin: August 1937. Reprinted *Science,* 168: 1314–1315; 1970b.

Deleuze, G., *Nietzsche and Philosophy.* Translated by Hugh Tomlinson. New York: Columbia University Press, 1983.

Deleuze, G., *Cinema 2: The Time Image.* Translated by Hugh Tomlinson and Robert Galeta. Minneapolis: University of Minnesota Press; (First published in France by Les Editions de Minuit as *Cinéma 2, L'Image-temps,* 1985) 1989.

Deleuze, G. and F. Guattari, *A Thousand Plateaus: Capitalism and Schizophrenia.* Translation and forward by B. Massumi. Minneapolis: University of Minnesota Press; 1987.

Dennett, D. C., *Darwin's Dangerous Idea: Evolution and the Meanings of Life.* London: Penguin Books; 1995.

DePinho, R. A., "The age of cancer," Insight Review Article. *Nature,* 408: 248–254; 2000.

de Rosa, R., J. K. Grenier, T. Andreeva, C. E. Cook, A. Adoutte, M. Akam, S. B. Carroll, and G. Balavoine, Hox genes in brachiopods and priapulids and protostome evolution. *Nature,* 399: 772–776; 1999.

Derrida, J., *Archive Fever: A Freudian Impression.* Translated by Eric Prenowitz. Chicago, University of Chicago Press; 1995.

Desmond, A., *Huxley: The Devil's Disciple,* vol. 1. London: Michael Joseph; 1994

Desmond, A., *Huxley: Evolution's High Priest,* vol. 2. London: Michael Joseph; 1997.

Desmond, A. and J. Moore, *Darwin: The Life of a Tormented Evolutionist.* New York: Warner; 1994.

Diamond, J., "Blitzkrieg against the Moas," Science's Compass—Perspectives (24 March). *Science,* 287: 2170–2171; 2000.

DiBerardino, M. A. *Genomic Potential of Differentiated Cells.* New York: Columbia University Press; 1997.

Dickson, D., "Parliament gives green light to stem-cell research." News (4 January). *Nature,* 409: 5; 2001.

Dobzhansky, T., The birth of the genetic theory of evolution in the Soviet Union in the 1920, pp. 229–242 in E. Mayr and W. B. Provine, *The Evolutionary Synthesis: Perspectives on the Unification of Biology.* Cambridge: Harvard University Press; 1980.

Doetsch, F., I. Caillé, D. A. Lim, J. M. Garcia-Verdugo, and A. Alvarez-Buylla, Subventricular zone astrocytes are neural stem cells in the adult mammalian brain. *Cell,* 97: 703–716; 1999.

Dominko, T., M. Mitalipo, B Haley, Z. Beyhan, E. Memili, B. McKusick, and N. L. First, Bovine oocyte cytoplasm supports development of embryos produced by nuclear transfer of somatic cell nuclei from various mammalian species. *Biol. Reprod.,* 60: 1496–1502; 1999.

Donoghue, M. J., Phylogenies and the analysis of evolutionary sequences, with examples from seed plants. *Evolution,* 43: 1137–1156; 1989.

Doolittle, W. F., Phylogenetic classification and the Universal Tree. *Science,* 284: 2124–2128; 1999.

Doolittle, W. F. and J. M. Logsdon, Jr., Archaeal genomics: do archaea have a mixed heritage? *Curr. Biol.,* 8: R209–R211; 1998.

Douglas, S., S. Zauner, M. Fraunholz, M. Beaton, S. Penny, L.-T. Deng, X. Wu, M. Reith, T. Cavalier-Smith & U-G. Maier, The highly reduced genome of an enslaved algal nucleus. *Nature,* 410: 1091–1096; 2001.

Driesch, H., The potency of the first two cleavage cells in echinoderm development. Experimental production of partial and double formations. Abridged and translated by L. Mezger, V. Hamburger, and T. S. Hall, pp. 38-50 in B. H. Willier and J. M. Oppenheimer, eds., *Foundations of Experimental Embryology.* Englewood Cliffs, NJ: Prentice-Hall; (1892) 1964.

Druffel, E. R. M., S. Griffin, A. Witter, E. Nelson, J. Southon, M. Kashgarian, and J. Vogel. Gerardia: Bristlecone pine of the deep-sea? *Geochimica et Cosmochimica Acta,* 59: (abstract) 5031–5036; 1995.

Dumit, J. and R. Davis-Floyd, Introduction. Cyborg Babies: Children of the third millennium, pp. 1–18 in R. Davis-Floyd and J. Dumit, eds., *Cyborg Babies: From Techno-Sex to Techno-Tots.* New York: Routledge; 1998.

Dworkin, R., *Life's Dominion.* London: Harper/Collins, 1993.

Edwards, R. G., "IVF and the history of stem cells," Commentary (27 September). *Nature,* 413:349–351; 2001.

Eldredge, N., *Time Frames: The Evolution of Punctuated Equilibria.* Princeton: Princeton Science Library; 1985.

Eldredge, N. and S. J. Gould, Punctuated equilibria: an alternative to phyletic gradualism. In T. Schopf, ed., *Models in Paleobiology.* San Francisco: W. H. Freeman; pp. 82–115; 1972.

Encyclopedia Britannica, CD. Standard Edition, Chicago: Merriam-Webster Collegiate Dictionary, Tenth Edition, 1998.

England, M. A., The human, pp. 207–220 in J. B. L. Bard, ed., *Embryos: Color Atlas of Development.* London: Mosby—Year Book Europe Limited; 1994.

Evans, M. J. and M. H. Kaufman, Establishment in culture of pluripotential cells from mouse embryos. *Nature,* 292: 154–156; 1981.

Ferrari, G., G. Cusella-De Angelis, M. Coletta, E. Paolucci, A. Stornaiuolo, G. Cossu, and F. Mavilio, Muscle regeneration by bone marrow-derived myogenic progenitors. *Science,* 279: 1528–1530; 1998.

Finkel, T., N. J. Holbrook, "Oxidants, oxidative stress and the biology of ageing," Insight Review Article (9 November). *Nature,* 408: 239–247; 2000.

Finnerty, J. R. and M. Q. Martindale, The evolution of the Hox cluster: Insights from outgroups. *Curr. Opin. Genet. Devel.,* 8: 681–687; 1998.

Fitch, W. M., R. M. Bush, C. A. Bender, and N. J. Cox, Long term trends in the evolution of H(3) HA1 human influenza type A. *Proc. Natl. Acad. Sci. USA,* 94: 7712–7718; 1997.

Foucault, M., *The Birth of the Clinic: An Archaeology of Medical Perception.* Translated by A. M. Sheridan Smith. New York: Pantheon; 1973.

Futeal, P. A., A. Kasprzk, E. Birney, J. C. Mullikin, R. Wooster, and M. R. Stratton, "Cancer and genomics," Analysis (15 February). *Nature,* 409: 850–851; 2001.

Gage, F. H., "Mammalian neural stem cells," Review (25 February). *Science,* 287: 1422–1438; 2000.

Gall, J., ed., *The Molecular Biology of Ciliated Protozoa.* New York: Academic Press; 1986.

Garcia-Bellido, A., Genetic control of wing disc development in *Drosophila. Ciba Found. Symp.,* 29: 161–183; 1975.

Garcia-Fernàndez, J. and P. W. H. Holland, Archetypal organization of the amphioxus *Hox* gene cluster. *Nature,* 370: 563–566; 1994.

Gardner, E. J., *History of Biology,* second ed., Minneapolis: Burgess Publishing, 1960.

Garstang, W., *Larval Forms: And other Zoological Verses.* With an Introduction by Sir Alister Hardy and a Foreword by Michael LaBarbera. Chicago: The University of Chicago Press; (1951) 1985.

Gasman, D., *Haeckel's Monism and the Birth of Fascist Ideology.* New York: Peter Lang; 1998.

Gearhart, J., "New potential for human embryonic stem cells," Perspectives: Cell Biology (6 November). *Science,* 282: 1051–1062; 1998.

Gehring, W. J., Homeoboxes in the study of development. *Science,* 236: 1245–1252; 1987.

Gerhart, J. and M. Kirschner, *Cells Embryos, and Evolution: Toward a Cellular and Developmental Understanding of Phenotypic Variation and Evolutionary Adaptability.* Oxford: Blackwell Science; 1997.

Gilbert, W., A vision of the grail, pp. 83–97 in D. J. Kevles and L. Hood, eds. *The Code of Codes: Scientific and Social Issues in the Human Genome Project.* Cambridge: Harvard University Press; 1992.

Gilbert, W., S. J. De Souza, and M. Long, Origin of Genes. *Proc. Natl. Acad. Sci. USA,* 94: 7698–7703; 1997.

Gillham, N. W., *Organelle Genes and Genomes.* New York: Oxford University Press; 1994.

Goff, L. J. and A. W. Coleman, Fate of parasite and host organelle DNA during cellular transformation of red algae by their parasites. *Plant Cell,* 7: 1899–1911; 1995.

Goff, L. J., J. Ashen, and D. Moon, The evolution of parasites from their hosts: a case study in the parasitic red algae. *Evolution,* 5: 1068–1078; 1997.

Gogarten, J. P., H. Kibak, P. Dittrich, L. Taiz, E. J. Bowman, B. J. Bowman, M. F. Manolson, R. J. Poole, T. Date, T. Oshima, J. Konishi, K. Denda, and M. Yoshida, Evolution of the vacuolar H^+-ATPase: Implications for the origin of eukaryotes. *Proc. Natl. Acad. Sci. USA,* 85: 6661–6665; 1989.

Goodell, M. A., K. Brose, G. Paradis, A. S. Conner, and R. C. Mulligan, Isolation and functional properties of murine hematopoietic stem cells that are replicating in vivo. *J. Exp. Med.,* 183: 1797–1806; 1996.

Goodwin, B. C., A relational or field theory of reproduction and its evolutionary implications, pp. 219–241 in M-W. Ho and P. T. Saunders, eds., *Beyond Neo-Darwinism: An Introduction to the New Evolutionary Paradigm.* Orlando: Academic Press; 1984.

Goodwin, B., *How the Leopard Changed its Spots: The Evolution of Complexity.* New York: Touchstone Book; 1994.

Gould, S. J., *Ontogeny and Phylogeny.* Cambridge: Belknap Press; 1977.

Gould, S. J., *Wonderful Life: The Burgess Shale and the Nature of History.* New York: W. W. Norton; 1989.

Gould, S. J. and E. S. Vrba, Exaptation—a missing term in the science of form. *Paleobiology,* 8: 4–15; 1982.

Greene, H. W., Diet and arborality in the emerald monitor, *Varanus prasinus,* with comments on the study of adaptation. *Fieldiana Zool.,* New Series, 31: 1–12; 1986.

Grell, K. G. and A. Ruthmann, Placozoa, pp. 13–27 F. W. Harrison and J. A. Westfall, eds., *Microscopic Anatomy of Invertebrates,* Volume 2: Placozoa, Porifera, Cnidaria, and Ctenophora, New York: John Wiley and Sons; 1991.

Grobstein, C., *Science and the Unborn: Choosing Human Futures.* New York: Basic Books; 1965.

Groves, A. K. and M. Bronner-Fraser, Neural crest diversification. *Current Topics in Developmental Biology,* 43: 221–258; 1999.

Guarente, L. and C. Kenyon, "Genetic pathways that regulate ageing in model organisms," Insight Review Article. *Nature,* 408: 255–262; 2000.

Gurdon, J. B., E. M. DeRobertis, and G. Partington, Injected nuclei in frog oocytes provide a living cell system for the study of transcriptional control. *Nature* (London), 260: 115–120; 1976.

Gussoni, E., Y. Soneoka, C. D. Strickland, E. A. Buzney, M. K. Khans, A. F. Flint, L. M. Kunkel, and R. C. Mulligan, Myotrophin expression in the *mdx* mouse restored by stem cell transplantation. *Nature,* 401: 390–394; 1999.

Haeckel, E. H. P., *The Riddle of the Universe at the Close of the Nineteenth Century.* Translated by Joseph McCabe. New York: Harper and Brothers; 1901. Reprint with an Introduction by H. James Birx: Buffalo: Prometheus Books; (1901) 1992.

Haffner, R. and M. Oren, Biochemical properties and biological effects of p53. *Curr. Opin. Genet. Dev.,* 5: 84–90; 1995.

Hagmann, M., "New genetic tricks to rejuvenate ailing livers," News of the Week (18 February). *Science,* 287: 1185–1186; 2000.

Hall, B. K. and M. H. Wake, Introduction: Larval development, evolution and ecology, pp. 1–19 in B. K. Hall and M. H. Wake, eds. *The Origin and Evolution of Larval Forms.* San Diego: Academic Press; 1999.

Hall, S. S., The recycled generation. *The New York Times Magazine,* January 30: 30–35, 46, 74, 78–80; 2000.

Hamburger, V., *The Heritage of Experimental Embryology: Hans Spemann and the Organizer.* New York: Oxford University Press; 1988.

Hanken, J., Larvae in amphibian development and evolution, pp. 61–108 in B. K. Hall and M. H. Wake, eds. *The Origin and Evolution of Larval Forms.* San Diego: Academic Press; 1999.

Hanson, E. D. *The Origin and Early Evolution of Animals.* Middletown: Wesleyan University Press; 1977.

Haraway, D. J., *Modest_Witness@Second_Millenium. FemaleMan©_Meets_Onco-Mouse™: Feminism and Technoscience.* New York: Routledge; 1997.

Haraway, D. J., *How like a Leaf: An Interview with Thyrza Nichols Goodeve.* New York: Routledge; 2000.

Harris, H., *The Birth of the Cell.* New Haven: Yale University Press; 1999.

Harris, J., Clones, genes, and human rights, pp. 61–94 in J. Burley, ed., *The Genetic Revolution and Human Rights*. The Oxford Amnesty Lectures 1998. Oxford: Oxford University Press; 1998.

Harrison, R. G., Observations on the living developing nerve fiber. *Anat. Rec.,* 1: 116–118. Reprinted pp. 100–103 in B. H. Willier and J. M. Oppenheimer, eds. *Foundations of Experimental Embryology*. Englewood Cliffs: Prentice-Hall; 1964.

Harvey, W., *Opera omnia: a Collegio Medicorum Londinensi edita/Guilielmi Harveii. Exercilioned de generatione animalium*. Londini: Guilielmus Bowyer; 1766.

Hayflick, Leonard, *How and Why We Age*. New York: Ballantine Books; 1994.

Hayflick. L., "The future of ageing" Insight Review Article (9 November). *Nature,* 408: 267–269; 2000.

Hesketh, R., *The Oncogene and Tumour Suppressor Gene* Facts Book. 2nd ed. San Diego: Academic Press; 1997.

Hickman, C. S., Larvae in invertebrate development and evolution, pp. 22–59 in B. K. Hall and M. H. Wake, eds. *The Origin and Evolution of Larval Forms*. San Diego: Academic Press; 1999.

Hillis, D. M., Homology in molecular biology, pp. 339–368 in Brian K. Hall, ed., *Homology: The Hierarchical Basis of Comparative Biology*. San Diego: Academic Press; 1994.

Holdaway, R. N. and C. Jacomb, Rapid extinction of the Moas (Aves: Dinornithiformes): Model, test, and implications. *Science,* 287: 2250–2254; 2000.

Holland, P. W. H. and J. Garcia-Fernàndez, *Hox* genes and chordate evolution. *Develop. Biol.,* 173: 382–395; 1996.

Holland, P. W. H., J. Garcia-Fernàndez, N. A. Williams, and A. Sidow, Gene duplications and the origins of vertebrate development, pp. 125–133 in M. Akam, P. Holland, P. Ingham, and G. Wray, eds., *The Evolution of Developmental Mechanisms*. Development 1994 Supplement. Cambridge: The Company of Biologists; 1994.

Holliday, R., Endless quest, *BioEssays,* 18: 3–5; 1996.

Hooper, M. L., *Embryonal Stem Cells: Introducing Planned Changes into the Animal Germline*. Poststrasse, Switzerland: Harwood Academic Publishers; 1992.

Hörstadius, S., *The Neural Crest*. Oxford: Oxford University Press; 1950.

Houck, M. A., J. B. Clark, K. R. Peterson, and M. G. Kidwell, Possible horizontal transfer of *Drosophila* genes by the mite *Protolaelaps regalis*. *Science,* 254: 1125–1129; 1991.

Hubbard, R., *The Politics of Women's Biology*. New Brunswick: Rutgers University Press; 1990.

Hughes, A., *A History of Cytology*. Ames: Iowa State University Press: History of Science and Technology Reprint Series; 1989.

Hutchinson, G. E., Homage to Santa Rosalia or Why are there so many kinds of animals? *American Naturalist,* XCIII: 145–159; 1959.

Imai, S-I, C. M. Armstrong, M. Kaeberlein, and L. Guarente, Transcriptional silencing and longevity protein Sir2 is an NAD-dependent histone deacetylase. *Nature,* 403: 795–800; 2000.

International Human Genome Sequencing Consortium, Initial sequencing and analysis of the human genome. *Nature,* 409: 860–921; 2001.

Jablonka, E. and M. J. Lamb, *Epigenetic inheritance and evolution: The Lamarckian dimension.* Oxford: Oxford University Press; 1995.

Jaffe, L. A. and M. Gould, Polyspermy-preventing mechanisms, pp. 223–250 in C. B. Metz and A. Monroy, eds., *Biology of Fertilization,* Vol. 3, *Fertilization Response of the Egg.* Orlando: Academic Press; 1985.

Jazwinski, S. M., Longevity, genes, and aging. *Science,* 273: 54–59; 1996.

Johnson, M. H., Three types of cell interaction regulate the generation of cell diversity in the mouse blastocyst, pp. 27–8 in G. M. Edelman and J.-P. Thiery, eds., *The Cell in Contact: Adhesion and Junctions are Morphogenetic Determinants.* New York: A Neurosciences Institute Publication, Wiley; 1985.

Joza, N., S. A. Susin, E. Daugas, W. L. Stanford, S. K. Cho, C. Y. J. Li, T. Sasake, A. J. Elia, H.-Y. M. Cheng, L. Ravagnan, K. F. Ferri, N. Zamzami, A. Wakeham, R. Hakem, H. Yoshida, Y-Y Kong, T. W. Mak, J. C. Zúñiga-Pflücker, G. Kroemer, and J. M. Penninger, Essential role of the mitochondrial apoptosis-inducing factor in programmed cell death. *Nature,* 410: 549–554; 2001.

Judson, H. R., *The Eighth Day of Creation: Makers of the Revolution in Biology.* New York: Simon and Schuster; 1979.

Just, E. E., *Biology of the Cell Surface.* Philadelphia: P. Blakiston's Son and Co.; 1939.

Kageura, H. and K. Yamana, Pattern regulation in isolated halves and blastomeres of early *Xenopus laevis. J. Embryol. Exp. Morphol.,* 74: 221–234; 1983.

Kalthoff, K., Analysis of a morphogenetic determinant in an insect embryo (*Smittia* spec., Chironomidae, Diptera), pp. 97–126 in S. Subtelny, ed., *Determinants of spatial organization,* 37th Symposium of the Society for Developmental Biology. Orlando, Academic Press; 1979.

Kato, Y., T. Tani, Y. Sotomaru, K. Kurakawa, J-y. Kato, H. Doguchi, H. Yasue, Y. Tsunoda. Eight calves cloned from somatic cells of a single adult. *Science,* 282: 2095–2098; 1998.

Kauffman, S. A., *The Origins of Order: Self-Organization and Selection in Evolution.* New York: Oxford University Press; 1993.

Kay, L., *The Molecular Vision of Life: Caltech, the Rockefeller Foundation and the Rise of the New Biology.* New York: Oxford University Press; 1993.

Kevles, D. J., *In the Name of Eugenics: Genetics and the Uses of Human Heredity.* New York: Alfred A. Knopf; 1985.

Kevles, D. J. and L. Hood, Out of Eugenics: The historical politics of the human genome, pp. 3–80 in D. J. Kevles and L. Hood, eds. *The Code of Codes: Scientific and Social Issues in the Human Genome Project.* Cambridge: Harvard University Press; 1992.

Kidwell, M. G., Lateral transfer in natural population of eukaryotes. *Ann. Rev. Genetics,* 27: 235–256; 1993.

Kinzler, K. and B. Vogelstein, "Life (and death) in a malignant tumour." News and Views (4 January). *Nature,* 379: 19–20; 1996.

Kirkwood, T., *Time of our Lives: The Science of Human Aging.* Oxford: Oxford University Press; 1999.

Kirkwood, T. B. and S. N. Austad, "Why do we age?" Insight Review Article. *Nature,* 408: 233–238; 2000.

Kiyono, T., S. A. Foster, J. I. Koop, J. K. McDougall, D. A. Galloway, and A. J. Klingehutz, Both Rb/p16^{INK4a} inactivation and telomerase activity are required to immortalize human epithelial cells. *Nature,* 396: 84–88; 1998.

Knoll, A. H. and S. B. Carroll, "Early animal evolution: emerging views from comparative biology and geology," Review. *Science,* 284: 2129–2137; 1999.

Kobayashi, M., H. Furuya, and P. W. H. Holland, Dicyemids are higher animals. *Nature,* 401: 762; 1999.

Kolata, G., *Clone: The Road to Dolly and the Path Ahead.* New York; William Morrow and Company; 1998.

Kolm, P. J. and H. L. Sive, Retinoids and posterior neural induction: a reevaluation of Nieuwkoop's two-step hypothesis. *Cold Spring Harbor Symposia on Quantitative Biology,* LXII: 511–521; 1997.

Kornberg, A., *Supplement to DNA Replication.* San Francisco: W. H. Freeman; 1982.

LaBarbera, M., Foreword to Garstang, W., *Larval Forms: And other Zoological Verses.* With an Introduction by Sir Alister Hardy. Chicago: The University of Chicago Press; (1951) 1985.

Lajtha, L. G., Stem cell concepts. *Differentiation,* 14: 23–34; 1979.

Lamarck, J. B., *Zoological Philosophy: An Exposition with Regard to the Natural History of Animals.* Translated by Hugh Elliot. Chicago: University of Chicago Press; (1809) 1984.

Lamour V., S. Quevillon, S. Diriong, V. C. N'Guyen, M. Lipinski, and M. Miranda, Evolution of the Glx-tRNA synthetase family: the glutaminyl enzyme as a case of horizontal gene transfer. *Proc. Natl. Acad. Sci., USA,* 91: 8670; 1994.

Lane, D. P., The regulation of P53 function. *Int. J. Cancer,* 57: 623–627; 1994.

Lang, B. F., G. Burger, C. J. O'Kelly, R. Cedergren, G. B. Golding, C. Lemieux, D. Sankoff, M. Turmel, and M. W. Gray. An ancestral mitochondrial DNA resembling a eubacterial genome in miniature. *Nature,* 387: 493–497; 1997.

Lanza, R. P., J. B. Cibelli, and M. D. West, Human therapeutic cloning. *Nature Medicine,* 5: 975–977; 1999.

Larousse: Dictionary of Scientists. Hazel Muir, ed., Edinburgh: Larousse Kingfisher Chambers; 1994.

Latham, K. E. Epigenetic modification and imprinting of the mammalian genome during development. *Curr. Topics Develop. Biol.,* 43: 1–49; 1999.

Latour, B., *Pandora's Hope: Essays on the Reality of Science Studies.* Cambridge: Harvard University Press; 1999.

Lawrence, J. G. and H. Ochman, Amelioration of bacterial genomes: rates of change and exchange. *J. Mol. Evol.,* 44: 383–397; 1997.

Lawrence, J. G. and H. Ochman, Molecular archeology of the *Escherichia coli* genome. *Proc. Natl. Acad. Sci. USA,* 95: 9413–9417; 1998.

Leblond, C. P. and B. E. Walker, Renewal of cell populations. *Physiol. Rev.,* 36: 255–279; 1956.

Le Douarin, N. M., *The Neural Crest.* Cambridge: Cambridge University Press; 1982.

Lewontin, R., Confusion about cloning. *New York Review of Books,* 23 October: 18–23; 1997.

Lewontin, R., *The Triple Helix: Gene, Organism, and Environment.* Cambridge: Harvard University Press; 2000.

Lewontin, R. C. and J. L. Hubby, A molecular approach to the study of genic heterozygosity in natural populations. II. Amount of variation and degree of heterozygosity in natural populations of *Drosophila pseudoobscura. Genetics,* 54: 595–609; 1966.

Libby, W., *History of Medicine, in its Salient Features.* Boston: Houghton Mifflin; 1922.

Lin, S-J., P-A. Defossez, L. Guarente. Requirement of NAD and *SIR2* for life-span extension by caloric restriction in *Saccharomyces cerevisiae. Science,* 289: 2126–2128; 2000.

Liotta, L. A., "An attractive force in Metastasis," News and Views (1 March). *Nature,* 410: 24–25; 2001.

Logsdon, J. M., Jr. and D. M. Faguy, Evolutionary genomics: *Thermotoga* heats up lateral gene transfer. *Curr. Biol.,* 9: R747–R751; 1999.

Lom, J., Phylum Myxozoa, pp. 26–52 in Lynn Margulis et al., eds., *Handbook of Protoctista.* Boston: Jones and Bartlett Publishers; 1990.

Longo, F. J., *Fertilization.* New York: Chapman and Hall; 1987.

Lovelock, J., *The Ages of Gaia*. New York: Bantam Books; 1990.

Lovelock, J., The Gaia hypothesis, pp. 13–31 in P. Bunyard, ed., *Gaia in Action*. Cambridge: Cambridge University Press; 1996.

Lyotard, J-F., *The Lyotard Reader*, Edited by Andrew Benjamin. Oxford: Basil Blackwell; 1989.

McClay, D. R. and G. M. Wessel, Spatial and temporal appearance and redistribution of cell surface antigens during sea urchin development, pp. 165–184 in E. H. Davidson and R. A. Firtel, eds., *Molecular Biology of Development*. New York: Alan R. Liss; 1984.

Macdonald, F. and C. H. J. Ford, *Molecular Biology of Cancer*. Oxford: Bios Scientific Publishers; 1997.

McDonald, J. W., X-Z. Liu, Y. Qu, S. Liu, S. K. Mickey, D. Turetsky, D. I. Gottlieb, and D. W. Choi, Transplanted embryonic stem cells survive, differentiate and promote recovery in injured rat spinal cord. *Nature Medicine*, 5: 1410–1412; 1999.

McGreath, K. J, J. Howcroft, K. H. S. Campbell, A. E. Schnieke, and A. J. Kind, Production of gene-targeted sheep by nuclear transfer from somatic cells. *Nature*, 405: 1066–1069; 2000.

McLaren, A., "Cloning: Pathways of Discovery," Pathways to a pluripotent future (9 June). *Science*, 288: 1775–1780; 2000.

MacWilliams, H. K., *Hydra* transplantation phenomena and the mechanism of *Hydra* head regeneration. *Develop. Biol.*, 96: 239–257; 1983.

Mahowald, A. P., The germ plasm of *Drosophila:* A model system for the study of embryonic determination. *Am. Zool.*, 17:551–563; 1977.

Mainenschein, J., Preformation or new formation—or neither or both? pp. 73–108 in T. J. Horder, J. A. Witkowsky, and C. C. Whylie, eds., *A History of Development*. New York: Alan R. Liss; 1985.

Maizels, N. and A. M. Weiner, The genomic tag hypothesis: modern viruses as molecular fossils of ancient strategies for genomic replication, pp. 577–602 in R. F. Gesteland and J. F. Atkins, eds., *The RNA World: The Nature of Modern RNA Suggests a Prebiotic RNA World*. Cold Spring Harbor: Cold Spring Harbor Laboratory Press; 1993.

Majerus, M. E. N., *Melanism: Evolution in Action*. Oxford: Oxford University Press; 1998.

Malpighi, M., *Works, Latin and Italian. Consulti di Marcello Malpighi,* 1675–1694. Opera in IV volumi. Bologna: Instituto per la Storia dell'Universita di Bologna; 1988–1992.

Marcum, B. A. and R. D. Campbell. Development of hydra lacking nerve and interstitial cells. *J. Cell Sci.*, 29: 17–33; 1978.

Margulis, L., Symbiosis in evolution: origins of cell motility. In S. Osawa and T. Honjo, eds., *Evolution of Life: Fossils, Molecules, and Culture.* Tokyo: Springer-Verlag; 305–324; 1991a.

Margulis, L., Symbiogenesis and symbionticism, pp. 1–24 in L. Margulis and R. Fester, eds., *Symbiosis as a Source of Evolutionary Innovation: Speciation and Morphogenesis.* Cambridge: MIT Press; 1991b.

Margulis, *Symbiosis in Cell Evolution: Microbial Communities in the Archean and Proterozoic Eons,* 2 edn. New York: Freeman; 1991c.

Margulis, L., Jim Lovelock's Gaia, pp. 45–57 in P. Bunyard, ed., *Gaia in Action.* Edinburgh: Flores; 1996.

Margulis, L., *Symbiotic Planet: A New Look at Evolution.* New York: Basic Books; 1998.

Margulis, L. and J. E. Cohen, Combinatorial generation of taxonomic diversity: implication of symbiogenesis for the Proterozoic fossil record, pp. 327–334 in S. Bengtson, ed., *Early Life on Earth,* Nobel Symposium No. 84. New York: Columbia University Press; 1994.

Margulis, L., J. O. Corliss, M. Melkonian, D. J. Chapman, *Handbook of Protoctista.* Boston: Jones and Bartlett Publishers; 1990.

Margulis, L., R. Guerrero, and P. Bunyard, We are all symbionts, pp. 160–177 in P. Bunyard, ed., *Gaia in Action.* Edinburgh: Flores; 1996.

Marshall, E., "The business of stem cells," News (25 February). *Science,* 287: 1419–1421; 2000.

Martin, E., The fetus as intruder: Mother's bodies and medical metaphors, pp. 125–142 in R. Davis-Floyd and J. Dumit, eds., *Cyborg Babies: From Techno-Sex to Techno-Tots.* New York: Routledge; 1998.

Martin, G. R., Isolation of a pluripotent cell line from early mouse embryos cultured in medium conditions by teratocarcinoma stem cells. *Proc. Natl. Acad. Sci. USA,* 78: 7634–7638; 1981.

Martin, G. M. and J. Oshima, "Lessons from human progeroid syndromes," Insight Review Article. *Nature,* 408: 263–266; 2000.

Martin, V. J. and M. B. Thomas, Elimination of the interstitial cells in the planula larva of the marine hydrozoan *Pennaria tiarellia. J. Exp. Zool.,* 217: 303–323; 1981.

Martin, V. J. and M. B. Thomas, Establishment and maintenance of morphological polarity in epithelial planulae. *Trans. Am. Micros. Soc.,* 102: 18–24; 1983.

Martindale, M. Q. and M. J. Kourakis, "Size doesn't matter," News and Views (24 June). *Nature,* 399: 730–731; 1999.

Mathon, N. F., D. S. Malcolm, M. C. Harrisingh, L. Cheng, and A. C. Lloyd, Lack of replicative senescence in normal rodent glia. *Science,* 291: 872–875; 2001.

Maturana, H. R. and F. J. Varela, *The Tree of Knowledge: The Biological Roots of Human Understanding,* Revised Edition. Translated by Robert Paolucci. Boston: Shambhala; 1998.

Maynard Smith, J. and E. Szathmáry, *The Origins of Life: From the Birth of Life to the Origin of Language.* Oxford: Oxford University Press; 1999.

Mayor, R., R. Young, and A. Vargas, Development of neural crest in *Xenopus. Curr. Topics in Develop. Biol.,* 43: 85–113; 1999.

Mayr, E., *Toward a New Philosophy of Biology: Observations of an Evolutionist.* Cambridge: Harvard University Press; 1988.

Mayr, E., Driving forces in evolution: an analysis of natural selection, pp. 29–48 in S. S. Morse, ed., *The Evolutionary Biology of Viruses.* New York: Raven Press; 1994.

Medawar, P., *The Thinking Radish: An Autobiography.* Oxford: Oxford University Press 1986.

Meinhart, H., *Models of Biological Pattern Formation.* London: Academic Press; 1982.

Melov, S., J. Ravenscroft, S. Malik, M. S. Gill, D. W. Walker, P. E. Clayton, D. C. Wallace, B. Malfroy, S. R. Doctrow, and G. J. Lithgow, Extension of life-span with superoxide dismutase/catalase mimetics. *Science,* 289: 1567–1569; 2000.

Mentor, S., Witches, nurses, midwives, and cyborgs: IVF, ART, and complex agency in the world of technobirth, pp. 67–89 in R. Davis-Floyd and J. Dumit, eds., *Cyborg Babies: From Techno-Sex to Techno-Tots.* New York: Routledge; 1998.

Mezey, E., K. J. Chandross, G. Harta, R. A. Maki, and S. R. McKercher, Turning blood into brain: cells bearing neuronal antigens generated in vivo from bone marrow. *Science,* 290: 1779–1782; 2000.

Michael, W. M., R. Ott, E. Fanning, and J. Newport. Activation of the DNA replication checkpoint through RNA synthesis by primase. *Science,* 289: 2133–2137; 2000.

Miller, J. B., L. Schaefer, and J. A. Dominov, Seeking muscle stem cells. *Curr. Topics Develop. Biol.* 43: 192–219; 1999.

Miller, R. A. The aging immune system: Primer and prospectus. *Science,* 273: 70–74; 1996.

Mintz, B. and K. Illmensee, Normal genetically mosaic mice produced from malignant teratocarcinoma cells. *Proc. Natl. Acad. Sci. USA.,* 72: 3585–3589; 1975.

Mittwoch, U., Parthenogenesis: Review article. *J. Med. Genetics,* 15:165–181; 1978.

Mocek, R., *Wilhelm Roux, Hans Driesch: Zur Geschichte der Entwicklungsphysiologie der Tiere. ("Entwicklungsmechanik").* Jena: Gustav Fischer Verlag, 1974.

Monod, J., *Chance and Necessity: An Essay on the Natural Philosophy of Modern Biology.* Translated from the French by A. Wainhouse. New York: Knopf; 1971.

Morgan, T. H., *Experimental Embryology.* New York: Columbia University Press; 1927.

Müller, A., B. Homey, H. Soto, N. Ge, D. Catron, M. E. Buchanan, T. McClanahan, E. Murphy, W. Yuan, S. N. Wagner, J. L. Barrera, A. Mohar, E. Verástegui, and A. Zlotnik, Involvement of chemokine receptors in breast cancer metastasis. *Nature,* 410: 50–56; 2001.

Murray, A. W. and D. Marks, "Can sequencing shed light on cell cycling?" Analysis (15 February). *Nature,* 409: 844–846; 2001.

Nagy, L. M. and M. Grbic, Cell lineages in larval development and evolution of holometabolous insects, pp. 275–300 in B. K. Hall and M. H. Wake, eds., *The Origin and Evolution of Larval Forms.* San Diego: Academic Press; 1999.

Nanny, D. L., Heredity without genes: Ciliate exploration of clonal heredity. *Trends Genetics,* 1: 295–298; 1985.

Nei, M., *Molecular Evolutionary Genetics.* New York: Columbia University Press; 1987.

Nei, M. and A. L. Hughes, Polymorphism and evolution of the major histocompatibility complex loci in mammals, pp. 222–247 in R. K. Selander, A. G. Clark, and T. S. Whittam, eds., *Evolution at the Molecular Level.* Sunderland: Sinauer Associates; 1991.

Nelson, K. E., R. A. Clayton, S. R. Gill, M. L. Gwinn, R. J. Dodson, D. H. Haft, E. K. Kickey, J. D. Peterson, W. C. Nelson, K. A. Ketchum. et al., Evidence for lateral gene transfer between Archaea and Bacteria from genome sequence of *Terrmotoga maritima. Nature,* 399: 323–329; 1999.

Nesse, R. M. and G. C. Williams, *Evolution and Healing: The New Science of Darwinian Medicine.* London: Phoenix; 1996.

Nijhout, H. F., Hormonal control in larval development and evolution—Insects, pp. 217–254 in B. K. Hall and M. H. Wake, eds., *The Origin and Evolution of Larval Forms.* San Diego: Academic Press; 1999.

Nuland, S. B., *How We Die: Reflections on Life's Final Chapter.* New York: Alfred A. Knopf; 1994.

Numbers, R. L. and J. Stenhouse, eds., *Disseminating Darwinism: The Role of Place, Race, Religion, and Gender.* Cambridge: Cambridge University Press; 1999.

Nüsslein-Vohlard, C., Maternal effect mutations that alter the spatial coordinates of the embryo of *Drosophila melanogaster,* pp. 185–211 in S. Subtelny, ed., *Determinants of spatial organization,* 37th Symposium of the Society for Developmental Biology. Orlando, Academic Press; 1979.

Ohta, T., The current significance and standing of neutral and nearly neutral theories. *BioEssays,* 18: 673–677; 1996.

Oliveira, M., J. R. Silva, M. Dansa-Petretski, W. de Souza, U. Lins, C. M. S. Braga, H. Masuda, and P. L. Oliveira, Haem detoxification by an insect. *Nature,* 400: 517; 1999.

Olshansky, S. J., B. A. Carnes, A Désesquelles, Prospects for human longevity. *Sciénce,* 291: 1491–1492; 2001.

Onishi, A., M. Iwamota, T. Akita, S. Mikawa, K. Takeda, T. Awata, H. Hanada, and A. C. F. Perry, Pig cloning by microinjection of fetal fibroblast nuclei. *Science,* 289: 1188–1190; 2000.

Oppenheimer, J. M., The non-specificity of the germ-layers. *Q. Rev. Biol.,* 15: 1–27; 1940. Reprinted pp. 256–294 in J. M. Oppenheimer, *Essays in the History of Embryology and Biology.* Cambridge: MIT Press; 1967.

Orlic, D., J. Kajstura, S. Chimenti, I. Jakoniuk, S. M. Anderson, B. Li, J. Pickel, R. McKay, B. Nadal-Ginard, D. M. Bodine, A. Leri, and P. Anversa, Bone marrow cells regenerate infarcted myocardium, *Nature,* 410: 701–705; 2001.

Oshima, J., "The Werner syndrome protein: an update," Review article. *BioEssays,* 22: 894–901; 2000.

Oyama, S., *The Ontogeny of Information: Developmental Systems and Evolution.* Second Edition, Revised and Expanded. Forward by Richard C. Lewontin. Originally published in 1985 by Cambridge University Press. Science and Cultural Theory. Durham, NC; Duke University Press; 2000.

Papaioannou, V. E. Microsurgery and micromanipulation of early mouse embryos, pp. 1–27 in P. F. Baker, ed., *Techniques in Cellular Physiology:* P116. Amsterdam: Elsevier Biomedical; 1981. Part I Physiology, Volume P1/1. Amsterdam: Elsevier/North-Holland Scientific Publishers; 1982.

Paradis, K., G. Langford, Z. Long, W. Heneine, P. Sandstrom, W. Switzer, L. Chapman, C. Lockey, D. Onions, The XEN 111 Study Group, E. Otto, Search for cross-species transmission of porcine endogenous retrovirus in patients treated with living pig tissue. *Science,* 285: 1236–1241; 1999.

Peled, A., I. Petit, O. Kollet, M. Magid, T. Ponomaryov, T. Byk, A. Nagler, H. Ben-Hur, A. Many, L. Shultz, O. Lider, R. Alon, D. Zipori, and T. Lapidot, Dependence of human stem cell engraftment and repopulation of NOD/SCID mice on CXCR4. *Science,* 283: 845–848; 1999.

Pence, G. E., *Who's Afraid of Human Cloning?* Lanham: Rowman and Littlefield Publishers; 1998.

Pennisi, E. and D. Normile, "Perseverance leads to cloned pig in Japan," News Focus (18 August). *Science*, 289: 1118–1119; 2000.

Pennisi, E. and G. Vogel, Clonage: la nature résiste: Les chercheurs peinent à transformer l'essai Dolly. *La Recherche,* 334: 28–40; 2000a

Pennisi, E. and G. Vogel, "Clones: A hard act to follow," News Focus (9 June). *Science,* 288: 1722–1727; 2000b.

Perkins, F. O., "Sporozoa": Apicomplexa, Microsporidia, Haplosporidia, Paramyxea, Myxosporidia, and Actinosporidia, pp. 261–331 in F. W. Harrison and J. O. Corliss, eds., *Microscopic Anatomy of Invertebrates: Protozoa.* Vol. 1. New York: Wiley-Liss; 1991.

Petersen, B. E., W. C. Bowen, K. D. Patrene, W. M. Mars, A. K. Sullivan, N. Murase, S. S. Boggs, J. S. Greenberger, and J. P. Goff, Bone marrow as a potential source of hepatic oval cells. *Science,* 284: 1168–1170; 1999.

Peterson, K. J., R. Andrew Cameron, and E. H. Davidson, Set-aside cells in maximal indirect development: evolutionary and developmental significance. *BioEssays,* 19: 623–631; 1997.

Philippe, H., A. Chenuil, and A. Adoutte, Can the Cambrian explosion be inferred through molecular phylogeny, pp. 15–25 in M. Akam, P. Holland, P. Ingham and G. Wray, eds., *The Evolution of Developmental Mechanisms.* Development 1994 Supplement. Cambridge: The Company of Biologists; 1994.

Piccini, P., D. J. Brooks, A. Björklund, R. N. Gunn, P. M. Grasby, O. Rimoldi, P. Brundin, P. Hagell, S. Rehucrona, H. Widner, and O. Lindvall, Dopamine release from nigal transplants visualized *in vivo* in a Parkinson's patient. *Nature Neurosciences,* 2: 1137–1140; 1999.

Poinar, Jr., G. and R. Poinar, *The Amber Forest: A Reconstruction of a Vanished World.* Princeton: Princeton University Press; 1999.

Polejaeva, I. A., H-H. Chen, T. D. Vaught, R. L. Page, J. Mullins, S. Ball. Y. Dai, J. Boone, S. Walker, D. L. Ayares, A. Colman, and K. H. S. Campbell. Cloned pigs produced by nuclear transfer from adult somatic cells. *Nature,* 407: 86–90; 2000.

Pollard, T. D., "Genomics, the cytoskeleton and motility," Analysis (15 February). *Nature,* 409: 842–843; 2001.

Polly, P. D., "Cope's rule," Letters (2 October). *Science,* 282: 50–51; 1998.

Ponting, C. P. and D. J. Blake, Predicting the evolution, structure and function of proteins from sequence information, pp. 199–213 in Martin J. Bishop, ed., *Genetics Databases.* San Diego: Academic Press; 1999.

Potten, C. S. and M. Loeffler, Stem cells: attributes, cycles, spirals, pitfalls and uncertainties. Lessons for and from the crypt. *Development,* 110: 1001–1020; 1990.

Prigogine, I and I. Stengers, *Order out of Chaos: Man's New Dialogue with Nature.* Toronto: Bantam Books; 1984.

Provine, W. B., *The Origins of Theoretical Population Genetics.* Chicago: Chicago University Press; 1971.

Provine, W. B., Genetics, pp. 51–58 in E. Mayr and W. B. Provine, *The Evolutionary Synthesis: Perspectives on the Unification of Biology.* Cambridge: Harvard University Press; 1980.

Quammen, D., *The Song of the Dodo: Island Biogeography in an Age of Extinction.* New York: Touchstone; 1996.

Raff, R. A., Developmental mechanisms in the evolution of animal form: origins and evolvability of body plans, pp. 489–500 in S. Bengtson, ed., *Early Life on Earth,* Nobel Symposium No. 84. New York: Columbia University Press; 1994.

Raff, R. A., *The Shape of Life: Genes, Development and the Evolution of Animal Form.* Chicago: University of Chicago Press; 1996.

Renfree, M. B., Implantation and placentation, pp. 26–69 in C. R. Austin, and R. V. Short, eds., *Reproduction in Mammals,* Book 2, *Embryology and Fetal Development,* 2nd ed., Cambridge: Cambridge University Press; 1982.

Ricklefs, R. E., Evolutionary theories of aging: confirmation of a fundamental prediction, with implications for the genetic basis and evolution of life span. *Am. Naturalist,* 152: 24–44; 1998.

Rieppel, O., Homology, topology, and typology: The history of modern debates, pp. 63–100 in B. K. Hall, ed., *Homology: The Hierarchical Basis of Comparative Biology.* San Diego: Academic Press; 1994.

Rietze, R. L., H. Valcanis, G. F. Brooker, T. Thomas, A. K. Voss, and P. F. Bartlett, Purification of a pluripotent neural stem cell from the adult mouse brain. *Nature,* 412: 736–739; 2001.

Roger, A. J., S. G. Svärd, J. Tovar, C. G. Clark, M. W. Smith, F. D. Gillin, and M. L. Sogin, A mitochondrial-like chaperonin 60 gene in *Giardia lamblia:* evidence that diplomonads once harbored an endosymbiont related to the progenitor of mitochondria. *Proc. Natl. Acad. Sci. USA,* 95: 229–234; 1998.

Rogina, B., R. A. Reenan, S. P. Nilsen, and S. L. Helfand, Extended life-span conferred by cotransporter gene mutations in *Drosophila. Science,* 290: 2137–2149; 2000.

Romanov, S. R., B. K. Kozakiewicz, C. R. Holst, M. R. Stampfer, L. M. Haupt, and T. D. Tisty, Normal human mammary epithelial cells spontaneously escape senescence and acquire genomic changes. *Nature,* 401: 633–637; 2001.

Rose, C. S., Hormonal control in larval development and evolution—Amphibians, pp. 167–216 in B. K. Hall and M. H. Wake, eds., *The Origin and Evolution of Larval Forms.* San Diego: Academic Press; 1999.

Rose, M., *Darwin's Spectre: Evolutionary Biology in the Modern World.* Princeton: Princeton University Press; 1998.

Rose, S., *Lifelines: Biology Beyond Determinism.* New York: Oxford University Press, 1998.

Rosenthal, B., Z. Mai, D. Caplivski, S. Ghosh, H. De La Vega, T. Graf, and J. Samuelson, Evidence for the bacterial origins of genes encoding fermentation enzymes of the amitochondriate protozoan parasite *Entamoeba histoloytica. J. Bacteriol.,* 179: 3736–3745; 1997.

Roth, V. L., Homology and hierarchies: Problems solved and unresolved. *J. Evol. Biol.,* 4: 167–194; 1991.

Roux, W., Contributions to the developmental mechanics of the embryo. On the artificial production of half-embryos by destruction of one of the first two blastomeres, and the later development (postgeneration) of the missing half of the body. Translation by Hans Laufer, pp. 2–37 in B. H. Willier and J. M. Oppenheimer, eds., *Foundations of Experimental Embryology.* Englewood Cliffs: Prentice-Hall; (1888) 1964.

Rubin, G., "Comparing species," News and Views (15 February). *Nature,* 409: 820–821; 2001.

Rudnicki, M. A. and M. W. McBurney, Cell culture methods and induction of differentiation of embryonal carcinoma cell lines, pp. 19–49 in E. J. Robertson, ed., *Teratocarcinomas and Embryonic Stem Cells: A Practical Approach.* Oxford: IRL Press; 1987.

Rudolph, K. L., S. Chang, M. Millard, N. Schreiber-Agus, R. A. DePinho, Inhibition of experimental liver cirrhosis in mice by telomerase gene delivery. *Science,* 287: 1253–1258; 2000.

Ruse, M., *Monad to Man: The Concept of Progress in Evolutionary Biology.* Cambridge: Harvard University Press; 1996.

Ruse, M., *The Darwinian Revolution: Science Red in Tooth and Claw.* Second edition. Chicago: The Chicago University Press; 1999.

Sapp, J., Concepts of organization and leverage of ciliate protozoa, 229–258 in S. F. Gilbert, ed., *A conceptual history of modern embryology. Developmental biology: a comprehensive synthesis.* Vol. 7. New York: Plenum Press; 1985.

Sapp, J., *Beyond the Gene: Cytoplasmic Inheritance and the Struggle for Authority in Genetics.* New York: Oxford University Press; 1987.

Sapp, J., *Where the Truth Lies: Franz Moewus and the Origins of Molecular Biology.* Cambridge: Cambridge University Press; 1990.

Sapp, J. *Evolution by Association: a history of symbiosis.* New York: Oxford University Press; 1994.

Scheer, U. and M. O. C. Dabauvalle, Functional organization of the amphibian oocyte nucleus, pp. 385–430 in L. W. Browder, ed., *Developmental Biology: A Comprehensive Synthesis,* Vol. 1, *Oogenesis.* New York: Plenum Press; 1985.

Scheler, M., *Ressentiment.* Edited, with an introduction by Lewis A Coser. Translated by William W. Holdheim. New York: The Free Press of Glencoe; 1961.

Schiffmann, D. A., Dorsoventral asymmetry in mitochondrial membrane potential in early *Drosophila* embryos. *Biochem. Soc. Trans.,* 25: S653; 1997.

Schiffmann, Y., An hypothesis, phosphorylation fields as the source of positional information and cell differentiation—(cAMP, ATP) as the universal morphogenetic Turing couple. *Prog. Biophys. molec. Biol.,* 56: 76–107; 1991.

Schiffmann, Y., Instability of the homogeneous state as the source of localization, epigenesis, differentiation, and morphogenesis. *Int. Rev. Cytol.,* 154: 309–375; 1994.

Schiffmann, Y., Self-organization in biology and development. *Prog. Biophys. molec. Biol.,* 68: 145–205; 1997.

Schlegel, M., J. Lom, A. Stechmann, D. Bernhard, D. Leipe, I. Dyková, and M. L. Sogin. Phylogenetic analysis of complete small subunit ribosomal RNA coding regions of *Myxidium lieberkuehni:* Evidence that Myxozoa are Metazoa and related to the Bilateria. *Arch. Protistenke.,* 147: 1–9; 1996.

Schnieke, A. E., A. J. Kind, W. A. Ritchie, K. Mycock, A. R. Scott, M. Ritchie, I. Wilmut, A. Colman, and K. H. S. Campbell, Human Factor IX transgenic sheep produced by transfer of nuclei from transfected fetal fibroblasts. *Science,* 278: 2130–2133; 1997.

Schrödinger, E., *What is Life?* Cambridge: Cambridge University Press; (1944) 1967.

Seilacher, A., P. K. Bose, F. Pflüger, Triploblastic animals more than 1 billion years ago: trace fossil evidence from India. *Science,* 282: 80–83; 1998.

Sgrò, C. M. and L. Partridge, A delayed wave of death from reproduction in *Drosophila. Science,* 286: 2521–2524; 1999.

Shamblott, M. J., J. Axelman, S. Wang, E. M. Gugg, J. W. Littlefield, P. J. Donovan, P. D. Blumenthal, G. R. Huggins, and J. D. Gearhart, Deviation of pluripotent stem cells from cultured human primordial germ cells. *Proc. Natl. Acad. Sci. USA,* 95: 13726–13731; 1998.

Shanley, D. P. and T. B. L. Kirkwood, Evolution of the human menopause. *BioEssays,* 23: 282–287; 2001.

Shay, J. W. and W. E. Wright, "When do telomeres matter?" Perspectives: Aging (2 February). *Science,* 291: 839–841; 2001.

Sherrington, C., *Man on his Nature.* New York: Mentor Book; (1951) 1964.

Shostak, S., Complexity in *Hydra*: Homeostasis, morphogenesis, control and integration. *Quart. Rev. Biol.,* 49: 287–310; 1974.

Shostak, S., Vegetative reproduction by budding in Hydra: A perspective on tumors. *Prosp. Biol. Med.,* 20: 545–568; 1977.

Shostak, S., Hydra and cancer: Immortality and budding, pp. 275–286 in C. J. Dawe, J. C. Harshbarger, S. Kondo, T. Sugimura, and S. Takayama, eds., *Phyletic approaches to Cancer:* Internat. Symp. Princess Takamatsu Cancer Res. Fund. Tokyo: Japan Sci. Soc. Press; 1981.

Shostak, S., *Embryology: An Introduction to Developmental Biology.* New York: Harper/ Collins; 1991.

Shostak, S., Symbiogenetic origins of Cnidaria: updating an hypothesis. *Invertebrate Reproduction and Development,* 23: 167–168; 1993a.

Shostak, S., A symbiogenetic theory for the origins of cnidocysts in Cnidaria. *BioSystems,* 29: 49–58; 1993b.

Shostak, S., Cnidaria, pp. 45–105 in K. G. and Rita G. Adiyodi, eds., *Reproductive Biology of Invertebrates,* Vol. VI, Part A, Asexual Propagation and Reproductive Strategies. New Delhi: Oxford and IBH Publishing; 1993c.

Shostak, S., *Death of Life: The Legacy of Molecular Biology.* London: Macmillan; 1998.

Shostak, S., *Evolution of Sameness and Difference: Perspectives on the human Genome Project.* Amsterdam: Harwood Academic Publishers; 1999.

Shostak, S., "Who's afraid of reductionism?" I am! In M. Van Regenmortel and D. Hull, eds., *Laudat Conference on Reductionism; in press.*

Shostak, S. and R. Tammariello, Supernumerary heads in *Hydra viridis,* in C. J. Dawe and J. C. Harshbarger, eds., *Neoplasms and Related Disorders of Invertebrate and Lower Vertebrate Animals. National Cancer Institute Monograph,* 31: 739–750; 1969.

Shostak, S. and V. Kolluri, Origins of diversity in cnidarian cnidocysts. *Symbiosis,* 19: 1–29; 1995.

Siddal, M. E., N. A. Stokes, and E. M. Burreson, Molecular phylogenetic evidence that the Phylum Haplosporidia has an alveolate ancestry. *Mol. Biol. Evol.,* 12: 573–581; 1995.

Signer, E. N., Y. E. Dubrova, A. J. Jeffreys, C. Wilde, L. M. B. Finch, M. Wells, and M. Peaker, DNA fingerprinting Dolly. *Nature,* 394: 329–330; 1998.

Slack, J. M. W., *From Egg to Embryo: Determinative Events in early Development.* Cambridge: Cambridge University Press; 1983.

Slack, J. M. W., *Egg and Ego: An Almost True Story of Life in the Biology Lab.* New York: Springer-Verlag; 1999.

Slack, J. M. W., "Stem cells in epithelial tissues," Review (25 February). *Science,* 287: 1431–1433; 2000.

Slack, J. M. W., P. W. H. Holland, and C. F. Graham, The zootype and the phylotypic stage. *Nature,* 361: 490–492; 1993.

Smith, I., *Life's other Secret: The New Mathematics of the Living World.* New York: John Wiley and Sons; 1998.

Smith, J. R. and O. M. Pereira-Smith, Replicative senescence: implications for in vivo aging and tumor suppression. *Science,* 273: 63–67; 1996.

Smith, M. W., D-F. Feng, and R. F. Doolittle. Evolution by acquisition: the case for horizontal transfer. *Trends Biochem. Sci.,* 17: 489–493; 1992.

Smothers, J. F., C. D. von Dohlen, L. H. Smith, Jr., and R. D. Spall. Molecular evidence that the myxozoan protists are metazoans. *Science,* 265: 1719–1721; 1994.

Sogin, M. L., The origin of eukaryotes and evolution into major kingdoms, pp. 181–192 in S. Bengston, ed., *Early Life on Earth.* New York: Columbia University Press; 1994.

Sohal, R. S. and R. Weindruch, Oxidative stress, caloric restriction, and aging. *Science,* 273: 59–63; 1996.

Solter, D., Dolly *is* a clone—and no longer alone. *Nature,* 394: 315–316; 1998.

Sonnonborn, T. M., The evolutionary integration of the genetic material into genetic systems, pp. 375–401 in R. A. Brink and E. D. Styles, eds., *Heritage from Mendel.* Proceedings of the Mendel Centennial Symposium, Sponsored by the Genetics Society of America, 1965. Madison: University of Wisconsin Press; 1967.

Spemann, H., *Embryonic Development and Induction.* New Haven: Yale University Press (Reprinted by New York: Hafner; 1962); 1938.

Steele, E. J., R. A. Lindley, and R. V. Blanden, *Lamarck's Signature: How Retrogenes Are Changing Darwin's Natural Selection Paradigm.* Reading: Perseus Books; 1998.

Steelman, J. T. and T. D. Kocher, From phenotype to genotype. *Evolution and Development,* 2: 166–173; 2000.

Stenseth, N. C., "The evolutionary synthesis," Perspectives: Evolutionary Biology (19 November). *Science,* 286: 1490; 1999.

Stevens, L. C., Embryonic potency of embryoid bodies derived from a transplantable testicular teratoma of the mouse. *Develop. Biol.,* 2: 285–297; 1960.

Stevens, L. C. Teratogenesis and spontaneous parthenogenesis in mice, pp. 93–106 in C. L. Markert and J. Papaconstantinou, eds., *The Developmental Biology of Reproduction.* 33rd Symposium of the Society for Developmental Biology. New York: Academic Press; 1975.

Stone, R., "U.K. backs use of embryos, sets vote," News of the Week (25 August). *Science,* 289: 1269–1270; 2000.

Sulston, J. E. and J. G. White, Regulation and cell autonomy during postembryonic development in *Caenorhabditis elegans. Develop Biol.,* 78: 577–598; 1980.

Swalla, B. J. and W. R. Jeffery, Requirement of the *Manx* gene for expression of chordate features in a tailless ascidian larva. *Science,* 274: 1205–1208; 1996.

Syvanen, M., Horizontal gene flow: evidence and possible consequences. *Ann. Rev. Genet.,* 28: 237–261; 1994.

Talbot, M., A desire to duplicate. *The New York Times Magazine,* February 4: 40–45, 67–68; 2001.

Tang, D. G., Y. M. Tokumoto, J. A. Apperly, A. C. Lloyd, and M. C. Raff, Lack of replicative senescence in cultured rat oligodendrocyte precursor cells. *Science,* 291: 868–871; 2001.

Tarkowski, A. K., Experimental studies on regulation in the development of isolated blastomeres of mouse eggs. *Acta Theriol.,* 3: 191–267; 1959.

Tartar, V., *The Biology of Stentor.* Oxford: Paragon Press; 1961.

Tateno, M., M. Mizutani, K. Yura, O. Nureki, S. Yokoyama, and M. Gō, Module structure and function of glutamyl-tRNA synthetase, pp. 53–63 in M. Gō and P. Schimmel, eds., *Tracing Biological Evolution in Protein and Gene Structure.* Amsterdam: Elsevier; 1995.

Thompson, D. W., *On Growth and Form: The Complete Revised Edition.* New York: Dover Publications, (1942) 1992.

Thomson, J. A., J. Itskovitz-Eldor, S. S. Shapiro, M. A. Waknitz, J. J. Swiergiel, V. S. Marshall, and J. M. Jones. Embryonic stem cell lines derived from human blastocysts. *Science,* 282: 1145–1147; 1998.

Tipler, F. J., *The Physics of Immortality: Modern Cosmology, God and the Resurrection of the Dead.* New York: Doubleday; 1994.

Tissenbaum, H. A. and L. Guarente, Increased dosage of a *sir-2* gene extends lifespan in *Caenorhabditis elegans. Nature,* 410: 227–230; 2001.

Tourasse, N. J. and M. Gouy, Accounting for evolutionary rate variation among sequence sites consistently changes universal phylogenies deduced from rRNA and protein-coding genes. *Molecular Phylogenetics Evolution,* 13: 159–168; 1999.

Toussaint, O., J. Ramacle, B. F. X. Clark, E. S. Gonos, C. Franceschi, and T. B. L. Kirkwood, Biology of ageing. *BioEssays,* 22: 954–956; 2000.

Turing, A. M., The chemical basis of morphogenesis. *Phi. Trans. R. Soc. London* B, 237: 37–72; 1952.

Turkle, S., Cyborg babies and cy-dough-plasm: Ideas about self and life in the culture of simulation, pp. 317–329 in R. Davis-Floyd and J. Dumit, eds., *Cyborg Babies: From Techno-Sex to Techno-Tots.* New York: Routledge; 1998.

Upcroft, J. and P. Upcroft. My favorite cell: *Giardia. BioEssays,* 20: 256–263; 1998.

van der Kooy, D. and S. Weiss, "Why stem cells?" Review (25 February). *Science,* 287: 1439–1441; 2000.

Van Valen, L., A new evolutionary law, *Evolutionary Theory,* 1: 1–30; 1973.

Vellai, T. and G. Vida, The origin of eukaryotes: the difference between prokaryotic and eukaryotic cells. *Proc. Roy. Soc., Lond.* B, 266: 1571–1577; 1999.

Venter, J. C., M. D. Adams, E. W. Myers, et al., The sequence of the human genome. *Science,* 291: 1304–1351; 2001.

Vickery, M. S. and J. B. McClintock. Regeneration in metazoan larvae. *Nature,* 394: 140; 1998.

Vogel, G., Harnessing the power of stem cells. *Science,* 283: 1432–1434; 1999.

Vogel, G., "Company gets rights to cloned human embryos," News Focus: Patents (28 January). *Science,* 287: 559; 2000.

Vogel, G., "British Parliament approves new rules," News (5 January). *Science,* 291: 23; 2001.

von Baer, K. E., *De Ovi Mammalium et Hominis Genesi.* Lipsiae (1827); Facsimili reproduction: Bruxelles: Culture et Civilisation; 1966.

von Baer, K. E., *Über Entwicklungsgeschichte der Thiere. Beobachtung und Reflexion.* Zweiter Theil. Königsberg (1837); Facsimili reproduction: Bruxelles: Culture et Civilisation; 1967.

Vossbrinck, C. R., J. V. Maddox, S. Friedman, B. A. Debrunner-Vossbrinck, and C. R. Woese, Ribosomal RNA sequence suggests microsporidia are extremely ancient eukaryotes. *Nature,* 326: 411–414; 1987.

Wadman, M., "Issue of patents on 'Dolly' technology stirs controversy." News (27 January). *Nature*, 403: 351–352; 2000.

Wakayama, T., A. C. F. Perry, M. Zuccotti, K. R. Johnson, and R. Yanagimachi, Full-term development of mice from enucleated oocytes injected with cumulus cell nuclei. *Nature,* 394: 369–374; 1998.

Wakayama, T., Y. Shinkai, K. L. K. Tamashiro, H. Niida, D. C. Blanchard, A. Ogura, K. Tenamura, M. Tachibana, A. C. F. Perry, C. F. Colgan, P. Mombaerts, and R. Yanagimachi, Cloning of mice to six generations. *Nature,* 407: 318–319; 2000.

Walsh, C. and C. L. Cepko, Clonally related cortical cells show several migration patterns. *Science,* 241: 1342–1345; 1988.

Walther, B. T., Origins vs. maintenance of sex and asex: a cellular view of sexuality. pp. 37–55 in H. Haukanes, ed., *Feminism 2000: Biology, Technology, Politics.* Norway: Centre for Women's and Gender Research, University of Bergen; 2000.

Wanntorp, H-E. Historical constraints in adaptation theory: Traits and non-traits. *Oikos,* 41: 157–159; 1983.

Wassarman, P. M., Early events in mammalian fertilization. *Annu. Rev. Cell Biol.,* 3: 109–142; 1987.

Watson, J. D., *The Double Helix: A Personal Account of the Discovery of the Structure of DNA.* New York: Mentor; 1969.

Watson, J. D. and F. H. C. Crick, Molecular structure of nucleic acids. A structure for deoxyribonucleic acid. *Nature,* 171: 737–738; 1953.

Webb, J. F. Larvae in fish development and evolution, pp. 109–158 in B. K. Hall and M. H. Wake, eds., *The Origin and Evolution of Larval Forms.* San Diego: Academic Press; 1999.

Weinberg, R. A., "Bumps on the road to immortality," News and Views (5 November). *Nature,* 396: 23–24; 1998.

Weismann, A., *Ueber die Dauer des Lebens.* Jena: Gustav Fischer Verlag; 1882.

Weismann, A., *The Germ-plasm: A Theory of Heredity* (German, 1886; first English translation 1893). Translated by W. Newton Parker and Harriet Rionnfeldt. New York: Charles Scribner's Sons; London: W. Scott; 1912.

Wellauer, P. K., R. H. Reeder, I. B. Dawid, and D. D. Brown, The arrangement of length heterogeneity in repeating units of amplified and chromosomal ribosomal DNA from *Xenopus laevis. J. Mol. Biol.,* 105: 487–505; 1976.

Wells, H. G., *The Time Machine: An Invention.* A Critical Text of the 1895 London First Edition, with an Introduction and Appendices. Edited by Leon Stover, The Annotated H. G. Wells, 1. Jefferson: McFarland and Company, 1996.

Werner, E. E., Size, scaling and the evolution of complex life cycles, pp. 68–81 in B. Ebenman and L. Persson, eds., *Size-structured Populations: Ecology and Evolution.* Berlin: Springer Verlag; 1988.

Willadsen, S. M., A method for culture of micromanipulated sheep embryos and its use to produce monozygotic twins. *Nature (London),* 277: 298–300; 1979.

Williams, G. C., *Plan and Purpose in Nature.* London: Phoenix; 1997.

Williams, T. and A. Polaszek, A re-examination of host relations in the Aphelinidae (Hymenoptera: Chalcidoidea). *Linnean Society, Biological Journal,* 57: 35–45; 1996.

Williamson, D. I., Incongruous larvae and the origin of some invertebrate life-histories. *Prog. Oceanog.,* 19: 87–116; 1988.

Williamson, D. I., Sequential chimeras, pp. 299–336 in Alfred I. Tauber, ed., *Organisms and the Origins of Self.* The Netherlands: Kluwer Academic Publishers; 1991.

Williamson, D. I., *Larvae and Evolution: Toward a New Zoology.* New York: Chapman and Hall; 1992.

Williamson, D. I., Types of evolution. *J. Natural Hist.,* 30: 1111–1112; 1996.

Williamson, D. I., Larval transfer and the origins of larvae. *Zoological J. Linnean Soc.,* 131: 111–122; 2001.

Williamson, D. I. and A. L. Rice., Larval evolution in the Crustacea. *Crustaceana,* 69: 267–287; 1998.

Wilmut, I., A. E. Schnieke, J. McWhir, A. J. Kind, and K. H. S. Campbell. Viable offspring derived from fetal and adult mammalian cells. *Nature,* 385: 810–813; 1997.

Wilmut, I., K. Campbell, and C. Tudge, *The Second Creation: The Age of Biological Control by the Scientists Who Cloned Dolly.* London: Headline Book Publishing; 2000.

Wilson, A. C., R. L. Cann, S. M. Carr, M. George, U. B. Byllensten, K. M. Helm-Bychowski, R. G. Higuchi, S. R. Palumbi, E. M. Prager, R. D. Sage, and M. Stoneking. Mitochondrial DNA and two perspectives on evolutionary genetics. *Biol. J. Linnean Soc.,* 26: 375–400; 1985.

Wilson, E. O., *Sociobiology: The New Synthesis.* Cambridge: Harvard University Press; 1975.

Woese, C. R., The universal ancestor. *Proc. Natl. Acad. Sci. USA,* 95: 6854–6859; 1998.

Wolfsberg, T. G., J. McEntyre, G. D. Schuler, "Guide to the draft human genome," Analysis (15 February). *Nature,* 409: 824–826; 2001.

Wolkow, C. A., K. D. Kimura, M-S. Lee, and G. Ruvkun. Regulation of *C. elegans* life-span by insulin signaling in the nervous system. *Science,* 290: 147–150; 2000.

Wolpert, L., Positional information and the spatial pattern of cellular differentiation. *J. Theor. Biol.,* 25: 1–7; 1969.

Wu, L. P. and K. V. Anderson, Related signaling networks in *Drosophila* that control dorsoventral patterning in the embryo and the immune response. *Cold Spring Harbor Symp. Quantitative Biol.,* LXII: 97–103: 1997.

Wyllie, A. H., The genetic regulation of apoptosis. *Curr. Opin. Genet. Develop,* 5: 97–104; 1995.

Yanagimachi, R., 1988. Sperm-egg fusion, pp. 3–43 in Düzgünes and F. Bronner, eds., *Current Topics in Membranes and Transport,* Vol. 32, *Membrane Fusion in Fertilization, Cellular Transport and Viral Infection.* Orlando: Academic Press; 1988.

Yang, D., Y. Oyaizu, H. Oyaizu, G. J. Olsen, and C. R. Woese, Mitochondrial origins. *Proc. Natl. Acad. Sci., USA,* 82: 4443–4447; 1985.

Yu, C-E., J. Oshima, Y. O. H. Fu, E. M. Wijsman, F. Hisama, R. Alisch, S. Matthews, J. Nakura, T. Miki, S. Ouais, G. M. Martin, J. Mulligan, and G. D. Schellenberg, Positional cloning of the Werner's syndrome gene. *Science,* 272: 258–262; 1996.

Zeh, D. W. and J. A. Zeh, Reproductive mode and speciation: the viviparity-driven conflict hypothesis. *BioEssays,* 22: 938–946; 2000.

Zhang, J. and M. Nei, Evolution of Antennapedia-class homeobox genes. *Genetics,* 142: 295–303; 1996.

Index

Abbé, Ernst, 103
absorptive (intestinal) cells, 13, 85, 87, 99, 100, 101
acquired-immune tolerance, 193
Actinosporea, 148
adaptive landscape, 54, 55
adaptive radiation, 57, 59, 220n. 56
adelphoparasites, 133, 148
adenocarcinoma, 77–78, 151
adenoma, 27
adenosine triphosphate (ATP), 138, 228n. 86
adenoviral protein, 77, 222n. 120, 223n. 124
adipocytes, 224n. 17
adrenal gland, 92, 150
Advanced Cell Technology, 12
agar cocoon, 176, 211n. 38
agastoparasites, 133, 148
aging: absence of, 66; accelerated, 7, 202; cellular, 5, 9, 76; delayed, 139; development and, 37; endocrine perturbations of, 139; endpoint of development, 95; evolution of, 215n. 108; genes and, 5, 29, 37, 65; humoral immunity and, 161; inheritance of, 5; inherited disorders of, 9; mitochondria and, 139; negligible, 66; normal, 26; panacea for, 15; premature, 10, 27; prepubescence and, 37, 164, 207; process of, 37, 208; reductionism and, 75; senescence and, 42, 44, 83, 130, 191
agribusiness, 187
alimentary system, 90, 92
alleles (allelomorphs), 31, 60, 73
Allman, George, 115
allopatric speciation, 55
alpha-feto-protein testing (AFT), 200
alternate splicing, 31
altruism, 36, 40, 79
Alvarez, Luis and Walter, 57

Alzheimer's disease, 42, 186, 213n. 64
amelioration, 128
American Society of Naturalists, 58
Ames dwarf mice, 8
Amici, Giovanni Battista, 103
amino acids, 79, 101: homologous sequences of, 62, 78, 109; in polypeptides, 30–31, 74
amitochondrial protozoa, 138
amniocentesis, 200
amnion, 101
amniotes, 101
amoeba-like (amoeboid), 147, 148–151
amphibian, 107: aging, 66; cloning, 166, 169, 171; gastrulation, 101; metamorphosis, 152; tadpole or larva, 26, 110
anemones, 66–67, 135, 147
aneuploidy, 71, 175
Animal Research Station, the, 210n. 36
annelids, 104, 111, 149
anterior-posterior axis (plane), 101, 104, 118, 147, 232n. 79
Anthozoa (anthozoans), 66, 147
antibodies, monoclonal, 134, 166, 237n. 52; to surface receptors, 190
antigenic complexion, 181, 182
antigen presenting cell (APC), 94
antigens, 22, 77, 178: embryo, 182, 238n. 69; marker, 183, 212n. 48, 237n. 52; stem cell, 178, 182, 183; viral, 77, 216n. 112
antioxidants, 6, 8
aphelinid wasps, 148
aplacophorans, 148
apoptosis, 25–26, 27, 77, 102, 123, 139, 152, 223n. 120
Aquifex aeolicus, 129
Archaea (Archaebacteria, archaeans), 129, 135